Actions of Chemicals
on Dividing Cells

Prentice-Hall Biological Science Series

William D. McElroy and Carl P. Swanson, *Editors*

Actions of Chemicals on Dividing Cells, BENGT A. KIHLMAN
*Biochemical Systematics,** RALPH E. ALSTON AND B. L. TURNER
The Cellular Functions of Membrane Transport, JOSEPH F. HOFFMAN, ED.
Classic Papers in Genetics, JAMES A. PETERS
Experimental Biology, RICHARD W. VAN NORMAN
Foundations of Experimental Embryology, BENJAMIN H. WILLIER AND
    JANE M. OPPENHEIMER
General and Comparative Physiology, WILLIAM S. HOAR
An Introduction to Animal Behavior: Ethology's First Century, PETER H. KLOPFER
    AND JACK P. HAILMAN
Mechanisms of Body Functions, DEXTER M. EASTON
Milestones in Microbiology, THOMAS D. BROCK
Molecular Architecture in Cell Physiology, TORU HAYASHI AND
    ANDREW SZENTGYORGYI, EDS.
Papers on Human Genetics, SAMUEL H. BOYER, IV
Poisonous Plants of the United States and Canada, JOHN M. KINGSBURY
Principles of Biology, NEAL D. BUFFALOE
Principles of Microbial Ecology, THOMAS D. BROCK
*Radiotracer Methodology in Biological Science,** C. H. WANG AND DAVID L. WILLIS
Readings in Ecology, EDWARD J. KORMONDY, ED.
Selected Botanical Papers, IRVING W. KNOBLOCH
Selected Papers on Virology, NICHOLAS HAHON
The Specifity of Cell Surfaces, BERNARD DAVIS AND LEONARD WARREN, EDS.
A Synthesis of Evolutionary Theory, HERBERT H. ROSS

BIOLOGICAL TECHNIQUES SERIES

Alexander Hollaender, *Editor*
Techniques in Ultraviolet Photobiology, JOHN JAGGER

CONCEPTS OF MODERN BIOLOGY SERIES

*Behavioral Aspects of Ecology,** PETER H. KLOPFER
Molecular Biology: Genes and the Chemical Control of Living Cells, J. M. BARRY
Processes of Organic Evolution, G. LEDYARD STEBBINS

FOUNDATIONS OF MODERN BIOLOGY SERIES

Adaptation, 2nd ed., BRUCE WALLACE AND A. M. SRB
Animal Behavior, 2nd ed., VINCENT DETHIER AND ELIOT STELLAR
Animal Diversity, 2nd ed., EARL D. HANSON
Animal Physiology, 2nd ed., KNUT SCHMIDT-NEILSEN
The Cell, 2nd ed., CARL P. SWANSON
Cell Physiology and Biochemistry, 2nd ed., WILLIAM D. MCELROY
Chemical Background for the Biological Sciences, EMIL H. WHITE
Growth and Development, 2nd ed., MAURICE SUSSMAN
Heredity, 2nd ed., DAVID M. BONNER AND STANLEY E. MILLS
The Life of the Green Plant, 2nd ed., ARTHUR W. GALSTON
Man in Nature, 2nd ed., MARSTON BATES
The Plant Kingdom, 2nd ed., HAROLD C. BOLD

* These titles are also in the PRENTICE-HALL INTERNATIONAL SERIES IN BIOLOGICAL SCIENCE.
Prentice-Hall, Inc.; Prentice-Hall International, United Kingdom and Eire; Prentice-Hall of
Canada, Ltd., Canada.

Actions of Chemicals on Dividing Cells

Bengt A. Kihlman

Fil. dr. Swedish Natural Science Research Council
Research Professor of Biochemical Cytogenetics
Institute of Physiological Botany
Uppsala, Sweden

PRENTICE-HALL, INC.
Englewood Cliffs, New Jersey

PRENTICE-HALL INTERNATIONAL, INC., *London*
PRENTICE-HALL OF AUSTRALIA, PTY. LTD., *Sydney*
PRENTICE-HALL OF CANADA, LTD., *Toronto*
PRENTICE-HALL OF INDIA (PRIVATE) LTD., *New Delhi*
PRENTICE-HALL OF JAPAN, INC., *Tokyo*

© 1966 by Prentice-Hall, Inc./Englewood Cliffs, New Jersey

Current printing (last digit):

10 9 8 7 6 5 4 3 2 1

Library of Congress Catalog Card Number 66–18128

Printed in the United States of America

C—00338

Preface

Nearly two years ago when I agreed to write a book on the effects of chemicals on dividing cells, I certainly did not expect it to be an easy task. Nevertheless, I underestimated the difficulties. I found myself confronted with an enormous literature, full of contradictory statements and with few questions finally solved. The way out obviously was to concentrate on certain aspects and problems. I hope the reader will excuse me for allowing my own preferences and interests to influence my choice when this necessary selection was made, although as a result the book is admittedly somewhat unbalanced.

A few comments about the title, ACTIONS OF CHEMICALS ON DIVIDING CELLS: It should be pointed out that only *harmful* effects of chemicals are described, i.e., effects such as inhibition of mitosis and the production of chromosomal aberrations. In most of the work discussed, the cells affected by the chemicals are either mammalian cells in tissue culture or root-tip cells of higher plants.

The book consists of two parts. In the first six chapters, which constitute Part I, the cell, the nucleus, DNA synthesis, chromosome duplication and the normal course of mitosis are described. Since this is not a textbook of cytology, I have not tried to give complete and detailed information about the structure and function of the cell. On the other hand, knowledge of certain structural and functional aspects of the cell are necessary for the comprehension of Part II. Part I has been written in order to save the reader the trouble of searching the literature for this information.

Obviously most of the known facts about cell division and chromosome structure and about the structure, chemistry and physiology of the interphase nucleus are relevant to the main theme of the book. Since the chemical has to penetrate the interior of the cell in order to be able to produce its effects, all information regarding this penetration is relevant. Two metabolic processes which have proved to be significant in connection with the disruptive effects of chemicals on cell division and chromosome structure are oxidative phosphorylation and DNA synthesis which are, therefore, described in Part I. The reader will repeatedly come across these processes which may be regarded as two of the major themes of the book.

The sector of biological research reviewed and discussed in this book is one of intense activity and rapid development. Important new discoveries are made almost every month and it has been impossible to keep the book entirely up to date technically. I hope the reader will make allowances for this and also excuse certain imperfections in expression and style which are the result of the book being written directly in English, a language which is not my own.

During the preparation of this work I have become indebted to many friends and colleagues. I would like to express my gratitude to Professor C. P. Swanson for the encouragement and support he has given me and to Professors J. J. Biesele, A. Levan, W. D. McElroy and G. Östergren, Fil. lic. Göran Odmark and Fil. lic. Torgny Unestam for critical reading of the manuscript, in part or in its entirety, and for many valuable suggestions. I particularly appreciated the constructive criticism I received from Dr. Biesele; his book "Mitotic Poisons and the Cancer Problem" has been of great help to me during my work and in many respects served as a model for my own book. Needless to say, any errors or misinterpretations are my sole responsibility.

To Mrs. Eva Johansson, who has patiently typed the manuscript and helped to prepare the indices and the list of references, to Miss Anne Rentzhog for help with the proofreading, and to Mr. Åke Danielsson, who assisted in the preparation of the photographic material, I am greatly indebted. Thanks are also due all those people who kindly provided materials for the illustration of this work.

My personal research mentioned in this book was supported by grants from the Swedish Natural Science Research Council, the Swedish Cancer Society, and by grant No. GM 9319 from the National Institutes of Health, U.S. Public Health Service.

BENGT A. KIHLMAN

Contents

The
Interphase Cell
and the
Mitotic Cycle

Cytoplasmic Structures in the Interphase Cell and Their Function

In this chapter we shall briefly describe some of the structures of the interphase cell, as revealed by the light and the electron microscope (Fig. 1-1), and their function, as indicated by physiological and bio-

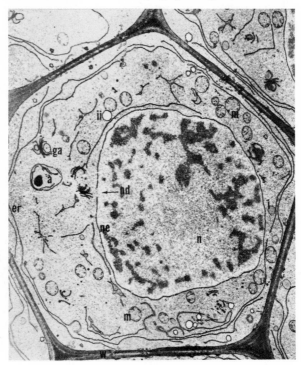

Fig. 1–1. Electron micrograph of a meristematic rootcap cell of maize showing the nucleus (n), nuclear envelope (ne), endoplasmic reticulum (er), mitochondria (m), and an amyloplast (a). (Whaley et al., 1960a; Amer. J. Bot. 47:423. Courtesy of the authors.)

chemical studies. More detailed information has been given when the structure and its function are likely to be particularly important in connection with the effects of chemicals on dividing cells. One such case is the plasma membrane and its permeability; another is the mitochondria and oxidative phosphorylation.

A. The Endoplasmic Reticulum, Ribosomes, the Golgi Apparatus, and Lysosomes

Even with the high resolution of the electron microscope, there remains a continuous ground or matrix substance which, although probably of high complexity, appears structureless. Porter (1961) has defined the matrix as "the 'structureless' medium in which are suspended all the resolvable elements of the cytoplasm."

The ground substance of almost all cells is traversed by a membrane-bound, more or less continuous vesicular system, which has been named the *endoplasmic reticulum* (ER) (Porter and Kallman, 1952). The interconnected lipoprotein membranes of the system separate the material inside the cavities of the ER from the surrounding cytoplasmic matrix. The ER is associated with the nuclear envelope, which consists of two membranes and an intervening, perinuclear, space. The outer of the two membranes of the nuclear envelope has been shown to be continuous with the membranes of the ER (Watson, 1955; Whaley et al., 1960*b*) and the nuclear envelope is apparently a part of the ER (compare Chapter 3). Elements of the ER extend to the cell surface. In plant cells, the ER-elements may even extend through the cell wall into neighboring cells (Whaley et al., 1960*a*).

The ER varies from cell to cell. In some cases the vesicles of the ER are few, whereas in other cases they are abundant. As a rule, the ER is not a prominent structure in undifferentiated cells; but when the cell begins to differentiate, the ER also develops. The morphological pattern of the system also tends to vary with the type of cell in which it occurs. The ER appears to be similar in cells with similar function.

Two main types of ER have been distinguished. These are the *granular* or *rough* form and the *agranular* or *smooth* form. The latter form predominates in cells such as the mature leukocyte and spermatocyte. The rough form (Fig. 1-2), which is easier to recognize, is associated with a particulate component of the ground substance. The particles are attached to the outer surface of the ER-elements. Chemically, they consist mainly of ribonucleic acid (RNA) and protein and are particularly abundant in protein-producing cells. The particles, which are called *ribosomes,* are known to be the structures on which the cytoplasmic protein synthesis of the cell occurs. The ribosomes are not necessarily localized on the surface of the ER, but may also be freely

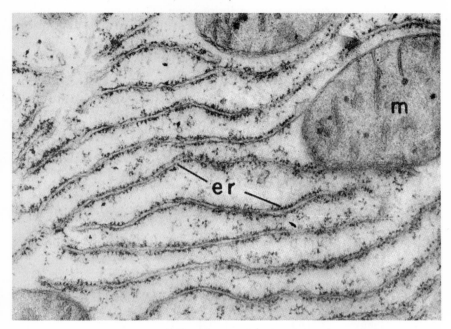

Fig. 1–2. Endoplasmic reticulum (er), rough type, in a rat liver cell. (Porter, 1961; The Cell II, p. 628, Brachet and Mirsky, eds. Reprinted by permission of Academic Press, Inc.)

distributed within the ground substance.

In cell division, the nuclear envelope and the other elements of the ER are broken down into fragments, some of which associate with the separating chromosome groups at anaphase. At telophase, when the daughter nuclei are formed, the fragments of the ER grow and fuse to form the new nuclear membrane (Whaley et al., 1960b). In plant cells, some of the fragments which do not participate in the formation of the nuclear envelope migrate toward the interzonal region of the spindle, where they form a lattice of microtubules along the equator of this region. It is within this network that the cell plate first appears.

The function of the ER is not known for certain. We do know that its rough form is involved in protein synthesis, but this is probably a function of the ribosomes rather than of the membrane system. It has also been suggested that the ER functions in intracellular transport, and that it carries "enzymes and metabolites important in physiological events taking place within the localized regions where it is found" (Porter, 1961). Finally, it may have a function as a conductor of intracellular impulses.

Since products of the *Golgi apparatus* appear to be involved in cell plate formation (compare Chap. 6, p. 82), a few words must be said

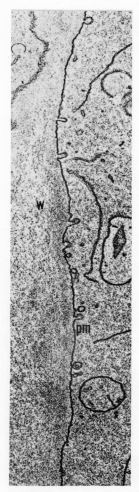

Fig. 1–3. Plasma membrane (pm), invaginated, in a meristematic cell of maize. (Whaley et al., 1960a; Amer. J. Bot. 47:439. Courtesy of the authors.)

about this cell organelle. The Golgi apparatus has its main function in connection with the formation of secretory products. In electron micrographs, the Golgi apparatus appears as a stack of membrane-bound cisternae, the membranes being of the same general thickness as those of the endoplasmic reticulum (Whaley et al., 1960a). In plant cells, the Golgi apparatus produces membrane-bound vesicles which secrete their content through the plasma membrane of the cell.

The *lysosomes* represent a class of cytoplasmic particles which have centrifugal properties between mitochondria and ribosomes. They are surrounded by a membrane and contain enzymes which are primarily hydrolytic in function. Among the lysosomal enzymes may be mentioned acid phosphatase, acid deoxyribonuclease (DNase) acid ribonuclease (RNase), cathepsin and α-glucosidase. Lysosomes are involved in the processes of pinocytosis and phagocytosis to be discussed later. They are also functioning in connection with the removal of intracellular and extracellular materials.

B. The Plasma Membrane and Its Permeability to Non-Electrolytes and Weak Electrolytes. Active Transport and Cytosis

The *plasma membrane* is more difficult to demonstrate than the membranes of the ER or the membranes surrounding the cell nucleus and the mitochondria; however, by the use of particular fixation procedures, considerable information has been obtained about the structure of the plasma membrane. By using fixation procedures which caused the plasma membrane to swell, Robertson (1959) found that the plasma membrane of maize root cells appeared as two thin dark lines separated by a light region. The thickness of the plasma membrane in both plant and animal cells has been estimated to be about 75 A, each of the dark lines being about 20 A thick.

The fundamental permeability studies of Overton (1899, 1902) indicated that the ability of a molecule to penetrate the plasma membrane was dependent on its solubility in lipids in such a way that the greater the solubility of the molecule, the greater also its ability to penetrate into the living cell. On the basis of these results, Overton concluded that the hypothetical cell or plasma membrane was impregnated with fatlike substances, i.e., with lipids. In support of this hypothesis, chemical analyses of red blood cell membranes (the "ghosts" of erythrocytes) have indicated the presence of lipids and proteins.

The molecular architecture of the plasma membrane is not known. According to a hypothesis by Danielli (1954), the membrane consists essentially of two layers of lipid molecules arranged with their hydrophilic or polar groups extending outwardly toward the surfaces of the structure. The double layer of lipid molecules would be sandwiched between two layers of protein molecules. The proteins consist of polypeptide chains, or meshworks of such chains, which are believed to be oriented in such a way that the hydrocarbon portions of the amino acid residues are dissolved in the lipid layer and the hydrophilic groups extend into the aqueous phase. The permeability properties of the membrane require that in some areas a polar structure extend right through the membrane (Fig. 1-4).

Danielli's plasma membrane model is in accord with the membrane structure seen in electron micrographs. Other biological membranes (the

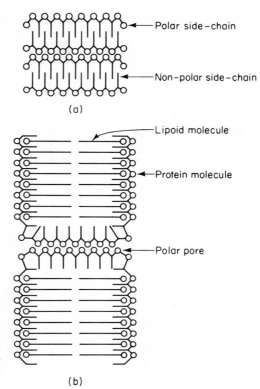

Fig. 1–4. The plasma membrane model of Danielli. (Danielli, 1954; Colston Research Society Papers, No. 7.)

membranes of the endoplasmic reticulum, the nuclear envelope, and the mitochondrial membranes) appear to be constructed according to the same general principle. However, although most workers favor Danielli's membrane model, some believe that the plasma membrane and other biological membranes are more likely to consist of a double-layered network of alternating protein and phospholipid units. The lipid molecules would be arranged in long rows (micelles) with their hydrocarbon portions joined by hydrophobic bonds and their hydrophilic groups facing outward. The protein molecules would be arranged in a similar way, i.e., with the hydrocarbon portions extending inward and with the hydrophilic groups on the surfaces of the membrane structure (Green, 1964).

It is possible to distinguish between two main types of movements of substances through the membrane: (1) movement in response to a concentration gradient (diffusion) and (2) active transport. When the first type of movement is discussed it is, both from a theoretical and a practical point of view, convenient to distinguish between the permeability to (a) nonelectrolytes, (b) weak acids and bases, and (c) strong electrolytes. Since the chemicals to be discussed in Part II of this book are either nonelectrolytes or weak electrolytes, we shall concentrate on these two groups.

According to the lipid theory of Overton mentioned above, it is the relative lipid solubility of a molecule, i.e., its distribution in a lipid/water system, that is decisive for the penetration power. The distribution or partition coefficient k is given as the ratio between the concentrations of the substance in the lipid phase and in the water phase. Thus, the greater the coefficient, the higher the relative lipid solubility and the faster the substance penetrates the plasma membrane. The experiments of Collander and Bärlund (1933) showed, however, that although the relative lipid solubility of a substance is of primary importance in determining its passage through the plasma membrane, the size of the molecule also influences the penetration power. It was found that as a rule small molecules penetrate faster than one would expect on the basis of their relative lipid solubility. This was interpreted as an indication that the otherwise continuous lipid layer of the plasma membrane in certain regions was provided with hydrophilic pores (the lipid sieve theory of Collander). Size is also important, inasmuch as very large molecules, such as starch or glycogen, are unable to penetrate into the cell by a diffusion process.

The movement of molecules through the cell membrane is more enhanced by temperature than is free diffusion. A ten-degree rise of temperature may result in a several-fold increase of the rate of penetration.

Strong electrolytes are completely dissociated and their solutions, therefore, contain only ions and no molecules. Ions have little ability to penetrate the lipid component of the plasma membrane and are, as a rule, taken up only by active transport.

Weak acids and bases have a position in between nonelectrolytes and strong electrolytes. The weaker the acid or base, the fewer ions its aqueous solutions contain. By lowering the pH of the solution of an acid and by increasing the pH of the solution of a base, the equilibrium can be changed still more in the direction of the undissociated molecule. The movement of an undissociated weak acid or base through the plasma membrane follows the same rules as the penetration of nonelectrolytes: the higher their relative lipid solubility and the smaller their size, the faster they penetrate.

The pH dependence is illustrated very nicely by the classical experiment of Osterhout (1925), who studied the distribution of hydrogen sulfide (H_2S) between the sea water and the cell sap of the alga *Valonia* (Fig. 1-5). The normal pH of the cell sap is 5.8, independent of the pH

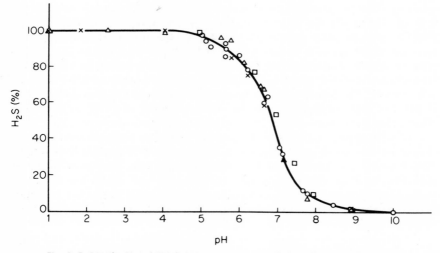

Fig. 1–5. Distribution of H_2S between sea water and the cell sap of *Valonia* at various pH values. (Osterhout, 1925. Reprinted by permission of The Rockefeller Institute Press from J. Gen. Physiol., September 1925, Vol. 8, No. 2, p. 135.)

outside the cell. Osterhout varied the pH of the sea water from pH 5 to pH 10 by adding hydrochloric acid or sodium hydroxide. Hydrogen sulfide was added to the sea water and the sulfide concentration in the cell sap was determined when equilibrium had been reached. At pH 5, H_2S exists almost entirely as undissociated free acid, whereas at pH 10 it is dissociated into bisulfide (HS^-) ions. Osterhout found that at all pH values from 5 to 10, the sulfide concentration inside the cell was directly proportional to the concentration of the undissociated acid outside the cell. This means that at pH 10, the sulfide concentration inside the cell was almost zero, whereas at pH 5 it was almost the same as outside the cell.

Several similar examples can be found in the literature. Here we shall mention only one more case, which is significant for the discussion of the effects of chemicals on dividing cells.

2,4-Dinitrophenol (DNP) is an uncoupling agent; i.e., it inhibits oxidative phosphorylation but not respiration. Since the respiration-coupled phosphorylation, as a rule, is the most important of the various ways by which the cell can generate the energy-rich phosphate bonds required for so many of its activities, treatments with DNP will affect many different processes in the cell, including growth, division, movement, cytosis, and absorption of ions and certain metabolites. The effect of DNP on these processes is dependent on the pH of the solution, being much stronger at low than at high pH. This means that to produce a certain inhibitory effect, much higher concentrations of DNP are needed at high than at low pH.

Stenlid (1949) studied the effect of DNP on glucose absorption in wheat roots at various pH values. He found that the DNP concentration necessary for obtaining a significant inhibition of glucose uptake was 8×10^{-7}M at pH 4.6, 3×10^{-6}M at pH 5.8, and 2×10^{-5}M at pH 7. DNP is a weak acid with a pK_a of 4.0, which means that DNP is dissociated to 50 per cent at pH 4. At pH 3, 90 per cent of the DNP molecules would be undissociated; at pH 5, 90 per cent would be dissociated. Stenlid also studied, spectrophotometrically, the uptake of DNP into the wheat roots. He found a much faster absorption of DNP at pH 4.5 than at pH 7.0, and concluded that the stronger effect of DNP in acid solution is due to a more rapid absorption of the undissociated acid.

It will appear in Chaps. 10 and 12 that the chromosome-breaking effects of the weak acids maleic hydrazide and N-nitroso-N-phenylhydroxyl amine are stronger at low than at high pH. The most likely explanation is that the compounds in question are taken up better as undissociated molecules. That uncharged molecules enter the cell more rapidly than the charged ions appears to be a result of the plasma membrane's being electrically charged.

Active transport through the plasma membrane is indicated when the agent is taken up against a concentration gradient and when the uptake is dependent on respiration energy. The accumulation of potassium in cells is an example of active transport. Of more interest to us are cases in which the absorption of nonelectrolytes or weak electrolytes has been the result of active transport. Such a case has been described by Birt and Hird (1956). They found that carrot slices can take up amino acids from the medium against a concentration gradient. The process of uptake was inhibited by DNP and by cyanide, which indicated that respiration energy was needed for the absorption.

Another probable case of active transport is the above-mentioned absorption of glucose by wheat roots, which was studied by Stenlid (1949), since the absorption was inhibited by DNP and by sodium azide. Stenlid's paper does not reveal if the other criterion for active transport, transport against a concentration gradient, is fulfilled.

Rickenberg and Maio (1961) have observed that mouse cells in tissue culture (strain L) take up galactose and glucose from the medium against a concentration gradient. The uptake was inhibited by anoxia, but was not significantly affected by inhibitors of oxidative phosphorylation (DNP, sodium azide) or glycolysis (iodoacetate). The lack of an effect of the inhibitors of oxidative phosphorylation indicates that active transport was not involved in the uptake of sugars by L-cells, particularly since uptake against a concentration gradient may also occur when the substance is transformed inside the cell, for example, by being polymerized.

Among the various theories proposed to explain active transport, those involving a carrier molecule are most popular. At the outer surface of the plasma membrane the substance to be transported forms, in the presence of an enzyme, a complex with an organic carrier molecule containing an energy-rich bond. The membrane is permeable to the complex, which moves across the membrane to its inner surface, where the substance is split off from the complex by another enzyme. Metabolic energy is believed to be required for the synthesis of the carrier and, possibly, for the splitting of the complex (Kramer, 1956).

The type of active transport described above does not apply to very large molecules, such as protein molecules or DNA molecules, which may be taken up by a mechanism called *pinocytosis* or *phagocytosis*. The process may vary in structural appearance and dimensions, but its essential feature appears to be that "a certain area of the surface membrane of the cell encloses a droplet of the surrounding medium, separates from the surface and migrates into the cell" (Holter, 1961).

According to Brandt (1958), pinocytosis in amoeba is initiated by the adsorption of charged solutes on the plasma membrane. The adsorption results in a decrease of the tension and structural rigidity of the membrane. The weakened membrane with the attached solute would then be drawn into the cytoplasm, where it forms an invagination which becomes detached from the membrane and freed in the cytoplasm. Studies by de Terra and Rustad (1959) in amoeba have shown that the formation of invaginations and vessels is inhibited by cyanide and carbon monoxide, which indicates that it is dependent on the oxidative metabolism of the cell.

Previously, it was customary to distinguish between *pinocytosis,* where the ingested material is invisible, and *phagocytosis,* where the ingested material is visible. However, recent biochemical and electron-microscopic studies have shown that there is no real distinction between pinocytosis and phagocytosis, which may merely be regarded as two different types of a basically similar process. Novikoff (1961) has suggested the term *cytosis* to separate these processes "from the continuous intake into cells by diffusion or 'active transport' across the cell membrane."

Cytosis has essentially been observed in animal cells, but electron micrographs indicate that the process may also occur in plant cells. The plasma membrane of plant cells is often very irregular, forming bags and invaginations which "may course around what appear to be particles outside the protoplast" (Whaley et al., 1960a) (see Fig. 1-3). The electron micrographs, of course, do not tell anything about the direction of the process, which could be an excretion as well as an uptake. That proteins are able to penetrate into plant cells is indicated by the studies

11

of Kaufmann and Das (1955), who found that treatment of onion-root tips with the enzyme ribonuclease resulted in mitotic abnormalities, and by the observations of Brachet (1956) that protein synthesis is inhibited and ribonucleic acid (RNA) broken down in onion-root tips treated with crystalline ribonuclease.

Of particular interest from a genetic point of view is the observation that mammalian cells in tissue culture are able to take up whole deoxyribonucleic acid (DNA) molecules from the intercellular environment by cytosis, because it indicates that the phenomenon of DNA-mediated genetic transformation, now well established in bacteria, may also be possible in mammalian cells. During the last few years, conclusive evidence has been presented for the incorporation of extracellular high-molecular-weight DNA into the nuclear DNA of mouse (e.g., Gartler, 1960; Kay, 1961; Bensch and King, 1961; Hill, 1961) and human (e.g., Hoskins and Montgomery, 1962; Szybalska and Szybalski, 1962) cells in tissue culture. That this incorporation may indeed result in transformation of genetic characteristics has been demonstrated by Szybalska and Szybalski (1962). They treated a human cell line which lacked the enzyme inosinic acid pyrophosphorylase (IMPPase) with DNA isolated from IMPPase-positive cells. The treatment resulted in the appearance of IMPPase-positive, genetically transformed cells. The transforming activity was abolished by deoxyribonuclease, but not by ribonuclease. DNA isolated from IMPPase-negative cells or from cells of other mammals had no transforming activity.

That not only DNA or DNA-protein complexes (Cocito et al., 1962), but also whole chromosomes are taken up by mammalian cells has been shown by Chorazy et al. (1963b). They found that in vitro exposure of mouse macrophages, HeLa cells, and rat embryo fibroblasts to chromosomes isolated from leukemic mouse cells resulted in the uptake of these chromosomes by a mechanism resembling cytosis. Since the chromosomes were labeled with H^3-thymidine, they could be traced by radioautography as well as by staining techniques and phase-contrast microscopy. The uptake of chromosomes during the first six hours was found to be restricted to the cytoplasm, but penetration into the nucleus occurred after longer exposures. The uptake was enhanced by glucose and inulin and inhibited by iodoacetate. The authors concluded, "There is no reason *a priori* to exclude the possibility that some new biological activity or property may appear in cells which have acquired new chromosomes by the process of pinocytosis or phagocytosis."

C. Mitochondria, Respiration, and Oxidative Phosphorylation

Mitochondria occur in the cytoplasm of nearly all aerobic plant and animal cells. They may be either rod-shaped or spherical and they may change from one shape to another. The diameter of spherical mitochondria varies between 0.5 and 1μ, and the long diameter of rod-shaped mitochondria may be greater than 10μ. The number of mitochondria is different in different types of cells; in the rat liver cell there are 1000 to 2500 mitochondria. For identifying mitochondria in the living cell, staining with Janus Green B or with tetrazolium is the easiest and most commonly used method. Chemical analyses of mitochondria have shown that lipids and protein are the main constituents of dry mitochondria. The lipid content amounts to about 30 per cent of the dry weight and the protein content to 65 to 70 per cent. The lipids appear to be mostly of the phosphatide type. A small amount of RNA is generally found in mitochondria, but it is possibly derived from ribosomes contaminating the mitochondrial fraction. Good evidence has recently been obtained for DNA's being a mitochondrial component (e.g., Nass and Nass, 1963a, b; Guttes and Guttes, 1964).

The structure of mitochondria has been revealed in great detail by electron microscopic studies (Fig. 1-6). The electron micrographs show

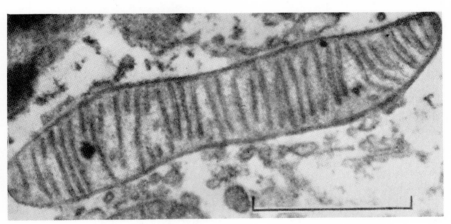

Fig. 1–6. Electron micrograph of mitochondrion in a mouse kidney cell. [Dalton and Felix, 1957; Symp. Soc. Exp. Biol. 10 (Fig. 4 A, Plate 2). Courtesy of A. J. Dalton.]

that the mitochondrion is surrounded by two membranes, each of which is about 60 A thick and separated from the other by a clear space. The inner membrane is folded to form the so-called *cristae*, which may be described as saclike extensions from the inner membrane into the interior of the mitochondrion. The membranes are believed to be built on the same principles as the plasma membrane. They contain lipids and proteins, but there is some disagreement about the molecular architecture of the membranes. According to one theory, the membranes consist of double layers of lipid molecules sandwiched between protein molecules; according to another, the membranes are networks of alternating protein and lipid units linked by hydrophobic bonds.

It has been known for some time that the mitochondria function as centers for the release of chemical energy by aerobic oxidation and the conversion of this energy into the energy-rich phosphate bonds of adenosinetriphosphate (ATP). This coupling of oxidation to synthesis of ATP has been called *oxidative phosphorylation,* and is the universal function of all mitochondria. In the energy-rich bond of ATP, the energy released by oxidation of foodstuff is stored in a form that can be utilized by the cell. Most of the energy required by the cell is provided in this way, and since most of the ATP is produced in mitochondria, they have been called "the powerhouse of the cell."

The substance oxidized by mitochondria is usually pyruvic acid ($CH_3COCOOH$) which has been produced outside the mitochondria from glucose by a mechanism which does not require the presence of oxygen. This mechanism, called *glycolysis,* is shown in Fig. 1-7. For each glucose molecule broken down by glycolysis, two molecules of pyruvic acid are formed, glucose containing six carbon atoms and pyruvic acid containing three. Glycolysis is a comparatively inefficient mechanism, resulting under anaerobic conditions in a gain of only two energy-rich phosphate bonds per molecule of glucose. In the glycolytic process, two molecules of NAD (nicotinamide-adenine dinucleotide, previously called diphosphopyridine nucleotide [DPN]) are reduced. Under anaerobic conditions, NAD may be regained by a reaction whereby the two pyruvic acid molecules are reduced by NADH to lactic acid. In alcoholic fermentation, pyruvic acid is first decarboxylated, whereupon the resulting acetic aldehyde is reduced by NADH to ethyl alcohol. In the presence of oxygen, on the other hand, pyruvic acid is further oxidized within the mitochondria, where the reduced NAD formed by glycolysis is also reoxidized. As already noted, it is in connection with these mitochondrial reactions that most of the ATP is formed.

Glycolysis is inhibited by *iodoacetate* (phosphoglyceraldehyde dehydrogenase reaction) and *fluoride* (enolase reaction).

Within the mitochondria, pyruvic acid is oxidized to carbon dioxide and water by way of the tricarboxylic acid (TCA) or citric acid cycle (Fig. 1-8). The first step is the conversion of pyruvic acid into the two-carbon compound acetic acid, which enters the TCA cycle in a combined or activated form with coenzyme A. By this oxidative decarboxylation process, one molecule of carbon dioxide is formed. Active acetate condenses with oxaloacetic acid to form the six-carbon compound citric acid.

In subsequent steps of the cycle, citric acid undergoes a series of rearrangements and degradations, resulting in the regeneration of oxaloacetic acid and the oxidation of the two carbons of the acetic acid to form two molecules of carbon dioxide. The TCA cycle is effectively inhibited by *fluoroacetate.*

In the oxidation of pyruvic acid, five pairs of electrons and five pairs of hydrogen atoms are removed from the substrate; four of each are picked up by NAD or possibly by NADP (nicotinamide-adenine dinucleotide phosphate, previously called triphosphopyridine nucleotide,

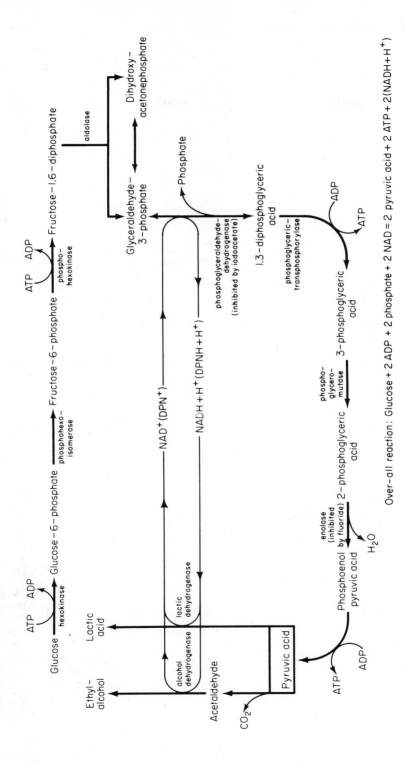

Fig. 1–7. The glycolytic sequence. (After Beevers, 1961; Respiratory Metabolism in Plants, p. 22.)

Over-all reaction: Glucose + 2 ADP + 2 phosphate + 2 NAD = 2 pyruvic acid + 2 ATP + 2(NADH+H⁺)

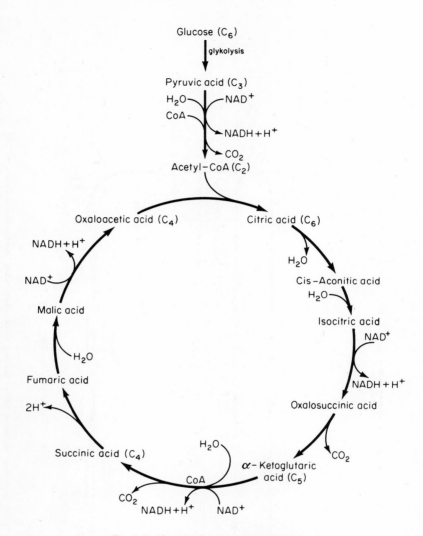

Fig. 1–8. The tricarboxylic acid (TCA) cycle.

TPN), which are the coenzymes of dehydrogenases catalyzing specific steps in the oxidation sequence. From the pyridine nucleotides the electrons and hydrogen atoms are transferred to flavoproteins and from the flavoproteins probably to a tetra-substituted benzoquinone, coenzyme Q.

The next reaction would be an oxidation of coenzyme Q by iron-containing cell pigments known as cytochromes, which pick up the electrons, the hydrogen atoms at the same time being given off into the cell fluid as hydrogen ions. The electrons are passed over the cytochrome chain to molecular oxygen, which then is capable of uniting with the hydrogen ions under the formation of water (Fig. 1-9). The transport

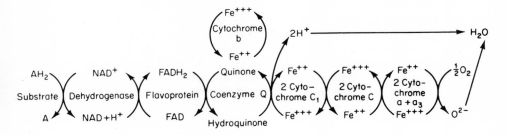

Fig. 1–9. Electron transport chain.

of one pair of electrons from the reduced pyridine nucleotide to molecular oxygen results in the formation of three molecules of ATP. One of the energy-rich bonds is formed between NADH and flavoprotein, another between flavoprotein and cytochrome C, and the third between cytochrome C and oxygen. As a result of the pyridine nucleotide mediated transfer of hydrogen and electrons from substrate to molecular oxygen, $4 \times 3 = 12$ ATP molecules are formed. The fifth pair of electrons, which is removed from succinic acid by the flavoprotein enzyme succinic dehydrogenase, is transferred directly to the cytochromes and, therefore, yields only two molecules of ATP.

When the five pairs of hydrogen ions combine with oxygen, five molecules of water are formed. However, since by the reactions of the TCA cycle, three molecules of water are consumed, the gain is two molecules of water per molecule of pyruvic acid. The number of carbon dioxide molecules formed from one molecule of pyruvic acid is three, and the over-all reaction may thus be written as

$$CH_3COCOOH + \tfrac{5}{2} O_2 = 3 CO_2 + 2 H_2O$$

The electron transport over the respiratory chain is strongly inhibited by *cyanide, azide,* and *carbon monoxide,* which react with the iron in the cytochrome oxidase. The inhibition of cytochrome oxidase by carbon monoxide is reversed by light. Cytochrome respiration is also inhibited by certain heavy-metal complexing agents such as *cupferron* (see page 137). The phosphorylation coupled to the respiratory chain is inhibited by *2,4-dinitrophenol.*

The enzymes connected with the TCA cycle appear to be located on the outer membrane of the mitochondrion, whereas those concerned with electron transfers leading to the synthesis of ATP are on the inner membrane (Green, 1964). The pyridine-adenine nucleotides pick up the electrons released in the outer membrane by the reactions of the TCA cycle and shuttle them across the liquid-filled space between the membranes to the electron-transfer particles on the inner membrane.

Many microorganisms and some embryonic tissue cells of higher organisms (e.g., embryonic chick cells; see Bullough, 1952) are able to fill their energy requirements through glycolysis. However, in most cells of higher organisms, ATP is produced by the processes of oxidative phosphorylation in the mitochondria. The effects of many chemical agents on mitosis and on chromosome structure have been found to be dependent on the aerobic generation of ATP. In some cases only the uptake of the chemical may be influenced; in others oxidative phosphorylation appears to be involved in the action mechanism of the chemical.

Before we leave the subject of respiration, it may be pertinent to consider the relationship which exists in organized tissues between oxygen concentration and oxygen uptake. An enzyme such as cytochrome

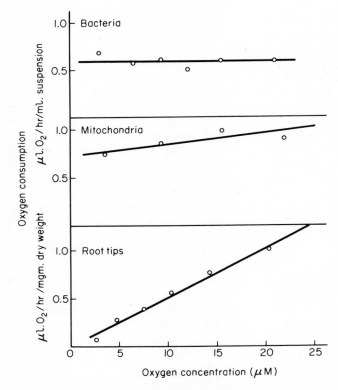

Fig. 1–10. The relationship between oxygen concentration and oxygen consumption in bacteria, bean root-tips, and mitochondria isolated from bean root-tips. (Odmark and Kihlman, 1962; Nature 194, p. 595. Reprinted by permission of the Editor of Nature.)

oxidase has a very high affinity toward oxygen and is saturated at very low concentrations of oxygen. The oxygen uptake of isolated mitochondria and of unicellular organisms with cytochrome oxidase as their terminal oxidase is, therefore, independent of oxygen tension from 100 per cent down to about 0.3 per cent oxygen in the gas phase. In organized tissues, such as root tips and anthers, the oxygen uptake decreases when the oxygen concentration is lowered below that in air. The decrease occurs because the diffusion of oxygen into the tissue is prevented by the oxygen consumption of the outer cell layers; therefore, fewer and fewer of the cells in the tissue in question are taking part in the oxygen consumption as the oxygen concentration in the surrounding fluid decreases.

The existence of such an oxygen gradient in roots is suggested by Fig. 1-10, which shows the relationship between oxygen concentration and oxygen consumption for bacteria (*Escherichia coli*), for broad bean roots (*Vicia faba*), and for mitochondria isolated from the broad bean roots (Odmark and Kihlman, 1962).

If the terminal oxidase is a flavo-protein enzyme which has a low affinity toward oxygen, the oxygen uptake is expected to increase with oxygen concentration, even in the absence of an oxygen gradient (James, 1953).

The Chemistry and Physiology
of the Interphase Nucleus

A. Chemistry of the Nucleus As a Whole

NUCLEIC ACIDS

The studies performed by Kossel and his collaborators around the turn of the century showed that the nucleic acids were composed of purine and pyrimidine bases, carbohydrate, and phosphoric acid. It further appeared from these studies that the nucleic acid isolated from yeast contained a carbohydrate component other than that isolated from tissues of animal origin. It was later found that the carbohydrate component of yeast nucleic acid was identical with the pentose sugar D-ribose, whereas the nucleic acid isolated from thymus gland contained D-deoxyribose. For this reason, the two types of nucleic acids are now called ribonucleic acid (RNA) and deoxyribonucleic acid (DNA). The two nucleic acids also differ in their base constituents, which are adenine, guanine, cytosine and *uracil* in RNA and adenine, guanine, cytosine and *thymine* in DNA.

The observation that yeast nucleic acid was of RNA type, whereas thymus nucleic acid was of DNA type, together with the subsequent identification of a nucleic acid isolated from wheat embryo as RNA, led to the conclusion that DNA occurred only in animal cells and was replaced by RNA in plant cells. It was also believed that all nucleic acid, independent of type and organism, always occurred in the nucleus, and only there (Fig. 2-1a).

However, in 1924 Feulgen found (with the aid of the staining method which is now known as the Feulgen technique) that DNA occurred in cell nuclei from both plant and animal tissues (Feulgen and Rossenbeck 1924). In subsequent experiments, Feulgen et al. (1937)

demonstrated chemically the presence of DNA in nuclei isolated from rye embryo. This was the definite evidence for the existence of DNA in plant cell nuclei. On the basis of these results, Feulgen claimed that DNA always occurred in cell nuclei and only there, whereas RNA would be the nucleic acid of the cytoplasm (Fig. 2-1b).

For a time it seemed as if Feulgen was right. Behrens (1938) iso-

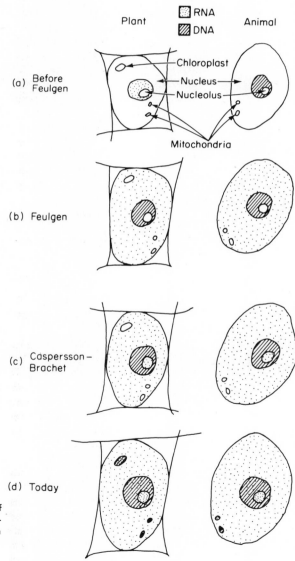

Fig. 2–1. The development of our concept of the distribution of RNA and DNA in plant and animal cells.

lated RNA from nucleus-free cytoplasm, and the ultraviolet microscopic analyses of Caspersson and his collaborators (1939, 1940, 1941) showed that the cytoplasm of both animal and plant cells contains a nucleic acid which, since it is Feulgen-negative, has to be RNA. Brachet demonstrated RNA in cytoplasm with the methyl-green-pyronin technique (1940, 1942). That RNA occurs in cytoplasm and DNA only in cell nuclei was confirmed by chemical analyses of cell fractions obtained by centrifugation of macerated cells (Schneider, 1946a; 1946b).

However, at the same time as the occurrence of RNA in cytoplasm was proved, it was found that RNA, along with DNA, is also one of the chemical constituents of cell nuclei. Independently of each other, Caspersson and Schultz (1940) and Brachet (1940) demonstrated the occurrence of RNA in the nucleolus (Fig. 2-1c). This discovery was subsequently confirmed by chemical analyses of isolated nucleoli (e.g., Vincent, 1952). That RNA also occurs in chromosomes has been shown by staining techniques (Brachet, 1942; Kaufmann et al., 1951), radioautographic experiments (Taylor, 1953b; Pelc and Howard, 1956), and chemical analyses of isolated interphase chromosomes (Mirsky and Ris, 1947; Gall, 1955).

The occurrence of RNA in the cell nucleus as a whole has become apparent from numerous analyses of isolated nuclei (e.g., Schneider, 1946a, b; Vendrely and Vendrely, 1948; Dounce et al., 1950; Davidson and McIndoe, 1949; Allfrey et al., 1952). Thus Feulgen, who had so elegantly demonstrated the incorrectness of the belief that DNA occurs only in animal cell nuclei and is replaced by RNA in plant cell nuclei, proved to be wrong when he claimed that RNA occurred only in the cytoplasm.

During the last decade it has been found that Feulgen's other statement, that DNA occurs exclusively in the cell nucleus, is not quite correct either. Extranuclear DNA has been reported in a variety of biological systems. The DNA is frequently associated with autonomous or semiautonomous cytoplasmic organelles such as the kinetoplast of trypanosomes (Steinert et al., 1958), mitochondria (Nass and Nass, 1963a, b; Guttes and Guttes, 1964), and chloroplasts of algae (Iwamura, 1960; Ris and Plaut, 1962) and higher plants (Kirk, 1963; Baltus and Brachet, 1963; Pollard, 1964) (Fig. 2-1d). The DNA-containing particles in the cytoplasm of amoeba (Rabinovitch and Plaut, 1962a), which multiply intracellularly, are probably infective organisms of bacterial or rickettsialike nature which have been taken up by cytosis from the medium (Roth and Daniels, 1961; Rabinovitch and Plaut, 1962b).

There are also cases, however, in which the cytoplasmic location of DNA has not been related to a recognizable structure. Chemical analyses performed by Vendrely and Vendrely (1948) indicated that the egg of the sea urchin contains several hundred times more DNA than the sperm cells. This result is incompatible with the idea that DNA occurs only in the cell nucleus and there in an amount related to the chromosome number. A few years later, Hoff-Jørgensen and Zeuthen (1952) showed that most of the DNA in the egg cells of amphibia are located in the cytoplasm, a finding which has subsequently been confirmed by several other authors (e.g., Finamore and Volkin, 1958; Bieber et al., 1959). The DNA in the cytoplasm of egg cells is probably of a low molecular weight (Bieber et al., 1959). A year before publication of the results of Hoff-Jørgensen and Zeuthen, Fraenkel-Conrat and Ducay (1951) reported that the compound avidin, which occurs in hen egg white, is a deoxyribonucleiprotein. The occurrence of DNA in the cytoplasm appears to be a characteristic of egg cells.

The nuclear DNA is generally believed to be located within the chromosomes. Thus, chromosomes isolated from interphase nuclei were found to contain DNA as one of their main constituents (Mirsky and Ris, 1947, 1951). The claim by Stedman and Stedman (1947) that DNA of the interphase nucleus occurs exclusively in the nuclear sap has not been confirmed; however, chemical analyses of the DNA content in the sap of newt oocyte nuclei have given somewhat contradictory results. Brown et al. (1950) did not obtain any evidence for the presence of DNA in the nuclear sap, whereas Izawa et al. (1963) found that the nucleoplasm contained as much DNA as the chromosomes.

As a rule, the DNA content of nuclei from different types of cells within the same organism is proportional to the number of chromosomes. Thus, a haploid cell nucleus, such as the sperm cell nucleus, has one-half the amount of DNA found in the diploid somatic cells, and a tetra-ploid cell has twice the DNA content of a diploid cell (Vendrely and Vendrely, 1948; Mirsky and Ris, 1949; see also Hauschka and Levan, 1951).

It has further been found that mitotic prophase nuclei, which have twice as many chromátids as the telophase nuclei, also have twice the amount of DNA. The prophase nuclei contained twice the diploid amount of DNA (4C) and the telophase nuclei contained the diploid value (2C). These findings show that DNA is synthesized during inter-phase (Swift, 1953).

The percentage of DNA is different in different types of cell nuclei. Thus, whereas the sperm cell nuclei may contain as much as 50 per cent of DNA (Stedman and Stedman, 1947), the dry substance of nuclei from the oocytes of amphibia contain only a small part of DNA. The percentage values are also influenced by the method used for the isolation of the nuclei. As a rule, the DNA content appears to be between 10 and 30 per cent of the dry weight (see, for instance, Dounce, 1952; Pollister, 1952; Allfrey et al., 1952). The RNA content is usually below 5 per cent and is thus considerably lower than the DNA content (Vendrely and Vendrely, 1948; Davidson and McIndoe, 1949; Allfrey et al., 1952; Pollister, 1952). In a recent study, Maggio et al. (1963a) found the nuclear fraction from guinea pig liver to contain $\sim$ 22. 3 per cent DNA, $\sim$ 4. 7 per cent RNA, and $\sim$ 33 per cent protein.

Chemical analyses have indicated the presence of several types of RNA in the nucleus. Allfrey and Mirsky (1957) found, "The ribonucleic acids of isolated thymus nuclei can be separated into two distinct fractions, one of which probably represents ribonucleic acid of the nucleolus." The fractions differed in their metabolic activities and susceptibility to an inhibition of RNA synthesis. The results of Maggio et al. (1963*b*) indicated that there are at least three types of RNA in nuclei isolated from guinea pig liver, "which differ from one another in NaCl-solubility, nucleotide composition, turnover, and possibly sequence." These observations are not surprising on the basis of our present concepts of the function of DNA and RNA.

The genetic information is contained in the nucleotide sequence of DNA. Since the phenotypical expression of this information is a result of the formation and activity of specific proteins, the nucleotide sequence in DNA has to be transformed into the amino acid sequence of the proteins. The various types of RNA apparently play the key role in this transformation.

It is customary to distinguish between three main types of RNA: messenger RNA (mRNA), transfer or soluble RNA (sRNA), and ribosomal RNA (rRNA). In the synthesis of mRNA from the nucleoside triphosphates, DNA functions as a template and mRNA is believed to contain a nucleotide sequence and genetic information corresponding to that of the DNA template. From the chromosomes where it is synthesized the mRNA is transferred to the cytoplasm where, attached to a ribosome, it functions as a template for the synthesis of a protein.

The DNA-like mRNA represents only about 10 per cent of total cellular RNA. Most of the RNA in the cell (75 to 80 per cent) is in the form of rRNA. The nucleotide sequence in rRNA has little resemblance to that in DNA, and rRNA appears to have only a passive role in information transfer. There is no clear-cut evidence that rRNA contains any information for protein structure, but it is a necessary component of the ribosomes on which protein synthesis occurs with mRNA as a template.

sRNA contains only about 70 to 80 nucleotides and has, thus, a low molecular weight. sRNA forms complexes with amino acids and functions in the transfer of amino acids and in their arrangement according to the information contained in mRNA (for literature on the subject of information transfer, see Sibatani, 1963; Volkin, 1963; Lipmann, 1963). There are probably at least as many molecular species of sRNA as there are amino acids in proteins.

The synthesis of DNA at the biochemical and cytological level will be described in separate chapters (Chaps. 4 and 5). Information about the synthesis of RNA is rather controversial. This is particularly true for the location of RNA synthesis, as will appear from the following pairs of quotations: "RNA synthesis was shown to be confined to the nucleus. . ." (Taylor, 1960*a*)—"These findings do not support the view that all the RNA of the cell is synthesized on the chromosomes; they indicate that substantial synthesis of RNA takes place in the cytoplasm. . ."

(Harris and LaCour, 1963); "The nucleolar ribonucleic acid is synthesized at the nucleolar organizers only. . ." (Pelling, 1959)—"Several lines of evidence indicated in *Smittia* that the synthesis of nucleolar RNA begins in the nucleolus proper and that the synthesis is dissociable from the synthesis in the organizer. . ." (Sirlin et al., 1963); ". . . it may be concluded that the primary site for transfer RNA synthesis is in N, the part of the nucleus containing the major portion of the chromosomes. . ." (Perry, 1962)—"The evidence presented above implicates transfer RNA as a product of this nucleolar synthesis. . ." (Birnstiel et al., 1965); ". . . a significant part of the ribosomal RNA has its origin in the nucleolus. . ." (Perry, 1963)—"It is concluded that the bulk of the ribosomal RNA—if not all—is manufactured by nonnucleolar regions of the chromatin. . ." (Chipchase and Birnstiel, 1963).

Although considerable confusion exists regarding the exact location of the syntheses of the various types of RNA, most authors seem to agree that RNA is synthesized within the nucleus, on the chromosomes as well as in the nucleolus, and then passed to the cytoplasm (Woods, 1959; Taylor, 1960a; Prescott and Bender, 1962; Muramatsu et al., 1964). Results obtained in radioautographic studies on RNA synthesis during mitosis in plant (Woodard et al., 1961; Das, 1963) and mammalian (Taylor, 1960a; Prescott and Bender, 1962; Feinendegen and Bond, 1963; Konrad, 1963; Reiter and Littlefield, 1964) tissues have shown that nuclear RNA synthesis in daughter cells begins at late telophase, continues during all stages of interphase, and stops in mid or late prophase.

According to Sirlin and his coworkers, chromosomal RNA synthesis is totally inhibited by 5,6-dichloro-1-(β-D-ribofuranosyl)benzimidazole (DRB) and by benzamide at concentrations which have only slight effects on nucleolar RNA synthesis (Sirlin and Jacob, 1964). Proflavine and actinomycin D, on the other hand, suppress the RNA synthesis in the nucleolus completely, but that on the chromosomes only partially (Sirlin et al., 1963; Muramatsu et al., 1964). That actinomycin D is a more effective inhibitor of nucleolar than of chromosomal RNA synthesis is somewhat surprising, because actinomycin is known to block DNA-dependent RNA synthesis selectively (e.g., Reich, 1964). This dilemma has been discussed by Perry (1962, 1963), who concludes that the inhibitory effect of actinomycin on nucleolar RNA synthesis is compatible with the idea that actinomycin blocks DNA-dependent RNA synthesis selectively, if it is assumed that the DNA of the nucleolar organizer region of the chromosomes has a particularly high affinity for actinomycin D.

PROTEINS

In his chemical analyses of salmon sperm, Miescher (1874) found that these cytoplasm-free cells contained, besides DNA, an organic base of high nitrogen content. Miescher called this base *protamine*. Kossel and his collaborators later found that protamine was a protein of low molecular weight. The basic character was a result of its high content of basic amino acids, among which arginine was predominant. According to Miescher's calculations, the dry substance of the salmon sperm heads consists of 30 per cent protamine and 60 per cent nucleic acid. Subsequent reports have appeared which indicate the presence of protein other than protamine in the heads of salmon sperm (Stedman and Stedman, 1947). However, the more recent analyses of Felix and his collaborators (1956) have confirmed Miescher's results.

In nuclei of somatic cells, protamine is replaced by *histone*. Like protamine, histone is a basic protein, but it contains a larger variety of amino acids and has a higher molecular weight than protamine. In spermatogenesis, histones are transformed into protamines (Allfrey et al., 1955*a*). The percentage values for the nuclear content of histones usually vary between 10 and 30 per cent of the dry weight of the nucleus.

The cell nucleus also contains proteins of nonbasic character. Best known is a water-insoluble, tryptophan-containing protein which probably was first isolated by the Stedmans (1943). They succeeded in isolating from different cell nuclei not only DNA and histone or protamine, but also a protein with acid properties which they called *chromosomin*. In contrast with histone, chromosomin contains relatively large amounts of tryptophan.

A few years later, Mirsky and Pollister (1946) extracted from tissues and isolated nuclei a DNA protein complex which they called *chromosin*. The protein component of chromosin contained, besides histone, another protein which, in contrast with histone, had a low nitrogen content and was soluble in $HgSO_4—H_2SO_4$. It differed from histone also in that it had a relatively high tryptophan content. It is possible that the tryptophan-containing protein in the chromosin of Mirsky and Pollister is identical with the chromosomin of the Stedmans. Subsequently, Mirsky and Ris (1947, 1951) found a tryptophan-containing protein, which they called *residual protein*, in chromosomes isolated from interphase nuclei.

In 1949, Thomas and Mayer obtained from boar sperm cells a protein fraction which, in contrast with histone, could be extracted with alkali but was insoluble in water and neutral salt solutions. Most of the protein fraction precipitated when the pH of the solution was lowered to pH 6. The protein fraction which precipitated at pH 6 contained the majority of the known amino acids, among them tryptophan. Subsequently, Wang and collaborators (1950, 1952, 1953) made a detailed analysis of this fraction, which they found in cell nuclei isolated from a variety of animal tissues. The fraction proved to consist of a lipoprotein, the lipid content being about 10 per cent; the complex also contained 0.8 per cent calcium. The same lipoprotein was found in chromosomes isolated from interphase nuclei by the method of Mirsky and Ris (Wang et al., 1952). Wang et al. believe that this lipoprotein is identical with the chromosomin of the Stedmans and probably also with the tryptophan-containing protein of Mirsky et al. Another possibility is that the lipid-containing protein is derived from the nuclear membrane (Wang et al., 1953).

Histone and the tryptophan-containing protein are evidently the principal protein constituents of chromosomes. In addition to these proteins, the cell nucleus is likely to contain a considerable fraction of non-basic proteins, which are easily soluble in water and which, therefore, are largely washed out from nuclei isolated in aqueous solution (Dounce, 1952).

As first shown by Allfrey et al. (1955a), isolated cell nuclei are capable of synthesizing proteins. The nuclear protein synthesis in root tips of *Vicia faba* was studied by Pelc and Howard (1952) by the radioautographic technique. Judged by the uptake of radioactive sulfur (S^{35}), the protein synthesis occurred approximately during the same period of interphase as the synthesis of DNA. Taylor and Taylor (1953) arrived at a similar conclusion regarding the protein synthesis during meiosis in *Lilium*. The photometric studies of Alfert (1955) and McLeish (1959) indicated that the synthesis of the basic proteins of the cell nucleus occurred simultaneously with the synthesis of DNA. However, some recent studies have indicated that the synthesis of histones continues during the entire interphase period and is interrupted only during mitoses (Woodard et al., 1961; Dounce, quoted by Busch, 1963). There is evidence that histone synthesis in both plant and animal cell systems is not dependent on active DNA replication or cell division (Flamm and Birnstiel, 1964; Ontko and Moorehead, 1964).

LIPIDS

The occurrence of lipids as one of the chemical constituents of the cell nucleus was demonstrated by the observation mentioned above that the protein fraction isolated by Wang and his collaborators was a lipoprotein. However, ten years earlier Stoneburg (1939) had demonstrated the presence of lipids in nuclei isolated by the citric acid method, which he developed. The lipids proved to be phospholipids and cholesterin. Chemical analyses subsequently performed by other workers have, on the whole, given similar results (Haven and Levy, 1942; Dounce, 1943; Williams et al., 1945; Levine and Chargaff, 1952; Polli and Ratti, 1953). It is agreed that the cell nuclei contain phospholipids, particularly lecithin. The total content of lipids in the cell nucleus is usually between 10 and 20 per cent of the dry weight. The lipids derived from the lipoprotein isolated by Wang amount to between two and five per cent of the dry weight of the nucleus. The nuclear lipids are reported to be localized in the nuclear membrane (Baud, 1948; Callan and Tomlin, 1950), in the nucleolus (Albuquerque and Serra, 1951; Vincent, 1952; Zagury, 1957; LaCour and Chayen, 1958), and in the chromosomes (Wang et al., 1950; Chayen et al., 1957; LaCour and Chayen, 1958).

METALS

Iron was one of the first metals to be found in cell nuclei. The studies by Macallum in the 1890's indicated the presence of iron in cell nuclei of a variety of animal species. Miescher found iron in the heads of salmon sperm. He believed that iron occurred as a component of a high-molecular organic compound which he called *karyogen* (Miescher, 1897). Burian (1906) also mentions karyogen as one of the chemical constituents of cell nuclei. According to Burian, karyogen occurred in small quantities but had a high iron content.

The reliability of results based on histochemical determinations of iron has been questioned, however. As early as 1892 Gilson pointed out that nucleic acids have a high post-mortem affinity to iron and that it therefore was possible that the positive iron reaction had been caused by contamination from the outside.

Gulick (1941) found that if a slide preparation was treated with ammonium sulfide to unmask organically bound iron, the nuclei could stand for weeks without showing any iron reaction provided contaminations were carefully avoided. However, if traces of iron were added to the slide, all the nuclei were strongly stained with FeS within a few days. Gulick concluded that the positive iron reactions which had previously been obtained in cell nuclei were caused, in most cases, by contaminations, and that the studies failed to reveal the localization of iron in the living cell in the few cases in which contamination could not be the explanation, since the iron released in the cell would be rapidly absorbed on the chromosomes. Since the publication of Gulick's critical review in 1941, facts have emerged which strongly suggest that iron is actually a component of the cell nucleus.

The radioautographic studies by Poulson and Bowen (1952), using Fe^{59} and larvae of *Drosophila* species as experimental material, indicated that the iron content in some tissues was up to ten times higher in the nucleus than in the cytoplasm. Bass and her collaborators (Bass et al., 1957; Bass and Saltman, 1959) found that iron is taken up by rat liver slices against a concentration gradient. The cell nucleus was involved in the accumulation. Staining and radioautographic studies identified the nucleus as the initial site for the greatest iron incorporation.

The radioautographic studies of Possingham and Brown (1958) demonstrated the presence of iron in the cell nuclei of *Pisum sativum* root tips. Their results show that iron is a normal constituent of cell nuclei and there functions as a link between DNA and other nuclear constituents. This explanation of the role of iron in the cell nucleus is based on conclusions drawn by Kirby (1956), who has studied a water-soluble DNA protein complex isolated from rat liver nuclei. DNA was released if the complex was treated with heavy metal-complexing agents. Kirby concluded that DNA is combined with protein through metallic bonds.

The results indicated that the DNA protein complex contained comparatively high concentrations of iron and manganese.

The presence of iron, copper, and manganese in DNA from various sources has also been demonstrated by several authors (e.g., Loring and Waritz, 1957; Eisinger et al., 1961; Tooze and Davies, 1963; Amoore, 1962b; Gol'dshtein and Gerasimova, 1963). Trivalent iron appears to be chelated to an interior site in DNA, whereas copper (Cu^{2+}) and manganese (Mn^{2+}) are bound to exterior DNA sites, probably to the phosphate groups (Eisinger et al., 1961). Besides functioning as links between DNA and another nuclear constituent, iron and copper may be significant in the production of ATP by an oxidative mechanism, which has been reported to occur in nuclei isolated from mammalian tissues (Allfrey et al., 1955b; Creasey and Stocken, 1959).

Yakusizi (1936a, b) demonstrated the presence of zinc in cell nuclei. He found that in nuclei of erythrocytes and pus cells the zinc content was more than twice as high as in the cytoplasm. According to the findings of Dounce and Beyer (1948), the nuclei of rat liver contain 0.0012 per cent zinc.

Two metals which have been reported to be constituents of nuclei and chromosomes more than the others are calcium and magnesium. Policard and his co-workers have shown that when tissue sections are incinerated, the chromatin leaves a white ash which appears to be oxides of calcium and magnesium. The electron microscopic studies of Scott (1940a, b) have shown that the metal component of the ash really consisted of calcium and magnesium.

Williamson and Gulick (1942) determined the concentration of calcium and magnesium in nuclei isolated from thymus and found that the nuclei contained (on a dry weight basis) 1.35 per cent calcium and 0.09 per cent magnesium. The concentration of both metals proved to be three to four times higher in the nuclei than in the cytoplasm. That calcium occurs in cell nuclei is also apparent from the studies of Wang (1953) and collaborators; the nuclear lipoprotein isolated by these authors contained 0.8 per cent calcium. The occurrence of calcium in the pollen tube nuclei of *Lilium longiflorum* has been demonstrated in radioautographic experiments by Steffensen and Bergeron (1959). Mazia (1954) and Steffensen (1955) have suggested that the chromosome has a particulate structure, the units being linked by bridges of calcium or magnesium or both.

B. Enzyme Systems in the Interphase Nucleus

During the past 15 years the enzyme activities in isolated cell nuclei have been investigated by several groups of workers, among whom those associated with Hogeboom, Schneider, Dounce, and Mirsky in the United States and with Lang and Siebert in Germany should be especially mentioned. Some very interesting results have been obtained by these studies, although many data have been rather difficult to interpret because of the technical difficulties connected with the isolation procedure. In many cases the most reliable data have been obtained in studies with nuclei isolated in nonaqueous media. When aqueous media are used, there is always the risk that water-soluble nuclear enzymes will be washed out during the isolation procedure. Another common source of error is that the nuclear fraction is contaminated with cytoplasmic organelles and enzymes.

Instead of reviewing all the rather controversial literature on the subject of nuclear enzymes, we shall concentrate on certain enzymic systems of particular interest for the topic of this book, such as those involved in the generation of the energy required for the various nuclear functions, and those which catalyze the synthesis of nucleic acids.

There is no doubt that the energy required for nuclear synthesis of RNA, DNA, and protein is supplied in the form of ATP. The question is how and where nuclear ATP is formed. Is it produced in the mitochondria or in the nucleus? If the latter alternative proved to be true, which is then the mechanism for ATP formation?

It soon became evident that the cell nucleus was strikingly badly equipped with enzymes catalyzing oxidative processes. It has repeatedly been found that of the enzymes involved in the TCA cycle, succinic acid dehydrogenase does not occur in cell nuclei (Dounce, 1952; Siebert, 1963). If this was true it would mean, as pointed out by Dounce (1952), that the most efficient system for synthesis of energy-rich bonds, the TCA cycle, cannot function in the cell nucleus.

The cell nucleus also seems to lack the cytochrome system which transports electrons from the reduced flavine enzymes to molecular oxygen. It is true that Dounce (1952) for some time claimed that cytochrome oxidase occurred in the cell nucleus, but according to Schneider and Hogeboom (1951) the cytochrome oxidase activity in the nucleus was a consequence of the nuclear fraction being contaminated with mitochondria. The explanation given by Schneider and Hogeboom has now been accepted by Dounce (Dounce et al., 1953).

Since apparently neither the TCA cycle nor the cytochrome system is functioning in the cell nucleus, it seemed unlikely that the cell nucleus should be able to synthesize energy-rich phosphate by aerobic respiration. This can also be concluded by the observations of Dounce (1952), and Lan (1943) that the cell nucleus is defectively equipped with flavoproteins.

On the background of these results, the finding of Allfrey et al. (1955b) that isolated thymus nuclei are able to synthesize ATP in the presence of oxygen was the more surprising. Since the discovery in 1955, this system has been the subject of studies in several laboratories, including those of Allfrey and Mirsky. The phenomenon of intranuclear ATP-generation has been shown to occur not only in thymus nuclei from calf (Allfrey et al., 1955b) and rat (Betel and Klouwen, 1963) but also in nuclei from various other rat tissues including spleen, bone marrow, lymph nodes and intestinal mucosa (Creasey and Stocken, 1959). The studies in the laboratories of Allfrey and Mirsky (McEwen et al., 1963a, b, c) have produced the following facts.

The process occurs only in the presence of oxygen. Besides being inhibited by anoxia, intranuclear ATP production is inhibited by cyanide, azide, and dinitrophenol and resembles in these respects oxidative phosphorylation in mitochondria. In contrast to the ATP production in mitochondria, nuclear ATP synthesis is not inhibited by methylene blue, Ca^{2+} ions and carbon monoxide. (Table 2/1) On the other hand, nu-

TABLE 2–1

EFFECTS OF INHIBITORS OF MITOCHONDRIAL OXIDATIVE PHOSPHORYLATION ON NUCLEAR ATP SYNTHESIS. (ALLFREY, 1963; EXP. CELL RESEARCH, SUPPL. 9, P. 422. REPRINTED BY PERMISSION OF ACADEMIC PRESS, INC.)

Inhibitor Added	Concentration	% Change in ATP Level	% Change in Uptake of Alanine-1-^{14}C
NaCN	10^{-3} M	−100	−76
2, 4 dinitrophenol	2×10^{-4} M	−100	−84
NaN$_3$	1×10^{-3} M	−100	−91
Antimycin A	1 μg/ml	− 61	−89
Dicumarol	3×10^{-5} M	− 47	−96
Amytal	1×10^{-3} M	—	−86
Methylene blue	2×10^{-5} M	+ 31	+ 3
Methylene blue	2.5×10^{-4} M	+ 21	−18
Ca^{2+} ions	2×10^{-3} M	0	0
Ca^{2+} ions	3×10^{-3} M	0	0
Ca^{2+} ions	4×10^{-3} M	0	0
Carbon monoxide	95% CO-5% O$_2$	0	0

clear respiration and phosphorylation is inhibited by DNase treatments, which do not affect oxidative phosphorylation in mitochondria. These differences show that ATP synthesis by thymus nuclei is not caused by mitochondria in the nuclear suspension. It has further been found that the nuclear ATP is derived from an intranuclear nucleotide pool. Added AMP or ADP are not phosphorylated by thymus nuclei because nucleoside phosphates do not penetrate as such into the nuclei but are hydrolyzed to nucleosides or free bases. Under anaerobic conditions, there is a rapid decrease in ATP-concentration, which cannot solely be accounted for by utilization of ATP. The facts suggested that ATP during anaerobic conditions is stored in a form which is not extractable in dilute acid. Allfrey (1963) proposes that ATP is conserved by storage in the form of polyadenylic acid.

It thus seems clear that at least certain mammalian cell nuclei are able to synthesize ATP and do not have to import this energy intermediate from the cytoplasm. The recent studies by McEwen et al. have also provided much information about the mechanisms of intranuclear ATP formation.

That cell nuclei contain all the enzymes required for the anaerobic break down of hexose diphosphate to pyruvic acid, i.e., the enzymes of the glycolytic sequence, has been known for some time (Dounce, 1952, 1952; Stern and Mirsky, 1952) and was confirmed in the studies of McEwen et al. (1963b). However, according to McEwen et al. (1963b) thymus nuclei are also equipped with all the enzymes involved in the TCA cycle, including succinic dehydrogenase. That the aerobic production of ATP in calf thymus nuclei is dependent on glycolysis and the TCA cycle is also indicated by the fact that it is blocked by inhibitors of glycolysis (iodoacetate) and of the TCA cycle (fluoroacetate) (McEwen et al., 1963c). The presence of enzymes of the hexose phosphate shunt in calf thymus nuclei has also been demonstrated (McEwen et al., 1963b). On the basis of these results, Allfrey (1963) concludes: "Thus it appears that the nucleus can carry out oxidative reactions and that these reactions are coupled to ATP synthesis. The nature of the coupling remains to be determined, although the role of DPN as an intermediary in electron transport seems to be quite clear."

NAD (DPN) is of interest in this connection also because the enzyme responsible for its formation, NAD pyrophosphorylase, is located in the cell nucleus (Hogeboom and Schneider, 1952). The presence of NAD-pyrophosphorylase has been demonstrated in nuclei from a large number of different tissues, and the specific activity of this enzyme in relation to DNA appears always to be constant. According to Siebert (1963), "DPN pyrophosphorylase can serve as an indicator of nuclear material in a tissue preparation with the same reliability as, e.g., analyses for DNA."

NAD pyrophosphorylase catalyzes the reaction:

$$\text{nicotinamide mononucleotide} + \text{ATP} \rightleftharpoons \text{NAD} + \text{pyrophosphate}$$

Another enzyme, nucleoside phosphorylase, which catalyzes the synthesis of nicotinamide riboside from nicotinamide and ribose-1-phosphate, also occurs in comparatively high concentration within cell nuclei (Stern et al., 1952). High concentrations of NAD have been found in nuclei isolated from calf liver (Stern and Mirsky, 1952).

When energy-yielding reactions in the cell nucleus are discussed, it should perhaps be noted that polyribonucleotides which occur and are synthesized within the nucleus are a potential source for energy-rich phosphate bonds. In the presence of the enzyme polynucleotide phosphorylase, which was discovered by Grunberg-Manago et al. (1955), nucleoside diphosphates are produced from RNA and polyribonucleotides according to the reaction:

$$(X\text{-}R\text{-}P)n + n\text{P} \rightleftharpoons n X\text{-}R\text{-}P\text{-}P$$

where X is a purine or pyrimidine base, R is ribose, and P is orthophosphate. ATP can be produced from nucleoside diphosphates by the nucleoside monophosphate kinase reaction:

$$XDP + ADP \rightleftharpoons XMP + ATP$$
$$MP = \text{monophosphate.}$$
$$DP = \text{diphosphate.}$$
$$TP = \text{triphosphate.}$$

Both polynucleotide phosphorylase and nucleoside monophosphate kinase have been found in cell nuclei (Hilmoe and Heppel, 1957; Harris and Watts, 1962; Miller and Goldfeder, 1961; Kessler and Chen, 1964).

The studies of Allfrey and Mirsky and their collaborators have shown that the cell nucleus contains most of the known ribonucleoside mono-, di-, and triphosphates. Not unexpectedly, the presence in cell nuclei of the corresponding deoxyriboside compounds has also been demonstrated. The studies of Bekhi and Schneider (1962, 1963) indicate that both deoxyribonucleosides and deoxyribonucleotides are concentrated several-fold in the nuclei of rat tissues. This fact supports the idea that the

TABLE 2–2

PROPORTIONALITY BETWEEN DNA CONTENT AND POLYMERASE ACTIVITY IN NUCLEI OF SEA-URCHIN EMBRYOS. (AFTER MAZIA, 1963; J. CELL. COMP. PHYSIOL. (SUPPL.) 62:127.)

DNA-Content Per Nucleus (mg)	Polymerase Activity (m μ moles TTP^{32} incorporated)
2.7×10^{-9}	0.76
2.8×10^{-9}	0.65
5.9×10^{-9}	1.27

synthesis of DNA occurs in the nucleus. The results of the first studies on the location of the enzyme catalyzing DNA synthesis were not in agreement with this idea, however. The enzyme, which has been called DNA polymerase, or DNA nucleotidyl transferase, was found in the cytoplasmic fraction and appeared to be absent from cell nuclei (e.g., Smellie, 1961). However, when subsequently nuclei were isolated in nonaqueous media, the specific activity of the DNA-polymerase proved to be several times higher in the nucleus than in the cytoplasm (Smith and Keir, 1963; Siebert, 1963). The failure to detect the enzyme in nuclei prepared in aqueous media is probably a result of the extreme solubility of the enzyme in such media. Mazia and Hinegardner (1963) have demonstrated the presence of DNA polymerase in nuclei isolated from sea-urchin embryos. There appeared to be a quantitative proportionality between the chromosome complement and the content of DNA polymerase. They found no evidence for the presence of the enzyme outside the nucleus. Keir and collaborators (Keir et al., 1963*b*; Keir and Smith, 1963) have obtained evidence indicating that calf thymus nuclei contain both DNA-polymerase and a physically distinct nucleotidyltransferase which catalyzes the addition of one nucleotide residue only to the end of polydeoxyribonucleotide chains. The latter enzyme, which was first described by Krakow et al. (1962) was called *terminal* DNA nucleotidyl-transferase and the DNA polymerase, *replicative* DNA nucleotidyl transferase by Keir et al. (1963*b*). The outstanding properites of the terminal nucleotidyltransferase are that it is not stimulated by the presence of all four deoxyribonucleoside triphosphates and that cysteine is required in the reaction.

The occurrence in cell nuclei of the RNA synthesizing enzyme RNA polymerase is indicated by several studies (e.g., Takahashi et al., 1963).

Structures of the Interphase Nucleus

A. The Nuclear Envelope

The first detailed descriptions of the structure of the nuclear envelope are those of Callan and Tomlin (1950). These authors succeeded in isolating nuclear membranes from amphibian oocyte nuclei. The isolated membranes were then studied both chemically and with the aid of the electron microscope. Callan and Tomlin found that the nuclear envelope consisted of a double membrane. The outer membrane contained pores with a diameter of 300 A; the inner was continuous and lacked visible structure. The elasticity and considerable strength of the nuclear envelope depend, according to these authors, on the inner membrane.

Since the paper of Callan and Tomlin appeared in print, a great number of electron microscopic studies on the structure of the nuclear envelope have been published. Nuclear membranes have been studied from types of organisms as different as protozoa, echinodermata, insects, mammals, and plants (e.g., Bairati and Lehmann, 1952; Harris and James, 1952; Afzelius, 1955; Bahr and Beermann, 1954; Kautz· and DeMarsh, 1955; Hassenkamp, 1957; Whaley et al., 1960b). The envelopes have proved to be of principally the same structure; i.e., they are double and contain pores, the size of which are 200 to 400 A. According to Harris and James (1952), in amoeba it is the inner membrane which contains pores; more recent electron micrography show both membranes to be penetrated by the pores (Afzelius, 1955; Watson, 1955; Whaley et al., 1960b). It is now clear that the nuclear envelope is continuous with and a component of the endoplasmic reticulum (Whaley et al., 1960b). The membranes of the nuclear envelope are distinguished from those of the reticulum only by the pores (Fig. 3-1). The electron micrographs of Whaley et al. (1960a, b) demonstrate that the membrane system in interphase cells extends from the nucleus to the cell surface and some-

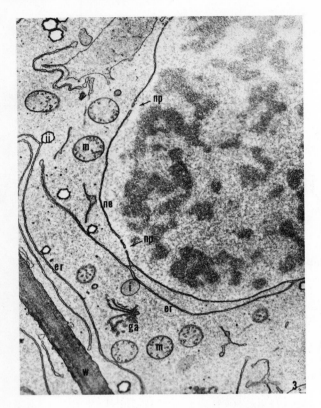

Fig. 3–1. Continuity between nuclear envelope and the membranes of the endoplasmic reticulum in a meristematic cell of maize. (Whaley et al., 1960a; Amer. J. Bot. 47:424. Courtesy of the authors.)

times even into the cytoplasm of adjacent cells. During cell division the system is fragmented. In telophase the fragments grow and fuse to form the envelope surrounding the daughter nuclei. The pores probably represent structures through which exchanges of substances may take place. However, they are not simple openings but contain a diffuse material of different nature and density than that of the cytoplasm and nucleoplasm.

Callan and Tomlin (1950) also studied the chemical composition of the nuclear envelope. They found that the outer membrane contained lipids in addition to proteins. The fact that the cell nucleus is surrounded by a lipid layer had been demonstrated previously by the work of several workers, including Monné (1942), Baud (1948), and Berg (1951). Monné also made the observation that the nuclear envelope was double and that the outer membrane was lipidic in nature.

The available information about the permeability properties of the nuclear membrane are contradictory. The results of Churney (1941) and Abele (1951) indicate that the nuclear membrane is semi-permeable. Callan (1949) studied the permeability of membranes isolated from oocyte nuclei. He found that the membrane was penetrated by water, simple electrolytes, various sugars (xylose, glucose, sackarose, raffinose) and depolymerized nucleic acid. The membrane was impermeable towards high-molecular compounds such as egg albumen, glycogen, acacia, and synthetic soluble celluloses.

In a review article Dounce (1954) concludes that the nuclear envelope is permeable to all kinds of molecules and does not function as a permeability barrier. However, most of the studies supporting this conclusion have been performed with isolated nuclei. Since the nuclear envelope is a part of the endoplasmic reticulum, the membrane structure in isolated nuclei is likely to have been damaged. Information about the permeability properties of the nuclear envelope which have been obtained in studies with isolated nuclei is, therefore, of doubtful value.

Loewenstein and Kanno (1963) have studied the electrical conductance and potential across the membrane of various types of cell nuclei. They were able to distinguish between two types of nuclear membranes. One has a high resistance and resting potential between nucleoplasm and cytoplasm, whereas the other "has a resistance indistinguishable from nucleoplasm and cytoplasm and no resting potential. The former kind of nuclear membrane is a formidable diffusion barrier even for particles of ion size; the latter is more permeable."

Feldherr and Feldherr (1960) have found that gammaglobulin (molecular weight approximately 160.000) injected into the cytoplasm near the nucleus does not penetrate the nuclear envelope in cells from the *Cecropia* moth. The findings by recent authors (e.g., Hill, 1961; Kay, 1961; Bensch and King, 1961) that extracellular high molecular weight DNA is incorporated into the cell nuclei of mammalian cells indicate, on the other hand, that the nuclear envelope is permeable at least to DNA. However, as pointed out by Stern and Mirsky (1953) and by Feldherr and Feldherr (1960), it is conceivable that molecules which cannot freely penetrate the nuclear membrane are transported into the nucleus by means of an energy-requiring mechanism.

B. The Nuclear Sap or Nucleoplasm

The amount of nuclear sap varies considerably. In the compact nuclei of sperm cells there is hardly any nuclear sap, whereas in the oocyte nucleus the nuclear sap constitutes the main part of the nuclear mass. According to Vincent (1955), the nuclear sap of the oocyte nucleus is in the nuclei of somatic cells concentrated in the nucleoli.

Brown et al. (1950) have isolated and analyzed chemically the nuclear sap of oocyte nuclei. The results of these studies lead to the conclusion that the nuclear sap contains two colloid phases which can be distinguished from one another experimentally; one of these phases is a disperse fluid, and the other is a structural colloid with mechanical rigidity. The analyses further indicated that the nuclear sap contains chiefly proteins and amino acids. According to the analyses of Busch et al. (1963), the greater portion of the acid-soluble nuclear proteins occur in the nuclear sap.

In the studies of Brown et al., nucleic acids and their hydrolytic products were not found in the nuclear sap. However, recently Izawa et al. (1963) have found, that the nucleoplasm of the newt oocyte contains as much DNA as the chromosomes. Part of the nucleoplasmic DNA is located in the numerous small nucleoli, which in this material are not attached to the chromosomes.

Evidence indicating the presence of ribosomes (particles consisting of ribonucleoprotein) in the nuclear sap has also been presented (Callan, 1956; Frenster et al., 1960).

C. The Nucleolus

Nucleoli occur in almost all cell nuclei. They are usually spherical but may also be rod-shaped or irregular. The nucleoli are formed during telophase at the so-called nucleolar organizer region in the nucleolar chromosomes. The number of nucleoli are, to begin with, equal to the number of nucleolar chromosomes, of which there is one for each haploid set of chromosomes in most plant species. However, the nucleoli have a tendency to fuse so that in most meristematic interphase cells of diploid plants there is only one nucleolus.

The density of the nucleoli is usually higher than that of the rest of the nucleus. The nucleoli isolated by Vincent (1952) from star fish oocyte nuclei had a density between 1.35 and 1.4 and appeared to be solid or semi-solid bodies. On the other hand, the main component of the prophase nucleoli in endosperm of several plant species which were studied by Bajer and Molè-Bajer (1956) had a half-liquid consistence. In addition to this half-liquid substance the prophase nucleoli in endosperm contained a material composed of small granules.

The existence of two or more phases in nucleoli has also been demonstrated by electron-microscopic studies. Thus early electron micrographs of animal cells indicated the presence of two phases. Of these phases, one, the *nucleoloplasm*, was structureless, whereas the other consisted of a fibrous, highly spiralized material called *nucleolonema* (for reference, see Vincent, 1955, and Serra, 1955). However, although recent electron-micrographic studies confirm the presence of different structures within nucleoli, they do not support the nucleolonema-nucleoloplasm concept. The most detailed light and electron microscopic studies of nucleoli of plant cells have been made by Lafontaine and collaborators (Lafontaine, 1958a, 1958b, Lafontaine and Chouinard, 1963), in *Allium cepa* and *Vicia faba*. Under the light microscope the preprophase nucleolus of *Vicia faba* consists of a densely stained material in which vacuole-like structures are embedded. The Feulgen-positive nucleolus-organizer region projects deeply into the nucleolus. Electron micrographs demonstrate the presence of two structurally distinct components in the densely staining material of the nucleolus (Fig. 3-2), which are described by the authors in the following way: "One of these components is represented by 150 A granules which, in places, are arranged into thread-like structures approximately 0.1 μ in diameter; the other component apparently consists of fibrils 60 to 100 A in diameter. . . . The granular and fibrillar components of the denser portion of the nucleolus persist as such during prophase and disperse throughout the nuclear cavity at the time of nucleolar disintegration. After nuclear membrane breakdown, these granules and fibrils, as well as those of the nucleoplasm, mix freely with similar elements already present within the forming spindle. No evidence has been obtained that, during or after nucleolar disintegration, the structural components of the nucleolus become associated as such with the chromosomes to form an external or internal matrix." (Lafontaine and Chouinard, 1963) The electron micrographs of Lafontaine and Chouinard further demonstrate the presence of granules and fibrils in the intranucleolar vacuoles. No evidence for the nucleolus' being surrounded by a membrane was obtained in the studies of Lafontaine or in those of other authors.

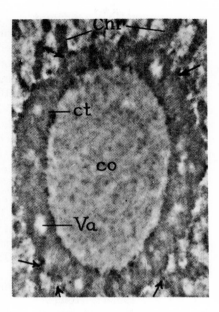

Fig. 3–2. Electron micrograph of the nucleolus in a root-tip cell of *Vicia faba*. Lafontaine, 1958. Reprinted by permission of the Rockefeller Institute Press from J. Biophys. Biochem. Cytol., November, 1958, Vol. 4, No. 6, pp. 777–784.)

That nucleoli contain ribonucleic acid (RNA) was shown by Caspersson and Schultz (1940). The absorption in ultraviolet light indicated the presence of nucleic acid, and since the nucleoli were Feulgen negative, Caspersson and Schultz concluded that the nucleic acid was RNA. The same year Brachet (1940) independently had found that nucleoli do not stain with pyronin after treatment with RNase, a fact which Brachet interpreted as evidence for the presence of RNA in nucleoli.

A definite proof for the existence of RNA in nucleoli was obtained by Vincent (1952). His chemical analyses of nucleoli isolated from starfish oocyte nuclei showed that the nucleolus contains 2.2 to 4.6 per cent nucleic acid, which was exclusively of the RNA type. According to Baltus (1954), the dry weight of nucleoli from starfish oocytes consists of about 5 per cent of RNA. Subsequent studies by Vincent (1957) indicated that the nucleolus contained several populations of RNA molecules which differed in their metabolic properties. One of these appeared to be transfer RNA (e.g., Sirlin et al., 1961; Vincent and Baltus, 1960; Birnstiel et al., 1965). Another, which was found to have a high rate of synthesis and a base composition resembling that of DNA, was identified as messenger RNA (Sibatani et al., 1962). On theoretical grounds it is to be expected that mRNA is formed on the chromosomes, an assumption which is supported by experimental evidence (e.g., Sirlin et al., 1962). Other observations indicate that RNA is synthesized also within the nucleolus (Woods, 1959; Sirlin et al., 1963; Perry, 1962, 1963; Birnstiel et al., 1965). Thus, transfer RNA has been reported to be of nucleolar origin (Birnstiel et al., 1965). Ribosomal RNA appears to be a nucleolar constituent (Perry, 1962; 1963; Chipchase and Birnstiel, 1963), but whether it is also synthesized in the nucleolus, as suggested by Perry (1962, 1963), or is merely collected there for final assembly into ribosomes (Chipchase and Birnstiel, 1963) is still in dispute. [Since this was written, evidence has been obtained which indicates that rRNA is synthesized at the nucleolus organizer region (Ritossa and Spiegelman, 1965; Wallace and Birnstiel, 1966.)]

At least a part of the RNA in nuceoli appears to be combined with proteins. The ribonucleoprotein particles thus formed can be extracted from nucleoli (Frenster et al., 1960; Birnstiel et al., 1963a). Chemical and electron microscopic analyses have shown that their chemical composition and structure is very similar to cytoplasmic ribosomes (Birnstiel et al., 1963a). However, so far there is no definite evidence for favoring the idea that cytoplasmic ribosomes are derived from the nucleolar ribosomes, although an exchange of ribosomes between nucleus and cytoplasm appears inevitable during mitosis. That the nucleolar ribosomes are functional in intranuclear protein synthesis has been demonstrated (Allfrey, 1963).

The results of the recent studies of Rees et al. (1963) and McLeish (1964) suggest that the nucleolus contains a DNA fraction, which is Feulgen negative and which is not easily detected by radioautographic technique. The possibility that this DNA was derived from accompanying chromosomal material was excluded. McLeish found the relationship between DNA and RNA content of the nucleolus to be 2:1. He suggests that the function of the DNA fraction in the nucleolus is to act as a primer in nucleolar RNA synthesis.

Vincent's (1952) chemical analyses indicated that 60 to 70 per cent of the dry weight of the isolated starfish oocyte nucleoli consisted of complex nonbasic proteins, which contained the amino acid tryptophan and 0.5 to 1 per cent phosphorus. Birnstiel et al. (1964) found in nucleoli from pea seedlings a considerable amount of acid-extractable proteins. These basic proteins were shown to be heterogeneous and to consist of nucleolar histone and basic, nonhistone protein. The nucleoli also contained small amounts of phospholipids. The presence of lipids in nucleoli and in the nucleolar organizer has also been indicated by several other studies (e.g., Shinke and Shigenaga, 1933; Mensinkai,

1939; Serra, 1947; Albuquerque and Serra, 1951; Zagury, 1957; LaCour and Chayen, 1958).

Enzymes found in nucleoli are acid phosphatase (Vincent, 1952), nucleoside phosphorylase, NAD pyrophosphorylase (Baltus, 1954) and the RNA-methylases (Birnstiel et al., 1963*b*). The apparent function of the RNA-methylase is to catalyze the alteration of the structure of transfer RNA by methylation of the base components (Birnstiel et al., 1963*b*).

D. The Chromosomes

The chromosomes in mitotic and meiotic division stages have been known and described by cytologists since the 1870's, and there is by now a tremendous descriptive literature on chromosome morphology as seen in the light microscope. We also have rather detailed information about the chemical composition of chromosomes. Thus, we know that chromosomes derived from the same organism contain constant amounts of DNA and histone and variable amounts of nonhistone protein and RNA. In addition, the chromosomes contain small amounts of lipids and metals such as calcium, magnesium, and iron. But in spite of this we still know very little about how these various constituents of the chromosomes are put together. There are three particularly important and controversial questions which so far have not been answered; these are

1. How many strands are present in chromosomes: is it a multistranded structure composed of 32 or 64 strands, or is it single-stranded?

·2. Should the structural backbone of the strand(s) be regarded as one molecule which runs uninterruptedly from one end to the other, or is the strand composed of smaller units linked end to end and kept together by bonds weaker than covalent bonds, i.e., bonds such as hydrogen bonds, ionic bonds, or hydrophobic bonds (van der Waal's attraction forces)?

3. Does the structural backbone consist of DNA, or of protein, or perhaps of both?

In the following, we shall examine the available evidence regarding the structure and chemistry of the chromosomes in interphase and prophase nuclei with these questions in mind.

Since the chromosomes during interphase generally are invisible, we know even less about the structural organization of the interphase chromosomes than about that of the chromosomes during the stages of active division.

When observed with the light microscope, the living cell nucleus frequently appears to be optically empty except for the nucleolus. In the fixed state, however, the chromosomes of the interphase nucleus appear as Feulgen positive material organized into a network of fine threads and granules. Frequently nuclei contain larger bodies of Feulgen positive material, the so-called chromocenters.

41

Electron microscopic studies by Ris, Kaufmann, and others (for references, see Kaufmann et al., 1960; Ris, 1961) indicate that the chromosome in interphase and prophase is a bundle of fibrils, each fibril being about 100 A in diameter. Since this fibril is about the smallest unit which is clearly resolved in electron micrographs, it is called the elementary chromosome fibril by Ris (1961). In the isolated leptotene chromosome of *Tradescantia,* which is a duplicated chromosome, Ris has estimated the number of 100 A fibrils to be about 32. The 100 A fibrils were also found in a nucleoprotein solution made by dissolving in distilled water chromosomes which had been isolated from calf thymus nuclei in saline versene at pH 6.5 (see below). When the chromosomes were prepared in saline versene at pH 8 and then dispersed in water, the 100 A fibrils separated into two 40 A thick subunits. In nuclei of late spermatids, where histone is replaced by protamine, the 100 A fibrils showed subunits about 40 A thick. Thus it appears as if the 100 A elementary chromosome fibril always is composed of two 40 A subunits and the leptotene chromosome of *Tradescantia* would then contain 64 such subunits, 32 in each chromatid. The diameter of the chromatid has been estimated to be 0.2 μ. According to Ris, the 40 A subunit represents a DNA double helix surrounded by histone.

All these studies support the multistranded hypothesis. Other support for this hypothesis comes from determinations of the relationship existing between DNA content and length of chromosomes (Read, 1961).

The single-strand hypothesis is supported by the electron-microscopic studies of Moses on paired meiotic chromosomes of primary spermatocytes and oocytes ["It is my present opinion that it is more difficult to fit a multistranded model (where "strand" is equivalent to 100 A microfibril) to our observations than a single-stranded one and I therefore favor the latter."] (Moses, 1963). It is further supported by the kinetic studies of Gall (1963a) on the action of DNase on lampbrush chromosomes, which indicated that there are two subunits of DNA (one DNA double helix) in the loops, where the chromosome is only one chromatid, and four subunits (a pair of DNA double helices) along the main axis, which consists of two chromatids, and by measurements of the diameter of the axis in lampbrush chromosomes, which is believed to be of the order of 200 A. On the basis of his autoradiographic studies, Taylor (see Chap. 5) concluded that each chromatid is composed of a DNA double helix with associated protein. The results of studies on the chromosome-breaking effects of chemicals and radiation are also more compatible with a chromosome model consisting of only a few strands (see below). The supporters of the single-stranded chromosome claim that the fact that chromosomes so often in electron micrographs appear to be composed of a multitude of independent strains is an illusion created by the single strand's winding and bending so frequently along its course that it has many parallel-lying segments.

Gall (1963b) has developed the surface-spread technique of Kleinschmidt et al. (1962) for the study of chromosomes from interphase nuclei with striking results. The material is spread on a water surface and picked up with carbon-coated grids for examination in the electron microscope. The nuclear material was found to consist exclusively of long fibers about 400 to 600 A in diameter. The fibers were believed to represent interphase chromosomes.

The surface-spread technique has also been used by DuPraw (1965) in his electron-microscopic studies on the macromolecular organization of nuclei and chromosomes. The results of these studies support the single-strand hypothesis.

The second and third questions, i.e., whether the chromosome is continuous or particulate, and whether DNA, protein, or both are responsible for the linear continuity of the chromosome, are just as controversial as the first one.

The above-mentioned studies of Gall (1963*a*) and DuPraw (1965), as well as those of Callan and Macgregor (1958; Macgregor and Callan, 1962) on the effects of DNase and other enzymes on lampbrush chromosomes and chromosomal fibers from interphase nuclei, indicate that DNA is

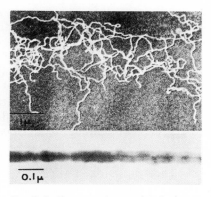

Fig. 3–3. Electron micrograph of chromosome fibers from a red-cell nucleus of the newt, *Triturus.* (Gall, 1963. Reprinted by permission of the author and the Editor of Science from Science, Vol. 139, No. 3550, p. 121, 1963.)

the structural backbone. Callan and Macgregor found that the axis of the loops in the lampbrush chromosomes is broken by DNase but not by trypsin, pepsin, or RNase, and concluded that uninterrupted fibers of DNA run throughout the lengths of lampbrush chromosomes. The studies of DuPraw show that the chromosomal fibers consist of a DNase-sensitive, trypsin-resistant core surrounded by a trypsin-sensitive sheath. That DNA is necessary for the structural integrity of the chromosome is also indicated by studies of the chromosome-breaking effects of inhibitors of deoxyribonucleotide synthesis such as 5-fluorodeoxyuridine (Taylor et al., 1962), deoxyadenosine (Kihlman, 1963*b*) and cytosine arabinoside (Kihlman et al., 1963).

On the other hand, Nebel and Coulon (1962) concluded on the basis of their electron-microscopic studies that the backbone of chromosome is protein and that DNA occurs in side loops. A similar structural organization of the chromosome has been suggested by Painter (1964), who believes ". . . that the backbone, or axis, of a chromosome is largely protein, with possibly an admixture of low molecular weight and nongenetic DNA, and that gene complexes are attached in side loops or branches similar to the cyclical 'chromosomes' of microorganisms."

The observations by Mazia that chromosomes are disintegrated when treated with trypsin but not when treated with pepsin and nucleases led him to conclude that the chromosomes contain a continuous backbone of basic protein (Mazia, 1941). However, subsequently Mazia (1954)

43

found that salivary gland chromosomes disintegrate into small particles when treated with citrate or with the chelating agent EDTA. Mazia was prompted to test the effect of chelating agents on chromosome structure by a previous biochemical study (Bernstein and Mazia, 1953) on the nucleoprotein in sperm cells of sea urchin. This previous study had shown that DNA-protein could be extracted from sperm heads only after pretreatments with citrate. After the citrate treatment, the DNA-protein dissolved in water in the form of particles which were 200 A thick and 4000 A long. Subsequent experiments showed that EDTA had the same effect.

On the basis of these experimental results Mazia suggested that the chromosome fibrils are composed by DNA-protein particles, linked end to end by bridges of divalent cations, probably Ca and/or Mg. Mazia's hypothesis was supported by Steffensen's observations that the frequency of spontaneous chromosomal aberrations in *Tradescantia* was increased if the plant was cultivated on Ca- and Mg-deficient medium (Steffensen, 1955).

That the chromosomal DNA is not just one long molecule running from one end of the chromosome to the other is also indicated by radio-autographic experiments, which show that there are several replicate units of DNA in a chromosome (see Chap. 5).

However, there is considerable disagreement regarding the way the units are linked together. In addition to the ionic bonds suggested by Mazia and Steffensen, hydrogen bonds (Ambrose and Gopal-Ayengar, 1953), nonhistone protein (Dounce and Sarkar, 1960), and phosphoserine (Taylor, 1963b; Borenfreund et al., 1964) have been suggested as linkers. In this connection it should be mentioned that Plaut and Nash have pointed out that there is really no need for linkers because even if the units of DNA replication are discrete DNA molecules, ". . . they could be held in a permanent longitudinal sequence by the surrounding material without direct connections between their ends." (Plaut and Nash, 1964.)

If the elementary chromosome fibril is composed of DNA-histone molecules linked together by nonhistone proteins (see above), both DNA and proteins would be essential for the structural integrity of the chromosome. Support for this alternative is obtained by the studies of Mirsky and Ris (1947, 1951) and by Chorazy et al. (1963a). Mirsky and Ris studied chromatin threads which had been isolated from vertebrate nuclei. These chromatin threads had many properties in common with mitotic chromosomes. They were Feulgen-positive, spiralized structures, and they contained primary and secondary constrictions. The chromatin threads contained all the chemical compounds which Mirsky and Pollister (1946) previously had found in chromosin (see above). The threads proved to be composed of DNA, histone, and a nonbasic, tryptophan-containing protein, which was called residual protein. In addition, the threads contained RNA and possibly lipids (Wang et al., 1950). Mirsky and Ris (1951) found that both DNA and residual protein were essential for the structural continuity of the threads. Removal of histone from the threads did not affect their structure, but they fell apart if either DNA or the residual protein was removed.

Chorazy et al. (1963a) studied the effect of various enzymes on the structure of isolated metaphase chromosomes and found that chymotrypsin, trypsin, and DNase caused a marked disintegration of the chromosomes.

DuPraw has pointed out, however, that the fact that chromosomes are disintegrated by trypsin as well as by DNase does not necessarily mean that both DNA and protein are responsible for the linear continuity of the chromosome. If the DNA chain exists as a regular secondary coil inside a proteinaceous sheath, it seems likely that the sheath proteins are responsible for maintaining this secondary configuration. Digestion of the sheath proteins by trypsin would result in ". . . a 'springing out' of the DNA secondary coil, in effect releasing the DNA core as a free molecule in solution. The linear continuity of the chromosome, however, would still be due to DNA alone and would remain intact even when DNA is released to solution (although a 'chromosome' as such would no longer be detectable)." (DuPraw, 1965.)

In conclusion, it may be said that the studies on fundamental chromosome structure have provided a wealth of frequently conflicting results and interpretations but few firmly established facts. It appears to be fairly generally accepted that the structural unit of the chromosome is a microfibril of the order of 100 A in thickness. Most authors also seem to favor the view that this fibril contains both DNA and protein and that the DNA component is involved in maintaining the structural integrity of the fibril. But whereas some authors regard the 100 A fibril as a true elementary fibril which cannot be further divided into identical subunits, others believe that it is a double structure composed of two 40 A fibers. According to a popular view, the 100 A fibril consists of a DNA core surrounded by a proteinaceous sheath or matrix. Some of the supporters of this view believe that the DNA exists as a single, long DNA double helix, running uninterruptedly from one end of the fibril to the other, whereas others prefer to think of the DNA core as a series of distinct DNA molecules held in an end-to-end position by linkers or by the surrounding matrix.

A controversial, still unanswered question is further whether the undivided chromosome thread consists of only one or of several 100 A fibrils.

Thus, there are many problems which remain to be solved before we can begin to understand the structural organization of the chromosome.

DNA Synthesis at the Biochemical Level

A. DNA Structure

The unit or monomer of the DNA polymer is the nucleotide, which itself is a complex molecule, being composed of a purine or pyrimidine

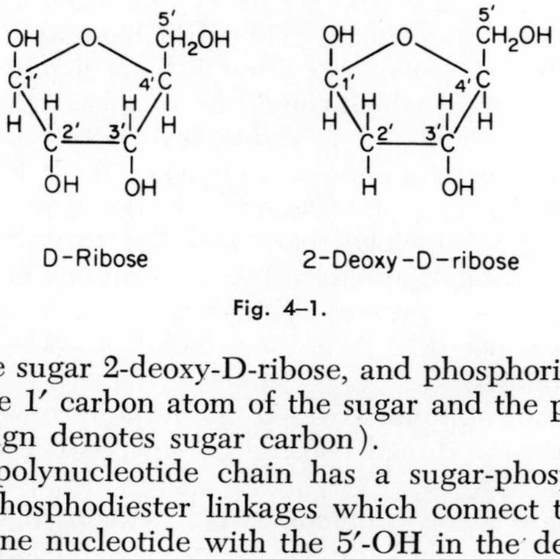

Fig. 4–1.

base, the pentose sugar 2-deoxy-D-ribose, and phosphoric acid. The base is attached to the 1' carbon atom of the sugar and the phosphate to carbon 5' (prime sign denotes sugar carbon).

The DNA polynucleotide chain has a sugar-phosphate backbone, constructed of phosphodiester linkages which connect the 3'-OH in the deoxyribose of one nucleotide with the 5'-OH in the deoxyribose of the adjacent nucleotide.

The purine bases in DNA are adenine and guanine, and the pyrimidine bases are thymine and cytosine. In plant DNA the cytosine is partly replaced by 5-methylcytosine.

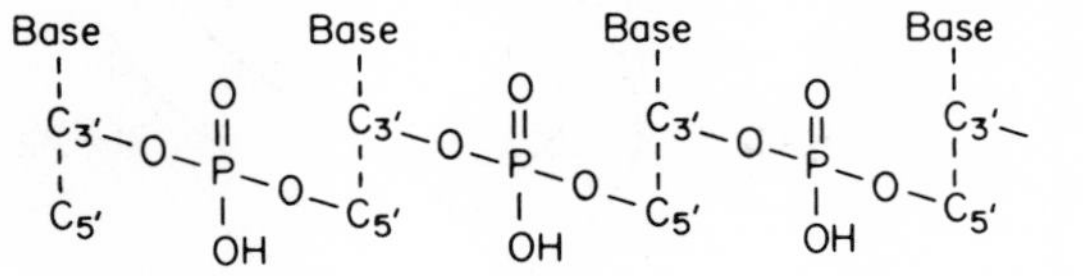

Fig. 4–2. The polynucleotide chain.

The pioneer work on base ratios in DNA and RNA was done by Erwin Chargaff and his collaborators, using chromatographic techniques.

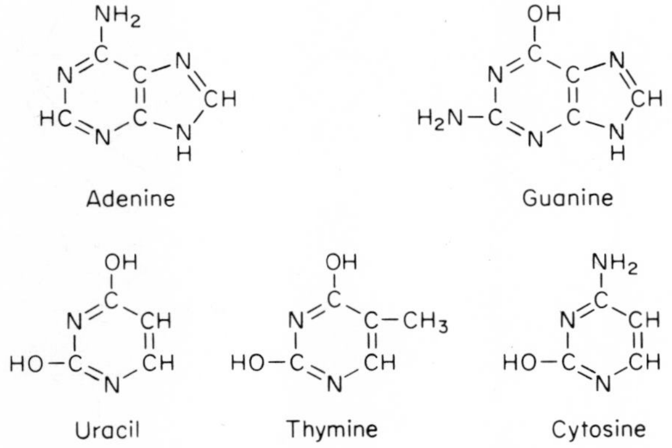

Adenine

Guanine

Fig. 4–3. The most commonly occurring of the purine and pyrimidine bases in DNA and RNA.

Uracil

Thymine

Cytosine

It has appeared that the relative amounts of each base vary from one DNA to another. Certain regularities have been established, however. Thus, it has been found that the sum of purines equals the sum of pyrimidines (adenine + guanine = thymine + cytosine), that the number of 6-amino groups equals the number of 6-keto groups (adenine + cytosine = thymine + guanine), and that adenine = thymine and cytosine = guanine. Another way of expressing the last relation is that the molecular ratios of adenine to thymine and guanine to cytosine are equal to one.

These facts, as well as evidence obtained by X-ray diffraction studies, led Watson and Crick (1953) to postulate their famous model of the structure of the DNA molecule. According to Watson and Crick, the DNA molecule consists of two polynucleotide chains wound around each other along a central axis to form a double-stranded helix. The two chains are held together by hydrogen bonds between the bases which lie inside the helix, perpendicular to the long axis. The bases are paired in a specific way, the adenine of one chain being linked to the thymine of the second, and, similarly, the guanine of one chain being linked to the

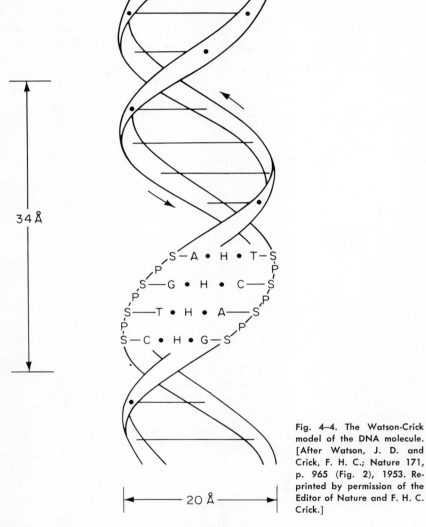

Fig. 4–4. The Watson-Crick model of the DNA molecule. [After Watson, J. D. and Crick, F. H. C.; Nature 171, p. 965 (Fig. 2), 1953. Reprinted by permission of the Editor of Nature and F. H. C. Crick.]

cytosine of the second. Thus, the sequence of nucleotides in the two chains is not identical, but complementary.

The model has proved to be essentially correct by the results of subsequent experiments, and is now generally accepted. However, recent evidence suggests that hydrophobic bonds rather than hydrogen bonds are responsible for holding the polynucleotide chains together in the DNA double helix, although hydrogen bonds may still be important for insuring specific base pairing.

In the chromosomes the DNA is associated with other compounds, of which the proteins are quantitatively most important. Polyvalent metal ions are strongly bound by DNA and may play an important role in the combination of DNA and protein in the DNA-protein complex. Metal ions appear also to be involved in the stabilization of the Watson-Crick double helix (see Eichhorn and Clark, 1965).

B. The Biosynthesis of DNA

The biosynthesis of DNA may be divided into three phases. The first of these is the *de novo* synthesis of the pyrimidine nucleotide uridy-

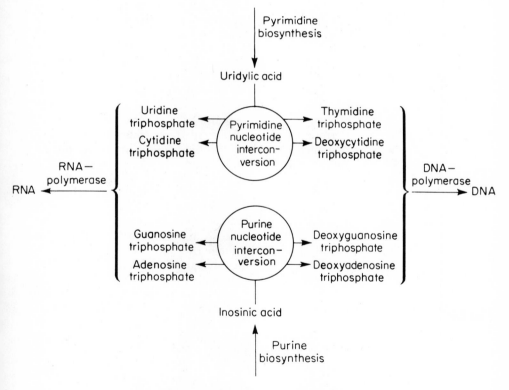

Fig. 4–5. The phases of DNA and RNA biosynthesis.

lic acid and the purine nucleotide inosinic acid, which are the ultimate precursors of all the different ribo- and deoxyribo-nucleotides occurring as constituents of RNA and DNA. The second phase is the synthesis of the four deoxyribonucleoside triphosphates, which are the immediate precursors of DNA, and the third phase is the polymerization of these deoxyriboside triphosphates in the presence of the enzyme DNA polymerase and a suitable DNA primer or template.

PHASE 1: THE SYNTHESIS OF INOSINIC ACID
(IMP) AND URIDYLIC ACID (UMP)

(For references, see Buchanan, 1960 and Crosbie, 1960.) The first step in the synthesis of IMP appears to be the formation of 5-phosphoribosylamine from 5-phosphoribosyl-1-pyrophosphate (PRPP) and glutamine. The reaction is catalyzed by the enzyme 5-phosphoribosyl pyrophosphate amidotransferase. The second step involves the reaction of 5-phosphoribosylamine, ATP, and glycine to yield glycinamide ribonucleotide. In the third step, glycinamide ribonucleotide is converted to formylglycinamide ribonucleotide. The formyl group is donated by N^5,N^{10}-anhydroformyltetrahydrofolic acid, and since tetrahydrofolic acid is involved, the reaction is inhibited by folic acid analogues, such as *aminopterin* and *amethopterin*. The fourth step, which involves the reaction of formylglycinamide ribonucleotide, glutamine, and ATP to yield formylglycinamidine ribonucleotide, is strongly inhibited by the antibiotic *azaserine,* which, like aminopterin, is known as an effective mitotic inhibitor and chromosome-breaking agent. In the presence of ATP, formylglycinamidine ribonucleotide is converted enzymatically into 5-aminoimidazole ribonucleotide. Thus, the imidazole ring in the purine skeleton is formed before the pyrimidine ring. In the presence of the enzyme 5-aminoimidazole ribonucleotide carboxylase, 5-aminoimidazole ribonucleotide reacts with CO_2 to yield 5-amino-4-imidazolecarboxylic acid ribonucleotide. The next step involves the formation of 5-amino-4-imidazole-N-succinocarboxamide ribonucleotide from 5-amino-4-imidazolecarboxylic acid ribonucleotide, aspartic acid, and ATP. 5-Amino-4-imidazole-N-succinocarboxamide ribonucleotide is then cleaved into fumaric acid and 5-amino-4-imidazolecarboxamide ribonucleotide. This intermediate in purine biosynthesis accumulates when cultures of *Escherichia coli* are poisoned with *sulfonamides.* In the presence of the enzyme 5-amino-4-imidazolecarboxamide transformylase, 5-amino-4-imidazolecarboxamide ribonucleotide is formylated into 5-formamido-4-imidazolecarboxamide ribonucleotide, which then readily is converted enzymatically into inosinic acid. N^{10}-Formyltetrahydrofolic acid participates in the formylation reaction, which is even more strongly inhibited by *aminopterin* and *amethopterin* than is the formylation of glycinamide ribonucleotide.

Besides the reaction-sequence outlined above, IMP may be formed from hypoxanthine and PRPP under the liberation of pyrophosphate (Fig. 4-7). However, this reaction requires the presence of preformed purine and represents a "salvage" pathway, in contrast to the normal pathway which starts from PRPP and glutamine.

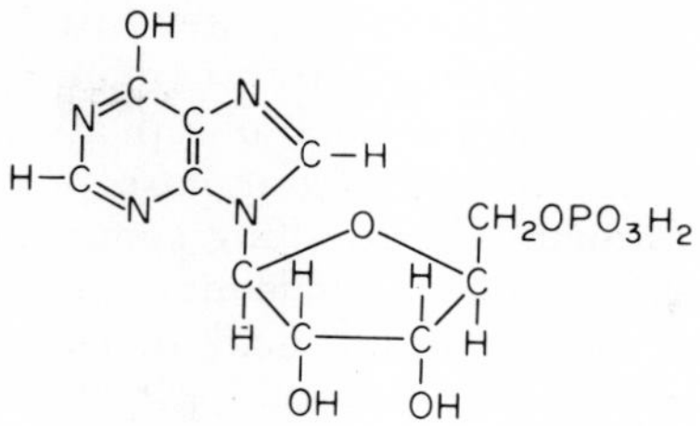

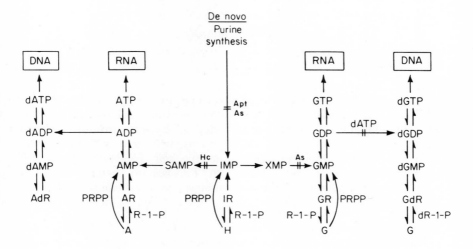

Inosinic acid

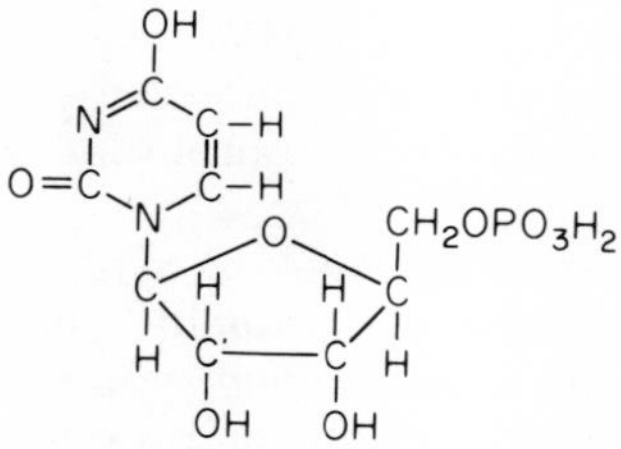

Uridylic acid

Fig. 4–6.

Fig. 4–7. The formation of the 5'-triphosphates of adenosine, guanosine, deoxyadenosine and deoxyguanosine from inosinic acid. (After Szybalski and Szybalska, 1961, Cancer Chemother. 11:87; and Warren, 1961, Metabolic Pathways, D. M. Greenberg, ed., Vol. II:459, Academic Press, Inc.)

The formation of carbamylphosphate from CO_2, ammonia, and ATP may be regarded as the first step in the synthesis of UMP. In the presence of the enzyme aspartate carbamyltransferase, carbamylaspartic acid (NH_2COOPO_3H) is formed from carbamylphosphate and aspartic acid under the liberation of inorganic phosphate. In the next step, which is catalyzed by the enzyme dihydro-orotase, water is split off and the pyrimidine ring is formed. The resulting compound, dihydro-orotic acid, is oxidized by flavineadenine dinucleotide to orotic acid, the reaction being catalyzed by dihydro-orotic acid dehydrogenase. The next step involves the condensation of orotic acid with PRPP to yield orotidine-5'-phosphate. It should be noted that in pyrimidine biosynthesis, the pyrimidine ring is formed first and then attached to ribosephosphate, whereas in purine biosynthesis, the purine skeleton is formed on the ribosephosphate. The final step in UMP biosynthesis, the conversion of orotidine-5'-phosphate to uridine-5'-phosphate (uridylic acid, UMP) (Fig. 4-6) is catalyzed by the enzyme orotidine-5'-phosphate decarboxylase.

Before the next phase in the DNA biosynthesis is discussed, the key position which PRPP holds in nucleic acid synthesis should be emphasized. This obligatory reactant in *de novo* synthesis of purine, pyrimidine, and pyridine nucleotides is formed in the presence of the enzyme ribosephosphatepyrophosphorylase according to the reaction:

ATP + ribose-5-phosphate →
5-phosphoribosyl-1-pyrophosphate (PRPP) + AMP

PHASE 2: THE SYNTHESIS OF DEOXYADENOSINETRI-

PHOSPHATE (dATP), DEOXYGUANOSINETRIPHOS-

PHATE (dGTP), DEOXYCYTIDINETRIPHOSPHATE

(dCTP), AND THYMIDINETRIPHOSPHATE (dTTP)

FROM INOSINIC ACID AND URIDYLIC ACID

The reaction sequence by which dATP and dGTP are formed from IMP appears in Fig. 4-7. IMP is first converted into adenylic acid (AMP) and guanylic acid (GMP). The first step in the formation of AMP from IMP involves the reaction of IMP with aspartic acid and guanosinetriphosphate (GTP) to yield adenylosuccinic acid (SAMP), guanosinediphosphate (GDP), and orthophosphate. This reaction, which is catalyzed by the enzyme adenylosuccinatesynthetase, is specifically inhibited by

$$OH$$
$$|$$

the L-aspartic acid analogue *hadacidin* ($OHC—N—CH_2COOH$). In the presence of the enzyme adenylosuccinase, adenylosuccinic acid is then split into AMP and fumaric acid.

The first step in the formation of GMP from IMP is the oxidation of IMP to xanthosine-5'-phosphate (XMP) by a nicotinamide-adenine dinucleotide (NAD)-dependent enzyme. XMP is then aminated to GMP by glutamine according to the reaction

XMP + ATP + glutamine + $H_2O \rightleftharpoons$
$$GMP + glutamic\ acid + AMP + pyrophosphate$$

It should be noted that in the xanthosine-5'-phosphate aminase reaction, ATP is split into AMP and pyrophosphate, rather than into the more usual products ADP and orthophosphate. The xanthosine-5'-phosphate aminase reaction is inhibited by *azaserine*.

The ribonucleotides of adenine and guanine are converted into the corresponding deoxyribonucleotides in the presence of the same enzyme system (cytidinediphosphate reductase) which converts pyrimidine ribonucleotides into pyrimidine deoxyribonucleotides (Larsson, 1963). The reduction, which apparently occurs at the diphosphate level, requires reduced lipoic acid, ATP and Mg^{++}. Reduced lipoic acid can be replaced by reduced nicotinamide-adenine dinucleotidephosphate (NADPH) and a heat-stable protein, called factor S_2. It is believed that these compounds, rather than reduced lipoic acid, are the physiological reducing agents in the CDP-reductase system (Moore and Reichard, 1963). The reduction of purine ribonucleotides to purine deoxyribonucleotides is inhibited by deoxyribonucleosidetriphosphates. The reduction of GDP to dGDP is strongly inhibited by dATP and dGTP (Reichard et al., 1961).

The deoxyadenosine- and deoxyguanosine-diphosphates formed by the CDP-reductase reaction are then phosphorylated by the corresponding deoxyribonucleosidediphosphate kinases to the immediate DNA-precursors dATP and dGTP according to the reactions:

$$dADP + ATP \rightleftharpoons dATP + ADP$$
$$dGDP + ATP \rightleftharpoons dGTP + ADP$$

The formation of deoxycytidinetriphosphate (dCTP) and thymidinetriphosphate (dTTP) from UMP is illustrated in Fig. 4-8. The first step involves phosphorylation of UMP by ribonucleoside mono- and diphosphate kinases to yield UDP and UTP. The second step in the formation of dCTP is the amination of UTP to cytidinetriphosphate (CTP). The reaction occurs only at the triphosphate level. CTP has to be dephosphorylated to cytidinediphosphate (CDP) before a reduction of the ribonucleotide to the corresponding deoxyribonucleotide can occur. The reduction of CDP to dCDP by CDP-reductase is strongly inhibited by the deoxyribonucleosidetriphosphates of thymine, guanine, and adenine, dATP being by far the most effective inhibitor (Reichard et al., 1961). Apparently, the reaction is also strongly inhibited by a phosphorylated derivative of *cytosine arabinoside*, probably cytosine arabinosidediphosphate (Chu and Fischer, 1962). The product of the CDP-reductase reaction, deoxycytidinediphosphate (dCDP), is then phosphorylated by a deoxyribonucleosidediphosphate kinase to the immediate DNA-precursor dCTP.

dCTP can also be formed from deoxycytidine (CdR) and ATP in the presence of the appropriate kinases.

It remains now to describe the formation of dTTP from UMP. As

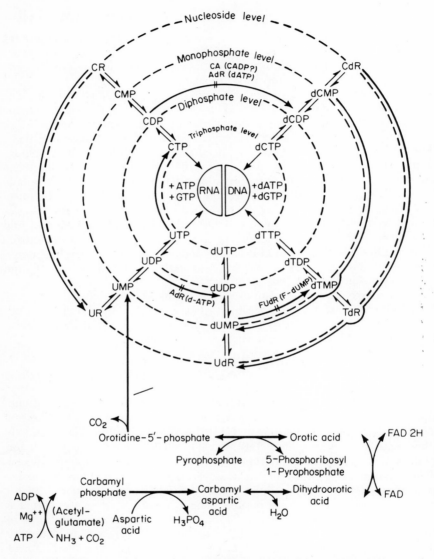

Fig. 4–8. The formation of the 5'-triphosphates of uridine, cytidine, deoxyuridine, deoxycytidine and thymidine from uridylic acid.

appears in Fig. 4-8, UMP is first phosphorylated to UDP, which is then reduced by CDP-reductase to deoxyuridinediphosphate (dUDP). The reduction of UDP is strongly inhibited by dUDP, dUTP, or both, but not by dUMP (Bertani et al., 1963). Since the methylation to thymidine phosphate occurs only at the monophosphate level, dUDP must be dephosphorylated to deoxyuridine monophosphate (dUMP). Other reactions which yield dUMP are deamination of deoxycytidinemonophosphate (dCMP) and the phosphorylation of deoxyuridine (UdR).

In the presence of the enzyme thymidylate synthetase and N^5,N^{10}-methylene-tetrahydrofolic acid (N^5,N^{10}-methylene-THFA), dUMP is converted to thymidylic acid (dTMP), the other product of the reaction being dihydrofolic acid, DHFA (Fig. 4-9).

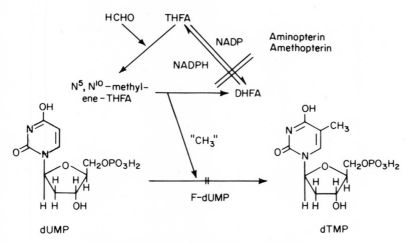

Fig. 4–9. The thymidylate synthetase reaction.

DHFA is reduced by NADPH to THFA, the reaction being catalyzed by the enzyme DHFA-reductase. N^5,N^{10}-Methylene-THFA is then reformed by the addition of a new one-carbon unit to THFA. The thymidylate synthetase reaction is strongly and specifically inhibited by *5-fluorodeoxyuridinemonophosphate (F-dUMP)* (Cohen et al., 1958). The formation of dTMP from dUMP can also be inhibited by *aminopterin* and *amethopterin*. By being strong inhibitors of the DHFA-reductase reaction, these folic acid derivatives prevent the reformation of N^5,N^{10}-methylene-THFA.

The immediate DNA-precursor dTTP is formed from dTMP and ATP in the presence of the enzymes thymidine mono- and di-phosphate kinase. A "salvage" pathway for the formation of dTTP is the phosphorylation of thymidine (TdR):

$$(1)\ \text{TdR} + \text{ATP} \underset{}{\overset{\text{TdR-kinase}}{\rightleftharpoons}} \text{dTMP} + \text{ADP}$$

$$(2)\ \text{dTMP} + \text{ATP} \underset{}{\overset{\text{dTMP-kinase}}{\rightleftharpoons}} \text{dTDP} + \text{ADP}$$

$$(3)\ \text{dTDP} + \text{ATP} \underset{}{\overset{\text{dTDP-kinase}}{\rightleftharpoons}} \text{dTTP} + \text{ADP}$$

$$\text{TdR} + 3\,\text{ATP} \rightleftharpoons \text{dTTP} + 3\,\text{ADP}$$

It has appeared in connection with the description of the biosynthesis of dATP, dGTP, dCTP, and dTTP that products of certain reaction steps inhibit their own formation by inhibiting enzymes required for the conversion of immediate or distant precursors to their reaction products. Such cases of negative *feedback* inhibition, which is something quite distinct from the product inhibition represented by mass-action effects, are the inhibition of the reduction of UDP to dUDP by dUTP (Bertani et al., 1963), or the reduction of CDP to dCDP by dTTP (Reichard et al., 1961). Other examples appear from the work of Potter and collaborators and of Maley and Maley. Ives et al. (1963) have reported an inhibition of TdR-kinase by dTTP and Maley and Maley (1962, 1963) have found that the enzymes UdR-kinase and dCMP-deaminase are strongly inhibited by dTTP. The enzyme CdR-kinase was inhibited by dCTP. In Fig. 4-10, these feedback reactions have been summarized.

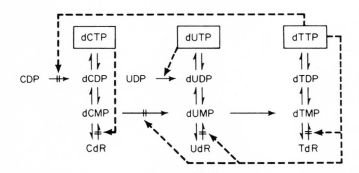

Fig. 4–10. Feedback inhibition of nucleotide interconversion. (After Potter, 1963; Exp. Cell Res. Suppl. 9, p. 261.)

They are of considerable interest, since they may provide a mechanism by which the supply of precursors needed for DNA biosynthesis is controlled.

PHASE 3: THE DNA-POLYMERASE REACTION

As first shown by Kornberg and his collaborators, DNA is synthesized from the four deoxyribonucleoside-5′-triphosphates, dATP, dGTP, dCTP, and dTTP in the presence of "primer" DNA and a purified enzyme system prepared from *Escherichia coli* (Kornberg, 1957; Bessman et al., 1958). Since then, the occurrence of similar enzyme systems in nuclei of animal cells and in other bacteria has been reported. The requirements for maximal activity of the enzyme system, which has been called DNA-polymerase or replicative DNA nucleotidyl transferase, are the presence of all the four deoxyribonucleoside-5′-triphosphates, Mg ions, and the DNA primer. Pyrophosphate is released by the reaction, which may be written as follows (Kornberg, 1960):

$$\left.\begin{array}{l} n \ \mathrm{dATP} \\ n \ \mathrm{dGTP} \\ n \ \mathrm{dCTP} \\ n \ \mathrm{dTTP} \end{array}\right\} + \mathrm{DNA} \xrightleftharpoons[\mathrm{DNA\text{-}polymerase}]{\mathrm{Mg^{++}}} \mathrm{DNA} \underline{\hspace{2cm}} \left[\begin{array}{l} \mathrm{dAMP} \\ \mathrm{dGMP} \\ \mathrm{dCMP} \\ \mathrm{dTMP} \end{array}\right]_n + 4n \text{ pyro-phosphate}$$

DNA-polymerase is inhibited by *ethidium bromide* (Elliott, 1963) and by *actinomycin D* (Elliott, 1963; Keir et al., 1963b).

Although maximal synthesis by the polymerase requires the presence of all deoxyribonucleoside-5′-triphosphates, a small but significant synthetic reaction occurs when only one of the deoxyribonucleoside-5′-triphosphates is present. It has been shown that this "limited" reaction results in the addition of a single or a few deoxyribonucleotide units to ends of the primer chain. The mechanism of the limited reaction appears to be the attack of the 3′-hydroxyl group at the end of the DNA chain on the nucleotidyl-phosphorus atom of the deoxyribonucleoside-5′-triphosphate with the elimination of pyrophosphate.

As pointed out in Chap. 2, there is evidence indicating that the addition of only one nucleotide residue to the end of polydeoxyribonucleotide chains is catalyzed by a physically distinct nucleotidyl transferase, named terminal nucleotidyl transferase by Keir and Smith (1963).

The function of the primer in the DNA-polymerase reaction is a most important question both from a biochemical and from a genetical point of view. Since DNA is believed to be the principal hereditary substance, which directs the synthesis of enzyme proteins and the development of the cell, it must also be copied in connection with cell division in order to provide for a similar development of the daughter cells. Watson and Crick have suggested that DNA is a hydrogen-bonded double helix of complementary chains of purine and pyrimidine deoxyribonucleotides. According to these authors, DNA replicates in a semiconservative manner, which means that the two strands separate and serve as *templates* for the synthesis of new complementary chains. Thus, the function of the DNA required for the polymerase reaction would be that of a template, which directs the formation of exact copies of itself, rather than that of a polymerization center where the elongation of DNA-chains is initiated. Support for this idea has been obtained by experiments, which show that the percentage composition of the bases in the product is very similar to that in the primer DNA. Results have also been obtained which indicate that denatured, or single-stranded, DNA is more effective as a primer than "native" DNA. The Watson-Crick scheme for DNA structure and replication is further supported by studies on the incorporation of base analogues. It has been found that in each case, the analogue substitutes specifically for the base it closely resembles. Thus, it has been found that in the DNA-polymerase reaction, 5-bromo-deoxyuridine-5′-triphosphate (B-dUTP) and dUTP can replace dTTP, but not dATP, dGTP, or dCTP. Similarly, 5-methyl- and 5-bromocytosine specifically replace cytosine, and hypoxanthine substitues only for guanine (Kornberg, 1960).

Although the expected template function of the primer DNA is strongly supported by experimental data, the exact mechanism by which DNA is replicated still eludes us. Bessman (1963) has pointed out that if DNA replicates by a mechanism similar to the limited reaction mentioned above, i.e., by adding deoxyribonucleotides to its ends, ". . . these new units must loop back in some manner to allow the directing influence of the DNA chain to be exerted." But this would require that there be ". . . some means of breaking this loop when the DNA has been duplicated." That chain ends are important for the reaction is demonstrated by the stimulating effect of sonication and of mild treatments with deoxyribonuclease on the priming activity (e.g., Sarkar et al., 1963). According to a hypothesis of DNA replication proposed by Bollum (1963), the first step is the production of denatured regions in the DNA, e.g., by mild DNase action. The next step is the formation of a complex between the enzyme protein and the denatured region in DNA. The catalytic complex provides a protected site where deoxyribonucleotide-5′-triphosphates can interact by hydrogen bonding with the pre-existing chain. Phosphoryl-protein interaction would possibly stabilize this interaction. The third step would then be the formation of oligonucleotides and pyrophosphate, with chain growth in either direction. For details of this attractive hypothesis, the reader is referred to the original article by Bollum (1963).

Finally the hypothesis of DNA replication proposed by Cavalieri and Rosenberg (1961) should be mentioned. According to these authors, DNA extracted from rapidly growing cells is four-stranded and the conserved unit in DNA replication is the double helix, rather than the single chain of the double helix, as suggested by Watson and Crick. During replication the fundamental configuration of the template would remain helical.

DNA Synthesis at the Cytological Level and Chromosome Duplication

A. DNA Synthesis

Cytophotometric studies in a large variety of plant and animal species have shown that there is a constant relationship between the amount of DNA per nucleus and the number of chromosomal sets. In dividing cells, the amount of DNA per nucleus doubles during interphase, and is equally distributed between the two daughter nuclei at anaphase. Thus, if the amount of nuclear DNA is 2C at anaphase and telophase, it is 4C at prophase and metaphase. However, the fact that DNA is doubled between telophase and prophase does not mean that DNA is synthesized during the entire interphase period.

Howard and Pelc (1953) have divided the interphase of *Vicia faba* root-tip cells into three stages on the basis of results obtained in autoradiographic studies. They found that radioactive phosphorous, P^{32}, was incorporated into chromosomal DNA during the middle third of interphase, which indicated that the synthesis of DNA occurs during this stage (the S period). Howard and Pelc estimated the duration of S to be about six hours and that of the period between the end of S and the beginning of prophase (the G_2 period) to be about eight hours. The duration of the time interval (G_1) between telophase and S was obtained by subtracting G_2 and S from the total interphase time. Since, according to Howard and Pelc, interphase lasts 26 hours in *Vicia*, the duration of G_1 would be 12 hours.

In principle, these results were confirmed by Deeley et al. (1957), who used a cytochemical method for studying DNA synthesis in *Vicia* root tips. However, since Deeley et al. estimated the average interphase time to be 20, rather than to 26 hours, they found the duration of G_1 to be only about six hours. In a recent autoradiographic study, the duration of G_1, S, and G_2 in *Vicia* root tips was reinvestigated by Evans and Scott (1964), using tritium(H^3)-labeled thymidine as the radioactive DNA-precursor. They found the duration of these periods to be 4.9, 7.5, and 4.9 hours, respectively. According to Evans and Scott, the total mitotic cycle in *Vicia* at 19°C lasts only 19.3 hours, and mitosis itself two hours (Fig. 5-1A).

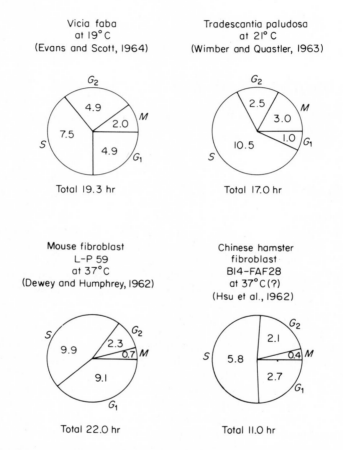

Fig. 5–1. Duration of G_1, S, and G_2 in root-tip cells of *Vicia faba* and *Tradescantia paludosa* and in tissue culture cells of mouse fibroblast and Chinese hamster fibroblast.

DNA synthesis has now been studied with the autoradiographic technique in many animal and plant species with essentially the same result. DNA synthesis occurs during a limited period of interphase, although the relative proportion of the interphase time spent in S may vary considerably between different species and tissues. This is also true for the relative duration of G_1 and G_2. In root tips of *Vicia faba* and in Chinese hamster fibroblast, G_1 and G_2 appear to be of about the same duration (Figs. 5-1A and D). In root tips of *Tradescantia paludosa*, G_2 is more than twice as long as G_1 (Fig. 5-1B), and in mouse fibroblast G_1 is about four times longer than G_2 (Fig. 5-1C). The microspore division in *Tradescantia* represents an extreme case. The interphase in this material is of the duration of a week, or more. Most of this time is spent in G_1, the S period occurring 24 to 36 hours before metaphase at 25°C (Moses and Taylor, 1955).

Although the periods G_1, S, and G_2 are very characteristic of the various stages of the interphase of dividing cells, they do not exist in the resting stage of differentiated and/or mitotically inactive cells. Lajtha (1963) has suggested the name G_0 for this "true" resting stage, which, in contrast to the stages G_1, S, and G_2, is not part of a mitotic cycle.

G_0 cells can be triggered into division. If this happens, the rule is that the cells go through the usual G_1-S-G_2 cycle before they divide. Polyploid cells have been reported to divide without a preceding DNA synthesis, however (compare Chaps. 6 and 7), and in these cases the cells pass directly from G_0 into G_2. The embryo cells of dry seeds may also be regarded as G_0 cells. The nuclei of these cells frequently have a DNA value of 4C (Avanzi et al., 1963; Stein and Quastler, 1963). When the seeds germinate, mitosis precedes DNA synthesis, and thus, the cells of the dormant embryo pass directly from G_0 into G_2.

Taylor (1953a) has pointed out that there is a coincidence in time between the onset of DNA synthesis and the time when the chromosomes cease to respond to radiation as single units. When cells are irradiated with X-rays in early interphase, the resulting aberrations are of the chromosome type. This type of aberration, in which the two chromatids of a chromosome are broken or exchanged at the same loci (compare Chap. 9) is believed to be induced before duplication, when the chromosomes are still single. X-ray irradiation of cells in late interphase results in aberrations of the chromatid type. In this case the unit of breakage is the single chromatid, and the interpretation is that these aberrations are induced in chromosomes which have already duplicated. In *Tradescantia* microspores (Taylor, 1953a; Moses and Taylor, 1955), as well as in *Vicia* root tips (Thoday, 1954), the transition from chromosome to chromatid-type aberrations coincides in time with the interphase period during which DNA is synthesized. The same correlation was found by Taylor in *Tulbaghia violaceae* (Taylor, 1958a). In the microspores of this plant, synthesis of DNA occurs at the very beginning of interphase, and aberrations of the chromatid type are produced by X-rays at any time between early and late interphase. After irradiation of Chinese hamster cells with X-rays, Hsu et al. (1962) found aberrations of the chromosome type only in cells irradiated while in G_1. Thus, the experimental evidence strongly indicates that the transition from aberration of the chromosome type to aberrations of the chromatid type occurs in connection with DNA synthesis. However, recent radioautographic studies by Wolff and Luippold (1964) and by Evans and Savage (1963) in *Vicia* have indicated that chromatid-type aberrations may be induced by X rays for a short time prior to the period of DNA synthesis. Evans and Savage suggest that this may result from a physical separation of replicating units which are preparing for replication. In the studies of Wolff and Luippold, as well as in those of Evans and Savage, H[3]-thymidine was used as radioactive DNA precursor.

B. Chromosome Duplication

The autoradiographic technique, which has proved to be so useful for determining the period of the cell cycle during which DNA synthesis takes place, has also given us important information about the mechanism of chromosome duplication. An important question, which has intrigued cytologists for decades, is whether one of the sister-chromatids in a chromosome is composed of entirely new material, whereas the other, which during duplication has acted as a template, contains original material, or whether both chromatids are half old and half new.

The first to use the radioautographic technique to solve this problem were Plaut and Mazia (1956). In their experiments, root tips of *Crepis capillaris* ($2n = 6$) were exposed for 12 hours to a solution containing C[14]-labeled thymidine. Since thymidine is incorporated only into DNA, it is the ideal precursor for studies of DNA synthesis. The roots were then transferred to a nonradioactive solution and fixed at various intervals during the first 24 hours after the C[14]-thymidine treatment. Radioautographs were prepared, and the distribution of the silver grains developed in the photographic emulsion over ana- and telophase nuclei was determined. If the newly formed DNA was distributed equally between the sister-chromatids, the two groups of chromosomes separating in ana- and telophase would contain equal amounts of labeled DNA. If, on the other hand, all the newly formed DNA was confined to one of the two sister-chromatids, there would be six labeled and six unlabeled chromatids, or daughter chromosomes, in anaphase. Since the chromatids separate at random in anaphase, one would expect the daughter nuclei in a certain proportion of cases to contain different amounts of radioactive material, because they have received a different number of labeled chromosomes. Plaut and Mazia found the distribution of labeled material between daughter nuclei to be so different that it hardly could be explained as an experimental error. Therefore, they conclude that the newly formed DNA is not equally distributed between daughter nuclei, indicating that an entirely new chromatid had been formed during replication.

The experiment by Plaut and Mazia, although important as a pioneer work, was too crude, however, and the results of subsequent experiments by Taylor and his collaborators, using more refined methods, have shown that their conclusions were incorrect.

Taylor et al. (1957) treated root tips of *Vicia faba* ($2n = 12$) with H^3-labeled thymidine in their already classical study of chromosome duplication. The β-particles emitted by tritium have a very low energy and travel only a fraction of a micron from their source of emission. Since the silver grains developed in the photographic emulsion are so very close to the labeled object, it is possible to detect, not only if both or only one of the sister-chromatids of the chromosome are labeled, but also if the labeling in a chromatid is restricted to a certain region(s).

Because of the excellent resolution obtained with H^3-thymidine, which by far exceeds that obtained with C^{14}-thymidine, the method used by Taylor et al. is much more reliable and sensitive than that of Plaut and Mazia. Another improvement was that Taylor et al., by adding colchicine to the nonradioactive solution to which the roots were transferred after the H^3-thymidine treatment, were able to tell how many divisions the analyzed cells had been through since labeling. Since colchicine prevents cell division but not chromosome division, every mitosis in the presence of colchicine will result in a doubling of the number of chromosomes (compare Chap. 8).

The result of the experiment of Taylor et al. was that all chromatids (Fig. 5-2) were equally labeled in the first division after the H^3-thymidine treatment. In the second division after the H^3-thymidine treatment, the chromosomes had one labeled and one unlabeled chromatid. When the chromosomes reached metaphase for the third time after the H^3-thymidine treatment, half of the now 48 chromosomes had one labeled chromatid, whereas the remaining 24 chromosomes were entirely unlabeled.

These results indicate that the thymidine incorporated into chromosomal DNA is part of a structural unit which remains intact during subsequent chromosome duplications. The experiments have further shown that the early interphase chromosomes are divided longitudinally in two units. During interphase these two units are doubled so that the chromosomes at the end of interphase are four-stranded. When the duplication occurs in the presence of H^3-thymidine, the labeled precursor will be confined to the two new strands. The chromatids of the prophase and metaphase chromosomes consist of an unlabeled old strand and a labeled new strand, which explains why the two sister-chromatids contain equal amounts of H^3-thymidine. If subsequent duplications occur in the absence of H^3-thymidine, the new strands will be unlabeled. In the second division after the H^3-thymidine treatment, three of the four strands in a chromosome are unlabeled, and one of the chromatids will contain two unlabeled strands and the other will contain one labeled strand and one unlabeled strand (Fig. 5-3). In the third division after the H^3-thymidine treatment, only half of the chromosomes contain one labeled strand.

Subsequently, Taylor found a similar "semi-conservative" chromo-

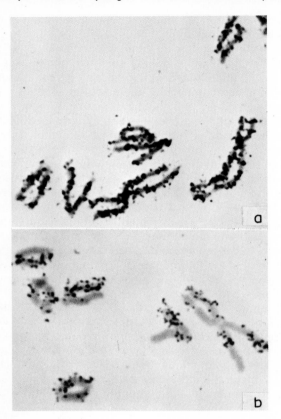

Fig. 5–2. Chromosomes of *Vicia faba* at the first (a) and second (b) division after incorporation of H³-thymidine during DNA replication. In a all chromatids are labeled, in b one chromatid of each chromosome is labeled. Sister-chromatid exchanges can be seen in b. (Taylor, 1962; Int. Rev. Cytol. 13:52, 53. Reprinted by permission of Academic Press, Inc.)

some duplication pattern in *Bellevalia* (Taylor, 1958c), *Crepis* (Taylor, 1958b), and in human cells in tissue culture (Taylor, 1960b). His results have also been confirmed by other workers (e.g., Woods and Schairer, 1959; Prescott and Bender, 1963).

An interesting phenomenon observed by Taylor (1958c) in connection with these experiments was the sister-chromatid exchanges. Although, as a rule, in the second division following the H³-thymidine treatment, the metaphase chromosomes were composed of one labeled and one unlabeled chromatid, it occurred that an otherwise labeled chromatid had an unlabeled segment. When this happened, the corresponding locus in the sister-chromatid was always labeled, indicating that a reciprocal exchange of segments between the two sister-chromatids had occurred (Fig. 5-2). The phenomenon was thoroughly analyzed by Taylor. Facts such as the absence of half-chromatid exchanges and the frequent occurrence of exchanges in pairs or twins led Taylor to conclude that the two subunits of the chromatid cannot reunite at random and, therefore, are not identical. Taylor believes, "This feature is likely

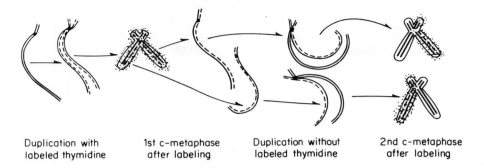

| Duplication with labeled thymidine | 1st c-metaphase after labeling | Duplication without labeled thymidine | 2nd c-metaphase after labeling |

Fig. 5–3. Diagrammatic representation of the structural organization and mode of replication of the chromosomes as revealed by autoradiographs. (Taylor, et al., 1957; Nat. Acad. Sci. (U.S.), Proc., 43:125. Courtesy of J. H. Taylor.)

although not necessarily related to the difference in the two strands of the DNA double helices which are complementary with respect to base pairs and have a different directional sense with respect to the 3'-5' phosphodiester linkages." (Taylor, 1962.)

There remains to mention one important feature of chromosome reproduction that has appeared from radioautographic studies: Different chromosomes of the same set, and even different parts of the same chromosomes, may duplicate at different stages of the S-period of interphase (asynchronous duplication). Thus Taylor (1958b) found in *Crepis capillaris* that the regions around the centromere were the last to duplicate. Lima-de-Faria (1959) has shown that the heterochromatic block formed by the sex chromosomes in the grasshopper *Melanoplus differentialis* synthesizes DNA later than the euchromatic autosomes. Late replication of sex chromatin has also been observed in mammalian cells in tissue culture (e.g., Taylor, 1960b; Grumbach et al., 1963). In rye, Lima-de-Faria (1959) found that the heterochromatin synthesizes DNA at a different period of time from the euchromatin. According to Wimber (1961), the terminal portions of the chromosome arms in the root-tip cells of *Tradescantia paludosa* continue DNA duplication at a time of the DNA synthesis period when other parts of the chromosomes have already ceased to synthesize. The sites of asynchronous duplication in *Tradescantia* were not related to any obvious heterochromatic segments. In root tips of *Vicia faba* Evans (1964) has found that the heterochromatic zones begin to synthesize their new DNA later than the euchromatic parts of the chromosomes and continue to synthesize for some time after the other parts have ceased. After having reviewed the available evidence on DNA replication in euchromatin and heterochromatin, Evans concludes that late replication is something characteristic of the DNA in positive heteropycnotic regions, whether they are in autosomes or in sex chromosomes.

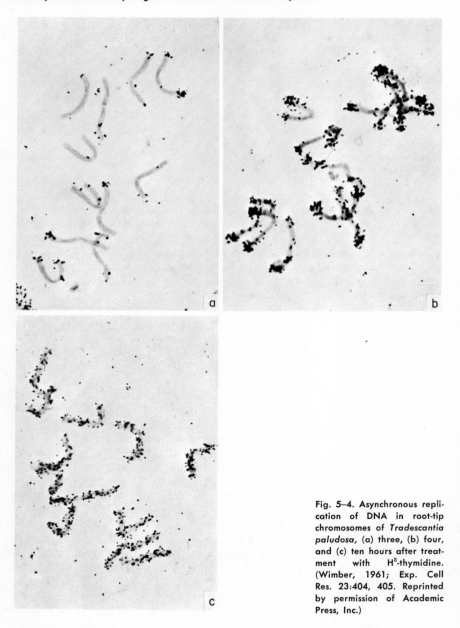

Fig. 5–4. Asynchronous replication of DNA in root-tip chromosomes of *Tradescantia paludosa*, (a) three, (b) four, and (c) ten hours after treatment with H³-thymidine. (Wimber, 1961; Exp. Cell Res. 23:404, 405. Reprinted by permission of Academic Press, Inc.)

However, there are data which do not fit with this picture. According to Taylor (1963c), "The various patterns suggest that the time of replication is under a genetic control more complex than that explained by two kinds of chromatin."

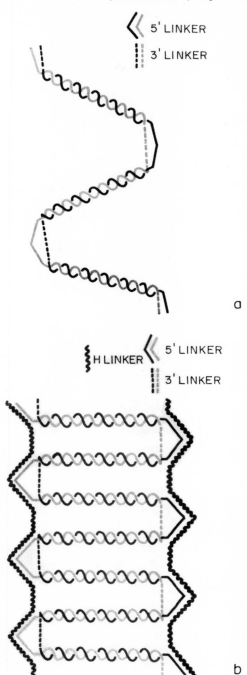

Fig. 5–5. Diagrammatic representation of the hypothetical organization of DNA in a portion of the chromosome. (a) The chromosome in G_1. (b) During replication (the S-period) the chromosome is assumed to be stabilized by folding and the establishment of H-linkers. (Taylor, 1963a; Molecular Genetics, Part 1, pp. 99, 100. Reprinted by permission of Academic Press, Inc.)

67

The observations further indicate that the chromosomes have many independent points where replication begins (Taylor, 1963b; Plaut, 1963; Evans, 1964), and that it is composed of many replicative units.

The results of his radioautographic experiments have caused Taylor to construct several chromosome models (Taylor et al., 1957; Taylor, 1957). The most recent one (Taylor, 1963a), which is shown in Fig. 5-5, is a modification of a model originally proposed by Freese (1958). The chromosome is visualized as a series of tandemly linked segments of DNA, which replicate as units, and which are connected with "R"-linkers. "During the condensed stages of division, in large chromosomes the long strand is assumed to be coiled, folded, and stabilized by H linkers that may give the chromatids a temporary doubleness during division stages." (Taylor, 1963b.) The existence and chemical nature of these hypothetical "R"- and "H"-linkers remain to be shown, but they are necessary to explain the properties of the chromosome. Recent findings by Bendich and collaborators (Bendich et al., 1963; Borenfreund et al., 1964) suggest that the "R"-linkers may be peptide esters (Taylor, 1963b).

C. Conclusions

The most important findings and conclusions of the radioautographic experiments described above may be summarized as follows:

The interphase of mitotic cells may be divided into three stages: (1) the S-(synthetic)-period during which labeled precursors are incorporated into chromosomal DNA, (2) the postsynthetic period G_2 between S and prophase, and (3) the presynthetic period G_1 between telophase and the beginning of S.

X-rays induce chromosome type aberrations in G_1 and aberrations of the chromatid type in S and G_2 The transition from chromosome-type aberrations to chromatid-type aberrations seems to occur in late G_1, just prior to the period of DNA synthesis.

The G_1 chromosome is divided longitudinally into two units or strands. During S these strands separate, each remaining intact and acting as a template for the formation of a new partner strand. The chromatid of the prophase and metaphase chromosomes, therefore, consists of one old and one new strand. The two strands in a G_1 chromosome or in a chromatid are not identical, and it is tempting to relate this difference to the difference existing between the strands in the DNA double helix, which are complementary and of opposite polarity (compare Chap. 4).

The chromosome has many sites where replication begins and is probably composed of many replicative units.

All these facts are best reconciled with a chromosome model which is composed of a series of tandemly linked DNA double helices with their associated protein.

Cell Division

A. Interphase

The stage between two succeeding divisions, when the chromosomes appear dispersed and are surrounded by a nuclear membrane, is called *interphase*. Viewed through the light microscope, interphase appears to be a rather inactive stage in comparison with the drastic changes occurring during the stages of active division. It is, therefore, particularly in the older cytological literature, referred to as the "resting stage." However, we know now that from a physiological point of view, interphase is far from being inactive. Interphase is the stage of synthesis and duplication which compensates for the halving of material and structures which takes place during the division stages. It would, therefore, be more appropriate to call interphase the *metabolic* stage rather than the resting stage.

During interphase the chromosomes are duplicated (compare Chap. 5), and material for the mitotic spindle is synthesized. New mitochondria and other cytoplasmic organelles are formed, and the cell increases in size. These processes require the synthesis of compounds such as nucleic acids, proteins, lipids, and carbohydrates. The intranuclear synthesis of nucleic acids and proteins has already been discussed (Chaps. 2 and 5). As mentioned in Chapter 2, the data indicate that RNA is synthesized from late telophase through the entire interphase period until mid-prophase. DNA synthesis is restricted to a period occupying in most cases one-third to one-half of the total time spent in interphase and is usually located in time in the middle of interphase. As mentioned in the preceding chapter, the period between the end of telophase and the DNA synthesis period (S-period) is called G_1 (gap 1), and the period between S and prophase is called G_2 (gap 2). Like the term *resting stage*, the terms G_1 and G_2 are somewhat unfortunate, since they seem to implicate that nothing of importance occurs during these periods.

However, we have already seen (p. 25) that RNA is synthesized during these periods. Histone synthesis begins in G_1 and continues through G_2 (Chap. 2).

The G_2 period corresponds roughly with the "antephase" of Bullough, which is defined by him as "that period immediately preceding the prophase when an energy store is created" (Bullough, 1952). The energy believed to be produced and stored in the antephase is that required for active division. The energy requirements of mitosis will be discussed in Chap. 7 in connection with the effects of inhibitors of respiration and oxidative phosphorylation on mitosis. It may, therefore, be sufficient to mention that recent experiments with both plant (Amoore, 1963a) and animal (Epel, 1963) material have shown that the concept of a mitotic energy store is superfluous. In the sea urchin egg, at least, mitosis appears to be dependent on the ATP level of the cell.

Even if there is no particular stage of energy production and storage at the end of interphase, many important processes occur between the end of DNA synthesis and the beginning of prophase, i.e., in G_2. During this period the physiological changes occur which result in chromosome spiralization and contraction and the onset of division. This is also the period during which ionizing radiation and certain chemical agents (e.g., methylated oxypurines) are most effective in producing chromosomal aberrations and mitotic delay. The fact that cells treated in G_2 with inhibitors of deoxyribonucleotide synthesis, such as 5-fluorodeoxyuridine, deoxyadenosine, and cytosine arabinoside, appear in metaphase with gaps and breaks in their chromosomes indicates that deoxyribonucleotide synthesis occurs at this stage (although DNA, or the bulk of DNA, is synthesized earlier), and is of importance for the structural integrity of the chromosomes. There are also facts indicating (Yost, 1951; Revell, 1959; Taylor et al., 1962) that most chromosomal aberrations are formed or realized shortly before prophase, although they may have been initiated, and their type determined, at a much earlier stage of interphase. All these facts make G_2 one of the most interesting phases of the cell cycle, and a better understanding of G_2 would, therefore, seem highly desirable.

We have seen that most of the anabolic processes connected with growth and duplication take place during interphase and not during the stages of active division. Other data indicate that the energy needed for anabolic processes and for division is also generated during interphase and not during division itself (compare Chap. 7). Thus, interphase appears to be a phase of physiological activity and morphological inactivity, whereas the opposite is true for active division.

The morphology and structural organization of the interphase cell have been described previously (Chaps. 1 and 3), and only a brief recapitulation of its appearance in the light microscope will be necessary here.

The structures of the interphase cell which are large enough to be detected in the light microscope are the cell nucleus, the mitochondria,

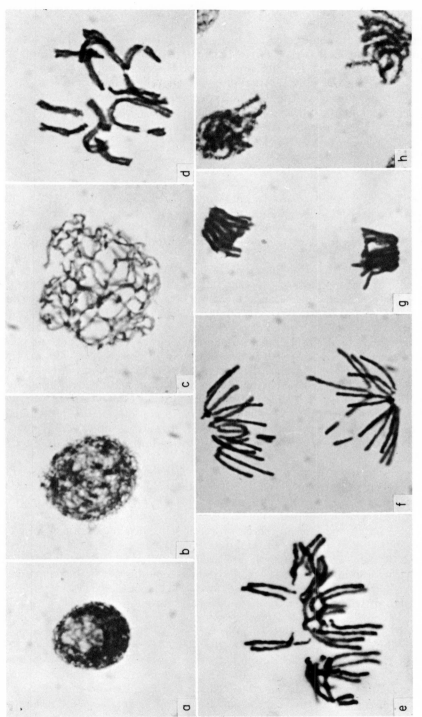

Fig. 6–1. Root-tip cells of *Vicia faba* in various stages of mitosis. (*a*) Interphase. (*b*) Early prophase. (*c*) Late prophase. (*d*) Metaphase. (*e*) Early anaphase. (*f*) Anaphase. (*g*) Telophase. (*h*) Late telophase.

and vacuoli. In plant cells it is further possible to see plastids of various kinds and the cell wall. The nucleus of the unfixed cell often appears homogenous except for the nucleoli and heterochromatic bodies. The nucleolus does not stain by the Feulgen technique, which indicates that it contains no or very little DNA. As a result of the synthetic processes which take place during the "metabolic-stage," both the cell and the nucleus are considerably larger at late than at early interphase.

B. Prophase

In slides made of fixed and stained root tips of plants such as the broad bean, *Vicia faba,* and onion, *Allium cepa,* the transition from interphase to prophase is characterized by the fact that the cell nucleus increases in volume and acquires a more granular structure. The cell is in early prophase when the chromatin within the nucleus has been organized in such a way that the chromosomes are visible as a network of thin threads. When the chromosomes in a more advanced stage of prophase become shorter and thicker, it is possible to see that they are divided longitudinally into two chromatids. Although the chromatids are joined only in the centromeric region (see below), they do not drift apart, but remain closely paired along their entire length, which indicates that attraction forces exist between the sister-chromatids. The pairing between the sister-chromatids is maintained until the end of metaphase, even when the chromatid is broken or when chromatid intra- and interchange has occurred. In metaphase, the chromatid interchanges resemble chiasmata in the diplotene stage of meiosis. The chromatid interchanges acquire this appearance as a result of the attraction forces between sister-chromatids in combination with the spiralization and contraction at prophase.

Since, in spite of the attraction between the sister-chromatids, the split between them is clearly visible, there seems to be some kind of barrier (surface charge, surrounding sheath) preventing the chromatids from coming too close together. This barrier also exists between chromosomes: "The long threads of the early prophase chromosomes appear to wind more or less at random throughout the nuclear cavity; but they never actually come in contact with one another, or indeed approach within a certain minimum distance: there is thus something which keeps them apart, which is probably in the nature of a generalized electrostatic repulsion distributed over the surface of the chromosome." (White, 1947.)

When the prophase is so far advanced that individual chromosomes can be distinguished, it is possible to see that the chromosomes are not stained uniformly from one end to the other, but that they contain achromatic segments or constrictions. As a rule, the chromosomes of both animal and plant cells are divided by a primary constriction or *centromere* into two arms, the length of which is dependent on the position of the centromere in the chromosomes. During metaphase and anaphase

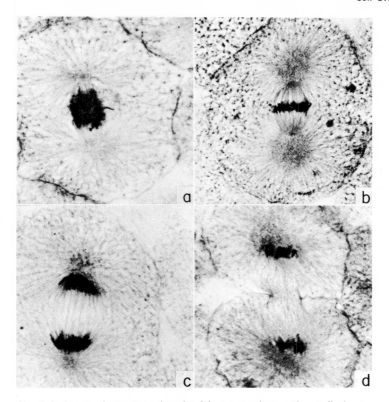

Fig. 6–2. Stages of mitosis in the whitefish. (a) Prophase with spindle begin-ning to form between asters. (b) Metaphase, the spindle now fully developed. (c) Anaphase. (d) Telophase with the furrow cutting the cell into two daughter cells. (Swanson, 1961. The Cell, p. 49. Courtesy of General Biological Supply House, Inc., Chicago.)

the chromosomes are attached to the spindle in the centromeric regions. Some chromosomes contain, in addition to centromeres, *secondary con-strictions*, which may be involved in the formation of nucleoli, in which case they are called *nucleolar constrictions*. Each chromosome has its characteristic morphology which is determined by the position of the primary constriction and, if secondary constrictions are present, also by their position and number.

The chemical nature of chromosomes has been discussed in Chap. 3. Therefore, it should be sufficient to mention such changes in the chemi-cal composition of chromosomes as occur during the stages of active division. Selective staining methods have indicated that the chromo-somes acquire an RNA component during prophase which remains on the chromosomes during metaphase and anaphase (e.g., Kaufmann et al., 1948; Jacobson and Webb, 1952). During telophase the RNA component disappears from the chromosomes. [This *deposition* of RNA-like material

73

onto mitotic chromosomes should not be confused with the *synthesis* of RNA, which stops at prophase when the nucleoli disintegrate, and begins at telophase in the pronucleolar bodies (Das, 1963).] At about the same time there is an increase of RNA in the interzonal region, and it seems reasonable to assume that the two processes are related. It should be pointed out, however, that Davidson in a recent radioautographic study (Davidson, 1964) could not find any evidence for a progressive increase in the amount of RNA on the prophase chromosomes. In agreement with the results of the earlier radioautographic studies of Prescott and Bender (1962), those of Davidson indicate that nuclear RNA is shed into the cytoplasm when the nuclear membrane breaks down and the nucleolus disintegrates.

The presence of phospholipids on the chromosomes during mitosis has been demonstrated by LaCour and Chayen (1958). These authors found that the chromosomes of plant root tips stain yellow with Orange G from mid-prophase to the end of anaphase. The substance stained by Orange G proved to be a phospholipid (LaCour et al., 1958). The similarity between the behavior of chromosomal RNA and phospholipid during the stages of active division is striking and, as pointed out by Mazia (1961), it calls to mind the association between ribonucleoprotein and lipoprotein in cytoplasmic structures.

LaCour and Chayen (1958) have discussed whether or not the lipoprotein could be regarded as a matrix substance. They conclude, ". . . it is not a 'matrix' in the sense that the fully spiralized chromosome is solidly embedded in it. Rather it is to be regarded as a coating to the nucleic acid-protein structure of the chromosomes, which is deposited about the time that spiralization begins."

The question of whether or not the chromosomes during the stages of active division are embedded in a matrix is a controversial one. Many workers, among them Darlington (1937) and Ris (1957), have questioned the reality of matrix, whereas others believe that if one does not distinguish between chromonema, which is the skeleton or permanent structure of a chromosome, and matrix, the substance in which the chromonema is embedded during the stages of active division, ". . . it is not possible to treat of the chemical composition of chromosomes in cytologically intelligible terms." (Serra, 1955.)

Electron-microscopic studies of Lafontaine and Chouinard (1963) suggest that the chromosomes during prophase, metaphase, and anaphase contain an achromatic matrix substance, the fine structure of which strongly resembles that of the chromonemata. This matrix substance, which fills the central core as well as the space between the chromonemata, could partly represent material from the nuclear sap and/or the nucleolus. Some of the matrix material is released during anaphase into the spindle.

In Chap. 3 various hypotheses on the structural organization of chromosomes were discussed. However, nothing was said about the spiralization and condensation processes responsible for the transformation of the late interphase chromosome to the metaphase chromosome. Unfortunately, hardly anything is known about these processes and their causes. The changes in length and diameter must be considerable. When fully despiralized, an ordinary interphase chromosome would be expected to be at least as long as the lampbrush chromosome in the meiotic prophase of the newt, which may be more than 1 mm. The chromatid diameter in the lampbrush chromosome appears to be of the order of 100 to 200 A (Gall, 1958). The same chromosomes are in metaphase only about 10 μ long, and the diameter of the mitotic prophase chromatid is of the order of 0.2 μ.

What kind of forces could be responsible for these remarkable changes of chromosome length and diameter?

Anderson et al. (1960) suggest that the condensation is the result of a discharge of negative groups on DNA with a polyvalent cation. These authors believe that histone, or a smaller basic polypeptide, or simple polyanions such as spermine, spermidine, cadaverine, or putresceine might be the polyvalent cations responsible for condensation. Support for this view was obtained in studies on the effect of polyamines on the state of chromosomes in isolated nuclei.

Also according to the recent hypothesis of Cole (1962), neutralization of DNA by a polyvalent cation is the main cause of chromosome coiling. The hypothesis is based on ". . . a co-linear, ionic bonding between a hydrated DNA double helix and histone in the α-configuration. The co-linear association would lead to neutralization of charged groups along the associated side, weakening bindings to water, and partially dehydrating the associated side. The unilateral dehydration would give rise to a secondary coiling of 138 A diameter" (Somers et al., 1963). By association with a second and a third histone species, further levels of coiling would be attained with the establishment of the metaphase chromosome as a result. The binding between DNA and histone would be strengthened by divalent metal ions and loosened by monovalent ions.

C. Contraction Stage and Prometaphase

The collapse of the nuclear envelope and the dissolution of the nucleolus mark the end of prophase. The ciné-micrographic studies of Bajer (e.g., 1954, 1957, 1958) on mitosis in endosperm have shown that the breakdown of the nuclear envelope is a very sudden process, whereas the (at that time) half-liquid nucleolus dissolves more gradually. The disintegration of the nucleolus is shown in Fig. 6-3. The appearance of a clear zone around the prophase nucleus precedes the breakdown of the nuclear envelope. The clear zone is usually structureless and appears to have a semi-liquid consistency. After the rupture of the nuclear envelope follows a stage which has been called "contraction stage" by Bajer and which is defined by him as ". . . the stage lasting for a few minutes prior to prometaphase (metakinesis), when

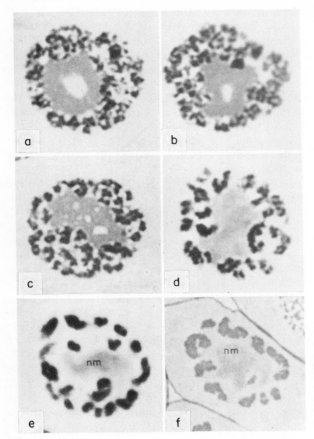

Fig. 6–3. The disintegration of the nucleolus during prophase in *Vicia faba*. (Lafontaine and Chouinard, 1963. Reprinted by permission of The Rockefeller Institute Press from J. Cell Biol., April, 1963, Vol. 17, No. 1, pp. 167–201.)

the scattered chromosomes which had in late prophase formed a loose ball aggregate suddenly into a tighter central mass" (Bajer and Molé-Bajer, 1956). After the contraction stage the interaction between the spindle and the chromosomes begins. The stretching of the centromeres which can be observed after the compression of the chromosome group in the contraction stage probably marks the attachment of the centromeres to the spindle. According to Bajer (1957), the spindle is formed as a result of an interaction between the clear zone, the nuclear sap, and the centromeres. The electron-microscopic studies of Lafontaine and Chouinard (1963) indicate that at least part of the granular and fibrillar components of the spindle are of nucleolar origin.

D. Metaphase

In metaphase the centromeres of the strongly spiralized chromosomes are in the equatorial plate of the spindle. The metaphase represents a stage of equilibrium between the convergent movements of prometaphase and the divergent movements of anaphase.

At metaphase the spindle is fully developed. Its structure in the fixed and unfixed cell as seen with the light and electron microscope, as well as its physical properties and chemical composition, will be briefly described below. For a detailed discussion, the reader is referred to the thorough review by Mazia (1961).

In the light microscope the spindle of the living cell appears as a clear, structureless area outlined by mitochondria and other large particles of the cytoplasm. However, if polarized light is used, it is evident that the spindle is a fibrillar structure (Bajer, 1961). The fibrous character of the spindle is also very apparent in fixed material. The fibers are of at least two kinds: chromosomal fibers, which are attached to the centromeres, and continuous fibers, which run from pole to pole. In contrast to the chromosomes, the spindle stains only very weakly with basic stains; it is, therefore, said to be achromatic.

Much of our knowledge of the chemical and physical properties of the spindle we owe to the studies of Mazia and his collaborators on the mitotic apparatus isolated from dividing sea urchin eggs. These studies have shown that the mitotic apparatus may be described as a gel which is formed by the polymerization of protein macromolecules. The proteins involved in the formation of the spindle are few, but they constitute a considerable part of the total protein fraction of the egg cell. The proteins of the spindle appear to be rich in sulfur, and there is evidence for the participation of S-S bonds in the formation of the spindle. According to one hypothesis, *intra*molecular S-S bonds in the spindle precursor proteins would be converted into *inter*molecular S-S bonds which, besides hydrogen bonds, would play an important role in holding the spindle gel together. Other constituents of the spindle are polysaccharides, lipids, and RNA. An interesting finding is that ATPase activity appears to be associated with the fibrous component of the mitotic apparatus. This enzyme, which splits ATP, but not ADP, GTP, CTP, or UTP, requires magnesium and has a pH optimum of 8.4. As pointed out by Mazia (1961), the fact that ATPase activity is associated with the mitotic apparatus is in agreement with the hypothesis that cellular motility is connected with this enzyme activity.

In most animal species and in some lower plants, a certain body, the *centrosome*, appears to participate in the formation and activity of the spindle. The centrosome is frequently a very conspicious structure. It consists of a small, refractile body surrounded by a clearer area from which a system of fibrillar rays, the aster or astral rays, radiate. According to the behavior of the asters, it is possible to distinguish between two types of cells. In one type, of which the cells of salamander are an example, the asters separate in early prophase and migrate towards the poles, the spindle being formed between them. In the other type, the separation of the asters may take place as early as in telophase of the preceding division.

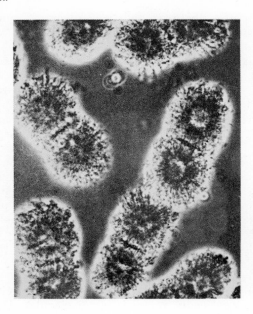

Fig. 6–4. Mitotic apparatus isolated from sea urchin eggs (*Strongylocentrotus purpuratus*) by the dithiodiglycol method. [Mazia, 1961b; The Cell III, Brachet and Mirsky, eds, p. 245 (Fig. 54-B). Reprinted by permission of Academic Press, Inc.]

E. Anaphase

The studies of Lima-de-Faria have shown that the region which holds the two sister-chromatids of each chromosome together at the very end of metaphase is the most proximal part of the arms (the part closest to the centromere) and not the centromere itself (Fig. 6-5). At this stage, the two longitudinal halves of the centromere are distinctly separated from each other (Lima-de-Faria, 1953, 1955). The material which holds the sister-chromatids together in the most proximal region appears to be a DNA-containing matrix substance, since at the end of metaphase the chromosome is divided into chromatids also in this region.

According to Lima-de-Faria (1955, 1958), the same weakly staining, DNA-containing matrix substance is responsible for keeping the sister-chromatids closely paired throughout their whole length at metaphase, the most proximal regions differing from other parts of the chromosome arms only by being the last to separate.

Whatever the cause of the pairing is, it suddenly ceases at the end of metaphase. Anaphase begins when the sister-chromatids separate also at the most proximal parts. The free sister-chromatids, or *daughter chromosomes* as they from now on are called, then begin to move towards opposite poles with the centromeric regions first and the chromosome arms trailing.

About the mechanism of chromosome movement we know almost as little as about the attraction forces operating between the sister-chromatids in mitosis and between homologous chromosomes in meiosis.

What we know is only that the centromeres of the chromosomes are attached to the so-called chromosomal fibers of the spindle, and that some obscure mechanism makes the chromosomal fibers to pull the centromeres towards the poles. For detailed discussions on the anaphase movement, the reader is referred to papers by Östergren (e.g., Östergren, 1950; Östergren et al., 1960) and to the review article by Mazia (1961).

Cells which during interphase have been treated with ionizing radiation or with chromosome-breaking chemicals often contain chromosomes which have been changed by breakage and/or chromatid exchange in such a way that they have no or two centromeres. During anaphase, the acentric chromosomes or chromosome fragments usually remain at the equatorial plate, whereas the dicentric chromosomes form bridges, if the two centromeres travel to opposite poles.

In addition to the movements of the chromosomes towards the poles, there is another movement during anaphase, which consists in an elongation of the spindle. In this other type of movement, the two groups of daughter chromosomes are further separated by the expansion of the middle region of the spindle.

Fig. 6–5. Chromosomes of *Allium cepa* at the very end of metaphase after colchicine treatment. The two longitudinal halves of the centromeres are separated from each other, the sister-chromatids being kept together by the most proximal part of the arms. [Lima-de-Faria, 1955; Hereditas 41: 238 (Plate 1:7–8). Courtesy of the author.]

F. Telophase and Cytokinesis

As a result of the elongation of the spindle, the two groups of daughter chromosomes may, at the end of anaphase, be further apart than the original distance between the poles of the metaphase spindle. The events occurring during telophase are essentially a reversal of those occurring during prophase. The chromosomes revert to their interphase condition, but, as pointed out by Mazia (1961), the process resembles a swelling, rather than a despiralization. Nucleoli are reformed, and each group of daughter chromosomes is enclosed by a nuclear membrane, formed by growth and fusion from fragments of the endoplasmic reticulum (Whaley et al., 1960a).

It has been possible to follow the formation of the nucleolus rather

TABLE 6–1.

Cyclical behaviour of various nuclear constituents during mitosis.

Method Used for Demonstration	Probable Chemical Nature of Compound	Localization of Compound During					References
		Interphase	Prophase	Metaphase	Anaphase	Telophase	
Silver-staining	Protein or lipoprotein	Nucleolus	Nucleolus → cytoplasm	Cytoplasm	Cytoplasm	Pre-nucleolar bodies on chromosomes	Das, 1962 ", 1963
Aniline blue-orange G	Phospholipid	Nucleolus, hetero-chromatin	Nucleolus → chromo-somes	Chromo-somes	Chromo-somes	—	La Cour and Chayen, 1958
Gentian violet-safranine	RNA						
Methylgreen-pyronin		Nucleolus, cytoplasm	Nucleolus → chromo-somes, cytoplasm	Chromo-somes, cytoplasm	Chromo-somes → cytoplasm	Chromo-somes → cytoplasm	Kaufmann et al., 1951
May-Grunwald Giemsa							Jacobson and Webb, 1952

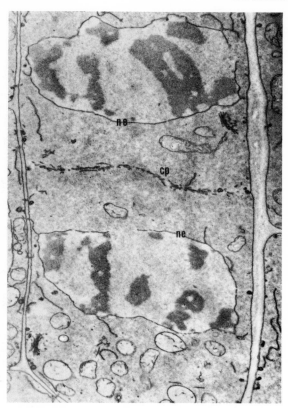

Fig. 6–6. Electron micrograph showing reconstruction of the nuclear envelope and the formation of the cell plate at telophase in a rootcap cell. Whaley et al., 1960a; Amer. J. Bot. 47, p. 445. Courtesy of the authors.)

in detail because it contains a characteristic silver-staining substance (Das, 1962). By taking advantage of this fact, Das (1962, 1963) has shown that nucleolar material is formed on the early telophase chromosomes or, rather, in the interchromosomal spaces. This prenucleolar material is then collected by the nucleolar organizers at the nucleolar constrictions, and nucleoli are formed. As indicated by the incorporation of H^3-cytidine, RNA-synthesis during telophase is confined almost exclusively to the prenucleolar bodies. A similar picture of the formation of nucleoli has been obtained by Lafontaine and Chouinard (1963).

At the same time as the two groups of daughter chromosomes are transformed into interphase nuclei, the cell divides into two daughter cells, each containing one nucleus. This process of *cytokinesis* is different in animal and plant cells. The animal cell, which is not surrounded by a rigid wall, divides by furrowing. The process starts as an invagination or constriction at the equatorial region which is accentuated until the cell is divided into two. In plant cells a cell plate is formed at the equatorial region of the telophase spindle or *phragmoplast*. As a rule, the cell plate is first formed in the central parts of the phragmoplast equator and grows towards the periphery of the cell. Further stages of

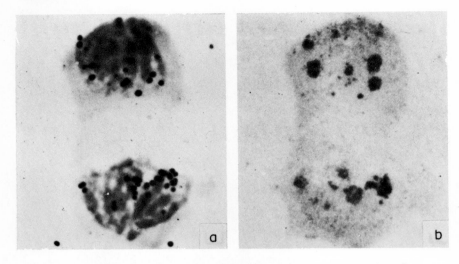

Fig. 6–7. Root-tip cell of *Nigella* in telophase showing incorporations of H³-cytidine (RNA-synthesis) (a) almost exclusively in the prenucleolar bodies (b). (Das, 1963. Reprinted by permission of the author and the Editor of Science from Science, Vol. 140, No. 3572, pp. 1231–1233, 1963.)

the process involve the development of a cell wall between the daughter cells. In this wall, the plate becomes the so-called *middle lamella.*

The exact mechanism by which the cell plate is formed is not known. According to Shimamura and Ôta (1956), RNA-containing material is concentrated in the phragmoplast, but the cell plate region itself appears to be free from it. An accumulation of RNA in the interzonal region at telophase has been observed in animal cells (Jacobson and Webb, 1952). Other cytochemical evidence (Olszewska, 1960) indicates that the first step in the formation of the cell plate is the appearance of neutral lipid droplets at the equatorial region. At successive later stages of cell plate development, phospholipids, lipoproteins, polysaccharides associated with proteins and, finally, only polysaccharides are found. The presence of pectic substances and cellulose can not be demonstrated until some time after the completion of cytokinesis.

Electron micrographs of telophase cells have shown the presence of a series of separated clear vesicles in the central zone of the equatorial plate (Buvat, 1963; Whaley and Mollenhauer, 1963). The cell plate is formed by a fusion of these vesicles, which apparently are a product of the Golgi apparatus (compare Chap. 1, pages 5–6). The electron-microscopic studies of Porter and Machado (1960) and of Whaley et al. (1960a) have further shown that fragments of the endoplasmic reticulum migrate towards the interzonal region, where they associate with the forming cell plate, but, apparently do not fuse with the vesicles of the plate (Whaley and Mollenhauer, 1963). This behavior of elements of the endoplasmic reticulum may account for the above-mentioned cyto-

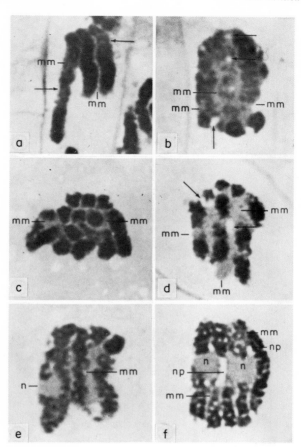

Fig. 6–8. The formation of the nucleolus during telophase in *Vicia faba*. (Lafontaine and Chouinard, 1963. Reprinted by permission of The Rockefeller Institute Press from J. Cell Biol., April, 1963, Vol. 17, No. 1, pp. 167–201.)

chemical observations that lipid and RNA-containing material accumulates in the interzonal region.

Fig. 6–9. The formation of the cell plate by fusion of the vesicles produced by the Golgi apparatus. (Whaley and Mollenhauer, 1963. Reprinted by permission of The Rockefeller Institute Press from J. Cell Biol. April, 1963, Vol. 17, No. 1, pp. 216–221.)

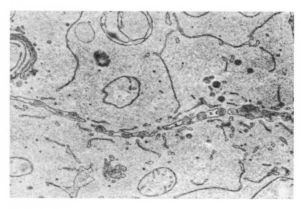

Inhibition
of Mitosis
and the
Production of
Chromosomal
Aberrations

Inhibition of Cell Division I: Prevention of Cells from Entering Mitosis

In this and the following chapter the inhibitory effects of chemicals on cell division will be discussed. Since almost any substance will, in some way or other, influence cell division if applied at sufficiently high concentration and under appropriate experimental conditions, an attempt to review all the available literature on the subject would be meaningless. Instead we shall concentrate on some chemicals, or group of chemicals, which are known to influence strikingly certain phases of cell divisions. These phases are (1) the entering of cells into division, (2) the formation of a functioning spindle, and (3) cytokinesis.

Agents which prevent cells from entering mitosis inhibit the division of the cell, the nucleus, and the chromosomes. But although they inhibit the formation of free chromatids or daughter chromosomes, they do not necessarily inhibit chromosome reproduction.

The stage affected is interphase, and sometimes early prophase, which then is caused to revert to the interphase condition. When these "preprophase inhibitors of mitosis" (D'Amato, 1949a) act on later stages of prophase, they often inhibit the normal evolution of prophase to metaphase, an effect called "prophase poisoning" by D'Amato (1949b, 1952).

Since interphase may be divided into three stages, i.e., the presynthetic stage G_1, the synthetic stage S, and the postsynthetic stage G_2, a classification of the preprophase inhibitors on the basis of their activity at these three stages would be useful. It would be expected that agents which act in G_1 or S would inhibit chromosome reproduction, as well as chromosome division, whereas agents which produce their effect mainly in G_2 would affect only the formation of free chromatids, since at this stage DNA and the chromosomes have already duplicated. Unfortunately, there is so far very little information on the precise stage of interphase which is affected by the various preprophase inhibitors, and what little there is is rather contradictory. It is, therefore, necessary to refrain from using this classification for the present. Instead the agents to be discussed will be classified according to the biochemical mechanism which is believed to be responsible for their action. Two groups of agents will be discussed here. One of these comprises agents which are known or believed to affect the synthesis or the structure of DNA (and RNA); the other group comprises agents which inhibit the production of the energy required for mitosis.

A. Agents Affecting DNA and DNA Metabolism

Doubling of DNA is not the only requirement for cell division, but inhibition of DNA synthesis will generally result in an inhibition of cell division (e.g., Edmunds, 1964). Therefore, as a rule, an S period during which DNA is doubled intervenes between two successive cell divisions. However, no DNA synthesis occurs during the brief interphase (interkinesis) between the first and second meiotic divisions. Cells of *Chlorella* (Iwamura, 1955) or of *Tetrahymena* (Zeuthen, 1963) may be induced to accumulate DNA, which is then used up in subsequent divisions without intervening DNA synthesis. Polyploid cells have been reported to divide without intervening DNA synthesis to yield daughter cells of lower ploidy (e.g., Rasch et al., 1959). An interesting case has been reported by Lindner (1959). He found that treatment of Ehrlich ascites tumor cells with 5-fluorouracil resulted in a halving of the amount of DNA per nucleus without affecting the number of chromosomes. As suggested by Biesele (1962), a possible explanation could be a moderate polyteny of the tumor chromosomes.

In these cases the lack of DNA synthesis did not result in an inhibition of the splitting of the chromosomes into chromatids. Cases are also known, however, in which cells enter mitosis with unsplit chromosomes, apparently as a result of a failure of the synthesis of chromosomal material (e.g., Beadle, 1933; Geitler, 1944; Östergren and Östergren, 1966). The failure of chromosome splitting appears to be gene-controlled in the cases reported by Beadle (1933) and Östergren and Östergren (1966).

Within the group of agents affecting DNA and DNA metabolism it may be useful to distinguish between inhibitors of the synthesis of DNA and DNA precursors, on the one hand, and agents which modify the structure of DNA, on the other. It should be pointed out, however, that although the mechanisma of action are different, the end result may often be the same. Thus, the activity of most of these agents is likely to result in an inhibition of DNA synthesis. Chemical and physical alteration of DNA makes it not only abnormal and unstable, but frequently also less suitable as a primer in the DNA polymerase reaction. Alkylated DNA precursors may inhibit DNA synthesis by interfering with the incorporation of normal DNA precursors.

INHIBITORS OF THE SYNTHESIS
OF DNA AND DNA PRECURSORS

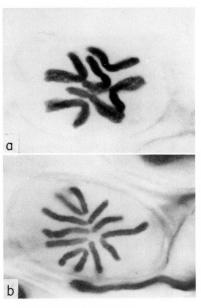

Fig. 7–1. Divided normal (a) and undivided (b) metaphase chromosomes in the pollen grain of *Tradescantia paludosa*. (Courtesy of G. Östergren.)

Azaserine. The antibiotic azaserine is known as a powerful inhibitor of mitosis in both plant and animal material. This is illustrated by the study of Tanaka and Sugimura (1956), and by that of Biesele (1958*b*). Tanaka and Sugimura, who used root tips of *Tradescantia paludosa* as experimental material, found that mitosis was completely suppressed in roots treated for 48 hours with 3×10^{-5}M, of azaserine. When the roots were treated for 30 minutes in 3×10^{-4}M, 1.4×10^{-3}M, and 3×10^{-3}M, the mitotic activity was suppressed to about one-tenth of its normal value within 12 hours. At 72 hours, the mitotic activity had returned to normal in all these cases.

Biesele studied the effects of 24-hour treatments with various concentrations of azaserine on tissue cultures of mouse embryonic skin and sarcoma 180. Both types of cells were completely inhibited by 10^{-3}M, whereas lower concentrations of azaserine suppressed the mitotic activity of S 180 more than that of embryonic skin.

Biochemical studies have shown that azaserine is a strong inhibitor of biosynthetic reactions requiring glutamine as the amino donor (for references, see Handschumacher and Welch, 1960). Several such reactions occur in the biosynthesis of purines and pyrimidines (compare Chap. 4). The glutamine-requiring reaction most sensitive to the inhibitory action of azaserine appears to be the amination of formylglycinamide ribonucleotide to formylglycinamidine ribonucleotide, and the mitotic inhibition induced by azaserine is also generally believed to be a result of the inhibitory action of azaserine on this particular step of purine biosynthesis. In agreement with this interpretation, the mitotic inhibition produced by azaserine is counteracted by preformed purines and by aminoimidazole carboxamide. However, if inhibition of purine biosynthesis is the only cause to the mitotic inhibition produced by azaserine, it is difficult to see why amino acids, such as phenylalanine and tryptophan, are able to reverse the mitotic inhibition (Tanaka and Sugimura, 1956).

Adenine and 2.6-diaminopurine. Adenine is a normal nucleic acid constituent, and 2.6-diaminopurine serves as a precursor of nucleic acid guanine (e.g., Bendich and Brown, 1948). The findings that these agents are strong inhibitors of mitosis and growth in both plant and animal tissues is, therefore, somewhat surprising. The effect of adenine on cell division and chromosome structure in root tips of *Allium cepa, Pisum sativum,* and *Vicia faba* has been studied by Kihlman (1950, 1952a, 1961a). In *Allium,* four hour treatments with 2×10^{-2}M adenine produced a complete arrest of mitosis which lasted for about one day (Kihlman, 1950). In *Pisum* a 24 hour treatment with 2.5×10^{-3}M adenine suppressed mitosis almost completely (Kihlman, 1952a). The mitotic inhibition was found to be stronger in the absence than in the presence of oxygen (Kihlman, 1961a). Other mitotic disturbances produced by adenine were chromosome contraction, inhibition of spindle and/or centromere function (metaphase poisoning) and chromosomal aberrations. Similar effects were produced by adenine in mouse tissue cultures (Biesele et al., 1952a, 1952b). The chromosome-breaking effect of adenine was counteracted by 2.6-diaminopurine (Biesele et al., 1952b). Explanation of these effects may possibly be provided by the finding of Henderson (1962) that purine biosynthesis in ascites tumor cells was strongly inhibited by adenine. However, in the experiments of Henderson, inhibition of purine biosynthesis was also obtained with hypoxanthine and purine ribonucleosides which did not have any marked effects on mitosis in plant root tips. The reaction step of purine biosynthesis which is affected by adenine appears to be the formation of glycinamide ribonucleotide from 5-phosphoribosylamine and glycine. Apparently, the synthesis of the enzyme required for this reaction is inhibited by adenine (Nierlich and McFall, 1963).

Twenty-four hour treatments with 2.6-diaminopurine at concentrations around 10^{-4}M almost completely inhibited mitosis in mouse tissue cultures (Biesele, 1958a). The mitotic inhibition was reversed by equimolar concentrations of adenine. Similarly, Setterfield and Duncan (1955) found that the mitotic inhibition produced by 9.6×10^{-5}M diaminopurine in root tips of *Vicia faba* was partially reversed by adenine. However, an even greater reversal was obtained with guanine, adenosine, and deoxyadenosine. Microphotometric measurements of Feulgen stain showed that about half of the inhibited nuclei in meristems treated with diaminopurine had the doubled ($4C$) amount of DNA, and about half the diploid ($2C$). The lack of nuclei with intermediate amounts of DNA indicated that diaminopurine inhibited the onset of DNA synthesis while permitting that underway to reach completion (G_1 inhibition). Diaminopurine also prevented the onset of prophase (G_2 inhibition), but had no inhibitory effect on cells already in division.

The mechanism of action of 2.6-diaminopurine as a mitotic inhibitor is still obscure. The fact that its inhibitory effect in several types of organisms is reversed by adenine or adenine nucleosides suggests that 2.6-diaminopurine acts as an adenine antagonist. Since 2.6-diaminopurine *in vivo* is readily converted into 2.6-diaminopurine ribonucleoside and the corresponding ribonucleoside mono-, di-, and tri-phosphates, it may also produce its inhibitory effect on mitosis by blocking the formation or function of one or several adenine-containing coenzymes (for references, see Handschumacher and Welch, 1960). Finally, there are facts which indicate that 2.6-diaminopurine inhibits the *de novo* synthesis of nucleic acid purine (for references, see Biesele, 1958a; Handschumacher and Welch, 1960).

Aminopterin and amethopterin. The 4-amino derivatives of folic acid (FA), aminopterin (4-aminopteroylglutamic acid) and amethopterin (4-amino-N^{10}-methylpteroylglutamic acid) are strong inhibitors of the enzymes folic acid reductase and dihydrofolic acid reductase, which catalyze the formation of tetrahydrofolic acid (THFA) from folic acid. Since derivatives of THFA act as coenzymes in one-carbon transfer reactions involved in the *de novo* synthesis of purines and in the formation of thymidylic acid from deoxyuridylic acid, inhibition of these reactions by aminopterin and amethopterin results in deficiency of nucleic acid precursors, and hence in inhibition of RNA and DNA synthesis. A direct inhibition of protein synthesis (in addition to that resulting from the inhibition of RNA synthesis) is also to be expected, since THFA-catalyzed one-carbon transfers are involved in the formation of methionine from homocysteine and serine from glycine. By adding to the medium all except one of the metabolites, the syntheses of which are blocked, a more specific inhibition· is obtained. Of the two THFA-requiring reactions involved in purine biosynthesis (see Chap. 4), the formylation of 5-amino-4-imidazole carboxamide ribonucleotide is particularly sensitive to the amino derivatives of folic acid. Of all THFA-dependent one-carbon transfers, the thymidylate synthetase catalyzed methylation of deoxyuridylic acid is probably the most sensitive to aminopterin and amethopterin.

At the cytological level the biochemical effects of the 4-amino derivatives of folic acid result in inhibition of cell division. It is clear, however, that different types of cells respond very differently to the inhibitory effects of aminopterin and amethopterin. Root-tip cells of *Vicia faba* appear to be very sensitive (Taylor, 1963b; Kihlman, unpublished results) and so are certain mouse cells in tissue culture, e.g., lymphoblasts L-5178Y (Handschumacher and Welch, 1960). The reason for the very high sensitivity of the lymphoblasts may be that they are deficient in the enzyme responsible for the formation of THFA from DHFA.

Cells have been reported to be inhibited by aminopterin and amethopterin both in metaphase (Hughes, 1952; Biesele, 1954 b) and in interphase; (Biesele, 1954b; Taylor, 1963b; for further references, see Gelfant, 1963). The metaphase inhibition has been questioned by Gelfant

(1963). According to Taylor (1963b), the labeling pattern in radioauto-graphic experiments indicated that most cells treated with aminopterin (10^{-7}M) in the presence of adenosine, hypoxanthine, and glycine (in order to inhibit only thymidylic acid synthesis) were arrested in late G_1 or in the beginning of S. Cells which were in G_2, mitosis, or G_1 at the beginning of the treatment, continue to advance through the mitotic cycle until late G_1 or early S, at which stage they are arrested until thymidylic acid becomes available. Cells already in early or middle S at the time of treatment are also arrested, whereas cells in late S may escape and reach division with damaged chromosomes.

5-Fluorodeoxyuridine (FUdR). The same type of inhibition as pro-duced by aminopterin and amethopterin in the presence of purines and amino acids is obtained with FUdR (Taylor, 1963b). However, that is only to be expected, since treatments with FUdR, like treatments with aminopterin and amethopterin, result in thymidylic acid deficiency. When thymidylic acid is no longer available, DNA synthesis stops. The 5'-monophosphate of FUdR, F-dUMP, is a strong and specific inhibitor of the enzyme thymidylate synthetase. As shown by Hartmann and Heidelberger (1961), the thymidylate synthetase of an enzyme fraction (S_3-fraction) prepared from Ehrlich ascites tumor cells was not in-hibited by FUdR in the absence of ATP (Table 7-1). In the presence of ATP, however, FUdR, like F-dUMP, becomes a powerful inhibitor (95 per cent inhibition at a concentration of 10^{-7}M), which shows that the S_3-fraction contained the kinase required for the phosphorylation of FUdR to F-dUMP.

Although F-dUMP is the true inhibitor of the thymidylate synthetase reaction, it is less effective than FUdR as an inhibitor of the incorpora-tion of formate into DNA-thymine in suspensions of Ehrlich ascites cells (Mukherjee and Heidelberger, 1962; Heidelberger, 1963). This is be-cause tumor cells, like most other cells (Bullough, 1952), are imperme-able to nucleotides, which are dephosphorylated at the cell membrane and enter the cell as nucleosides (Heidelberger, 1963).

Inhibition of thymidylic acid-synthesis and hence of DNA-synthesis, appears to be the only biochemical effect of low (10^{-8} to 10^{-6}M) con-centrations of FUdR. Thus, at these low concentrations, FUdR is a very specific inhibitor. At higher concentrations, there may be incorporation of 5-fluorouracil into RNA, with disturbed RNA and protein metabolism as a result (Heidelberger, 1963). Since cell division in both plant and animal cells is strongly inhibited after one or a few hours' treatment with FUdR at concentrations of 10^{-7}M or higher (Taylor et al., 1962; Kihlman, 1962; Chu and Fischer, 1962; Hsu et al., 1964), it seems reason-able to assume that the inhibition of mitosis is a result of the inhibition of DNA synthesis. This conclusion is supported by the fact that equi-molar or higher concentrations of thymidine, or thymidine analogues such as CUdR, BUdR, and IUdR, reverse the inhibition of both DNA synthesis (e.g., Salzman and Sebring, 1962; Paul and Hagiwara, 1962; Bell and Wolff, 1964; Odmark and Kihlman, unpublished) and mitotic

TABLE 7-1.

The inhibition of thymidylate synthetase by various pyrimidine derivatives in the presence and absence of ATP. (After Hartmann and Heidelberger, 1961; J. Biol. Chem. 235:3242-3249.)

Pyrimidine Derivative	ATP (2 μM) + or −	Preincubation (10 min) with ATP + or −	Per cent Inhibition at Indicated Concentrations of Pyrimidine Derivative						
			$10^{-3}M$	$10^{-4}M$	$10^{-5}M$	$10^{-6}M$	$2 \times 10^{-7}M$	$10^{-7}M$	$3 \times 10^{-8}M$
5-Fluorouracil (5-FU)	−	−	0						
5-Fluorouridine (5-FUR)	−	−	0						
5-Fluorodeoxyuridine (5-FUdR)	−	−	13	15					
5-Fluorouridine-5'-monophosphate (5-FUMP)	−	−	5						
5-Fluorodeoxyuridine-5'-monophosphate (5-FdUMP)	−	−					84		67
Thymidine-5'-monophosphate (dTMP)	−	−	0						
5-FU	+	+	0	0	0				
5-FUR	+	+	42		0				
5-FUdR	+	−			88	71		42	
5-FUdR	+	+						95	
5-CUdR	+	−	39	29		6		0	
5-BUdR	+	−	24	11	0				
5-IUdR	+	−	0	0					

93

inhibition (Taylor et al., 1962; Taylor, 1963*b*; Kihlman, 1962; Hsu et al., 1964). The inhibitory effect of FUdR on mitosis and its reversal by thymidine is illustrated for mouse L-M cells in Fig. 7-2.

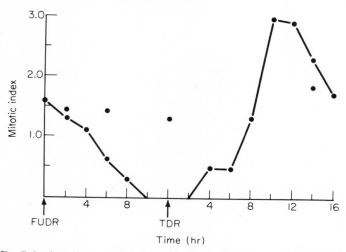

Fig. 7–2. The inhibitory effect of 0.01 µg/ml FUdR on mititoc activity of mouse cells (strain L-M) and its reversal by 10 µg/ml thymidine (TdR). (Hsu et al., 1964; J. Nat. Cancer Inst. 32:839–851, p. 841. Courtesy of T. C. Hsu.)

Deoxyadenosine (AdR). Inhibition of DNA synthesis through DNA-precursor deficiency can also be obtained by treatment of cells with deoxyadenosine (e.g., Klenow, 1959; Prusoff, 1959; Maley and Maley, 1960; Lark, 1960; Morris and Fischer, 1961; Kit and Dubbs, 1962). Such treatments result in the intracellular accumulation of dATP in both animal (Munch-Petersen, 1960; Klenow, 1962) and plant (Odmark and Kihlman, 1965) cells. As shown by Reichard et al. (1961), dATP is a strong inhibitor of the cytidine diphosphate reductase reaction by which deoxyribonucleotides are formed from the corresponding ribonucleotides. In the types of cells studied, e.g., Ehrlich ascites tumor cells (Klenow, 1959; Prusoff, 1959), chick embryo cells (Maley and Maley, 1960), bacteria (Lark, 1960), human leukocytes (Kihlman et al., 1963), and *Vicia faba* root-tip cells (Kihlman, 1963*b*), the inhibition of DNA synthesis was accompanied by an inhibition of growth and cell division. In bean root tips mitosis was completely, or almost completely, inhibited by a 24 hour treatment with 6×10^{-3}M AdR. Cell division was resumed about 12 hours after transferring the seedlings to an AdR-free medium (Kihlman, 1963*b* and unpublished).

Cytosine arabinoside (CA). Chu and Fischer (1962) observed that mitosis of L5178Y leukemic mouse cells in tissue culture was inhibited by CA. Biochemical studies showed that DNA synthesis was strongly suppressed in the CA-treated cells, whereas RNA synthesis was unaffected. The studies of Chu and Fischer further indicated that CA, probably in a phosphorylated form, inhibited DNA synthesis by inhibiting the reduction of cytidylic acid to deoxycytidylic acid. The inhibitory action of CA was reversed by CdR, but not by TdR, AdR, or GdR. The mechanism of the inhibitory action of CA appears to be similar to that of AdR. Figure 7-3 shows the effect of various concentrations of CA in the

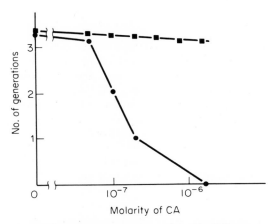

Molarity of CA

Fig. 7–3. The inhibitory effect of cytosine arabinoside (CA) on reproduction of mouse L5178Y cells and its prevention by deoxycytidine (CdR). *Circles*—CA; *squares*—CA + 5 × 10^{-6}M CdR. [Chu and Fischer, 1962; Biochem. Pharmacol. 11:425. Reproduced by permission of Pergamon Press.]

presence and absence of CdR on the reproduction of L5178Y cells.

The studies of Kihlman et al. (1963) have shown that mitosis in *in vitro* cultures of human leukocytes is effectively inhibited by CA at concentrations higher than 10^{-6}M. Like the mitotic inhibition produced by CA in L5178Y cells, that produced by CA in human leukocytes was reversed by CdR, but not by AdR, GdR, or TdR (Table 7-2). In root

TABLE 7–2.

THE EFFECT OF DEOXYRIBOSIDES ON THE MITOTIC INHIBITION PRODUCED IN HUMAN LEKOCYTES BY CYTOSINE ARABINOSIDE. (AFTER KIHLMAN ET AL., 1963; HEREDITAS 50:139–143.)

Cytosine Arabinoside (10^{-5}M) + or −	Deoxyriboside (2×10^{-4}M) Added	Per cent Cell Divisions
−	—	0.93
+	—	0.10
+	AdR	0.05
+	CdR	0.80
+	GdR	0.25
+	TdR	0.05
+	AdR, CdR GdR, TdR	0.95

tips of *Vicia faba,* CA behaved differently. Although tested at concentrations as high as 10^{-3}M, CA inhibited neither cell division nor DNA synthesis in this material (Kihlman and Odmark, unpublished).

AGENTS WHICH MODIFY THE CHEMICAL AND

PHYSICAL PROPERTIES OF DNA AND

ITS COMPLEXES

Alkylating agents. Perhaps best known and most thoroughly studied of the alkylating agents is nitrogen mustard or di(2-chloroethyl)methylamine (HN2). It is, therefore, somewhat surprising that the mode of action of this powerful mitotic inhibitor is still so little understood. There appears to be a general agreement that the cellular damage is primarily brought about by alkylation of DNA (compare Chap. 13), but as appears in a recent review article by Gelfant (1963), the questions of whether DNA synthesis is inhibited by HN2 or not and at which stage of interphase HN2-treated cells are arrested are particularly controversial ones. This may be illustrated by two recent studies, not included in the review by Gelfant.

Caspersson et al. (1963) have studied the effects of HN2 on mouse fibroblast cells in tissue culture. They found that although mitosis was almost completely inhibited by the HN2 concentrations used, DNA synthesis continued and DNA accumulated to predivisional amounts. These findings appear to support the suggestion of Gelfant (1963) that HN2 blocks cell division in G_2.

In contrast to this, Evans and Scott (Scott and Evans, 1964 and personal communication), using root tips of *Vicia faba* as experimental material, found that G_2 cells were not delayed by HN2 treatments in their development to the first mitosis, whereas cells exposed while in S were considerably retarded.

Mitomycin C and actinomycin D. Recent evidence indicates that the antibiotic mitomycin C, which is known to cause inhibition of DNA synthesis (Shiba et al. 1959) and degradation of DNA (e.g., Reich et al., 1961) may act as an alkylating agent (Schwartz et al., 1963) which links complementary DNA strands together by covalent bonds (Iyer and Szybalski, 1963). It seems likely that not only the degradation of DNA but also the inhibition of DNA synthesis is a result of alkylation of DNA by mitomycin C, since it has been found that DNA obtained from mitomycin-treated cells is a poor primer for DNA polymerase, although it still is an effective primer for RNA polymerase (Pricer and Weissbach, 1963).

Treatment of *Vicia faba* root tips with 0.1 per cent mitomycin C for one hour or with 0.01 per cent for two hours were lethal, death of the roots occurring within 48 hours. A one hour treatment with 0.001 per cent mitomycin C caused a marked inhibition of mitosis, the period with few or no mitoses lasting for 24 hours or more (Merz, 1961).

The effect of mitomycin C (0.0001 per cent, one hour) on human leukocytes *in vitro* has been studied by Nowell (1964). Cells treated at the time of planting, when they were still mitotically inactive (G_0 cells), were not inhibited in their development to the first mitosis. Similarly, treatment of cells at the postsynthetic or G_2 stage of interphase did not result in mitotic inhibition. A marked mitotic inhibition was obtained, however, when the cells were in G_1 or in S at the time of treatment.

Mitomycin C has a strong inhibitory effect on cell division and DNA synthesis without markedly influencing protein and RNA synthesis (e.g., Pricer and Weissbach, 1963; Kuroda and Furuyama, 1963). In contrast, the antibiotic actinomycin D is a strong inhibitor of DNA-dependent RNA synthesis at concentrations which have no effect on DNA polymerase (e.g., Reich, 1964). At higher concentrations, DNA polymerase is effectively inhibited as well. Since cell division apparently is inhibited by concentrations below those required for inhibition of DNA synthesis (e.g., Elliott, 1963), the growth inhibition obtained by treatments with actinomycin D appears to be the result of a suppressed RNA and protein synthesis, rather than of an inhibition of DNA synthesis.

Maleic hydrazide (MH) and 8-ethoxycaffeine (EOC). The biochemical and/or physicochemical mechanisms underlying the cytological effects of these two agents are still rather poorly understood. Maleic hydrazide is a structural isomer of uracil, and it seemed, therefore, possible that it acted as an antimetabolite in connection with the synthesis and metabolism of nucleic acids. However, all attempts to counteract the cytological effects of maleic hydrazide with uracil and thymine have failed (Loveless, 1953). Nor has it been possible to produce the maleic hydrazide-type of cytological effect with other structural isomers of uracil. On the other hand, it has been found that treatments of plant root tips with C^{14}-labeled MH results in a selective accumulation of MH in nuclei and nucleoli (Callaghan and Grun, 1961).

The relationship between DNA synthesis in *Vicia* root tips, on the one hand, and the mitotic inhibition and the chromosomal aberrations produced by MH in the same material, on the other, has been studied by Evans and Scott (1964). The authors conclude that on the basis of the available evidence it does not seem likely that MH is incorporated in place of a normal base into DNA and RNA. They believe that it is more plausible that MH is bound ". . . in some unspecific manner to nuclear proteins and possibly also to the nucleic acids" and that the cytological effect of MH ". . . may be due to alterations in the protein component of the chromosome or to an antimetabolite action of MH loosely linked to the DNA-RNA-protein complex, as is perhaps indicated by the considerable lengthening of the DNA synthesis phase."

According to another hypothesis, MH produces its cytological effects by reacting with sulfhydryl groups in the cell (Muir and Hansch, 1953). It has been found that MH irreversibly inhibits certain enzymes requiring free sulfhydryl groups and that MH in actively dividing tissues induces an increase of reduced glutathione at the expense of oxidized glutathione (Hughes and Spragg, 1958). The important role played by SH-groups in connection with cell division was discussed in the preceding chapter, and it seems to be a reasonable hypothesis that the inhibition of mitosis produced by MH is a result of the ability of MH to react with sulfhydryl groups. If this were true, however, it would put MH in the same class of antimitotic agents as the quinones, and the inclusion of MH under the heading "Agents affecting DNA. . ." would hardly be justified. The quinones are known as powerful inhibitors of mitosis and of many enzyme reactions, and in most cases these effects appear to be the result of an attack on sulfhydryl groups essential for the function of enzymes and structural proteins (for references on quinone effects, see Biesele, 1958*a* and Hoffmann-Ostenhof, 1963).

The mitotic inhibition produced by MH in root tips of *Vicia faba* has been described by McLeish (1953). Figure 7-4 shows the reduction

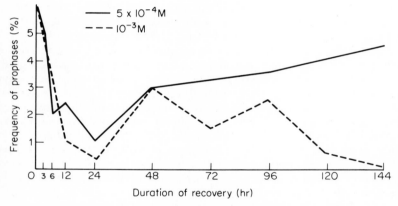

Fig. 7–4. Frequencies of cells in prophase at various times after 2-hour treatments of *Vicia faba* root-tips with 5×10^{-4}M (*solid line*) and 10^{-3}M (*broken line*) maleic hydrazide. (After McLeish, 1953; Heredity 6(Suppl. vol.):125–147.)

of the number of prophases obtained various times after two-hour treatments with 5×10^{-4}M and 10^{-3}M MH. After both treatments, a minimum frequency of mitoses is obtained at 24 hours. When root tips are treated with the lower concentration, there seems to be a nearly complete recovery 144 hours after the end of the treatment. At the higher concentration, a temporary partial recovery between 24 and 120 hours is followed by a new, even more severe, suppression at 144 hours.

As previously mentioned, Evans and Scott (1964) have studied the relationship between DNA synthesis and the effects of MH on mitosis. For determination of the period of DNA synthesis, tritium-labeled thymidine and the radioautographic technique were used. It was found that cells in G_2 were not delayed by the MH treatment, but that cells exposed to MH while in the S stage of interphase were considerably retarded in their development. Thus, the stage inhibited by MH in root-tip cells of *Vicia faba* is the same as that inhibited by HN2.

A very different type of inhibition is produced by EOC. Figure 7-5

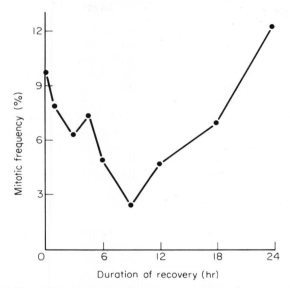

Fig. 7–5. Frequencies of mitoses at various times after 2-hour treatments of *Vicia faba* root-tips with 10^{-2}M 8-ethoxycaffeine.

shows the effect of a two-hour treatment with 10^{-2}M EOC at 17°C on the frequencies of mitosis in root tips of *Vicia faba* obtained during the subsequent recovery at 19°C. During the first hours following treatment, the mitotic incidence fell from about 10 per cent at 0 hours to 2.4 per cent at 9 hours. From then on the frequency of mitoses again increased, and at 24 hours a value of 12.2 per cent was obtained, which is even higher than the frequency in untreated roots. Such a compensatory wave of mitoses following mitotic inhibition has frequently been observed after radiation treatments (see, for instance, Carlson, 1954).

That late interphase or G_2 was the stage most sensitive to the cytological effects of EOC was already clearly indicated by the studies of Kihlman (1955a, 1955b, 1961b), and has recently been confirmed by the radioautographic studies of Scott and Evans (1964). By labeling the newly synthesized DNA with H^3-thymidine, these authors found that cells are arrested by EOC mainly in the G_2 stage of interphase, which is prolonged to approximately twice its normal duration.

The mechanism of action of EOC will be discussed in Chaps. 10 and 13. It may, therefore, be sufficient to mention here that it probably consists in a physicochemical attack on chromosomal DNA or DNA-protein complex, although the dependence of the effect on oxidative phosphorylation shows that enzymatic reactions are also involved.

B. The Energy Requirements of Mitosis, as Indicated by the Effect of Inhibitors

Since movement is a form of work, the movement of chromosomes during mitosis is obviously an energy-requiring process. Furthermore, the phases of active movement are preceded and succeeded by processes involving drastic morphological changes (contraction and condensation of chromosomes during prophase, reconstruction of the interphase nucleus during telophase and cytokinesis), and it is, therefore, understandable that the stages of active mitosis have been regarded as stages of particularly high energy requirement in comparison with interphase, the apparent "resting stage." The fact is, however, as recent experiments have shown, that the synthetic processes occurring during interphase are at least as energy-requiring as the chromosome movements during mitosis.

Support for the idea that the stages of active mitosis are particularly energy-requiring was obtained by the findings that cell division is inhibited by agents which suppress the energy-generating processes in the cell, i.e., inhibitors of glycolysis, respiration, and oxidative phosphorylation.

The relation between metabolic activity and cleavage in the egg cell of the sea urchin, *Arbacia punctulata,* has been reviewed by Krahl (1950), who concluded that the energy required for cleavage is produced by aerobic processes. Since both the inhibition of oxygen consumption and the inhibition of cleavage by carbon monoxide (CO) were light-reversible, the cytochrome system appeared to be involved in the oxidative energy-yielding reaction (compare Chap. 1). That oxidative phosphorylation was involved was indicated by ". . . the highly specific parallel between inhibition of cleavage and inhibition of a cell-free phosphorolyting system from the eggs by a series of substituted phenols" and by the fact that the same agents also blocked phosphorylation in the intact fertilized egg. Among the phenols highly effective in blocking cleavage and oxidative phosphorylation may be mentioned 4.6-dinitro-2(1.1-dimethylhexyl)phenol, 2.4.6-triiodophenol, 4.6-dinitro-o-cresol, 2.4-dinitro-α-naphtol, and 2.4-dinitrophenol. Oxygen consumption was drastically increased by low concentrations of these agents, and was still above normal at concentrations which completely blocked cleavage and phosphorylation.

Similar observations have been made with other experimental materials. It seems as if mitosis is possible in most animal and plant tissues only in the presence of oxygen, when the available substrates, usually carbohydrates, can be efficiently oxidized in the TCA cycle (compare Chap. 1). However, it is also known that some tissues, such as *in vitro* cultures of chick fibroblast, are able to maintain active cell division and growth under anaerobic conditions (Laser, 1933), or in the presence of inhibitors of aerobic respiration, such as CO, cyanide, and azide (Pomerat and Willmer, 1939). A suppression of mitotic activity in chick embryo fibroblast was obtained when inhibitors of glycolysis, such as fluoride or iodoacetate, were added (Pomerat and Willmer, 1939). Since glycolysis is a much less efficient mechanism for generation of energy-rich phosphate than is aerobic respiration, it would seem as if chick embryos required less energy for mitosis than most other tissues. However, as pointed out by Bullough (1952), a more likely explanation is that the chick fibroblast tissue is able to absorb unusually large quantities of glucose with the result that they are capable of producing considerable quantities of energy-rich phosphate by the relatively inefficient method of glycolysis.

According to the *antephase* hypothesis of Bullough (1952), the energy required for mitosis is produced during a particular stage of the mitotic cycle, the antephase. When this period begins is not known, but it ends when prophase begins.

Related to the antephase hypothesis of Bullough is the energy-reservoir hypothesis of Swann (1954), which was developed in order to explain the inhibitory effects of CO on cleavage in sea urchin eggs. As mentioned previously, CO is an effective and specific inhibitor of cytochrome oxidase, the terminal oxidase of the respiratory chain. Since the CO-cytochrome oxidase complex is stable only at wave lengths outside its absorption bands, ". . . it is possible, merely by altering the wave length of the illuminating beam, to switch on and off the inhibition of respiration while actually observing the eggs." (Swann, 1954.) The results of the experiments were that if the inhibition was applied before prophase, the first cleavage was delayed for a length of time roughly equal to the duration of inhibition. If the inhibition was applied during division, it had no effect on that division, but the next one was delayed by a period equal to the duration of the inhibition.

According to Swann, these facts are best explained in terms of a reservoir mechanism. Energy is steadily released by respiration and stored in the form of some organic compound containing energy-rich bonds. The reservoir siphons out when it is full, and this starts the division, which then continues even if the reservoir is not filled. The experimental results of Swann indicate that, normally, the reservoir begins to be refilled at once. This would mean that respiration would continue even during the division stages. Most of the available evidence indicates, however, that the respiration rate is much lower during the stages of active division than during interphase (Erickson, 1947; Stern and Kirk, 1948; Zeuthen, 1958).

The nature of the energy store has also been studied by Swann (1957), who concluded that it could not be ATP, and suggested thiol esters as possible candidates for this role. As pointed out in Chap. 2 we have in the polynucleotides of the cell another possible energy store worth considering.

The hypotheses of Bullough and Swann have in common the idea that the energy required for cell division is produced and stored before that particular division begins. But whereas Bullough believes that the production of energy for mitosis is restricted to a particular period of late interphase, Swann is of the opinion that the energy reservoir begins to be refilled immediately after it has siphoned out at the very end of interphase, and that the production of energy for the reservoir continues during division and the next interphase. An essential feature of both hypotheses is also that there is a "point of no return" (Mazia, 1961) in mitosis, after which it is impossible to prevent that division from being completed by inhibitors of respiration, glycolysis, and oxidative phosphorylation. Studies by Epel (1963) and Amoore (1963a) have shown, however, that there is no such point of no return, and that the energy-reservoir hypothesis is unnecessary.

Epel studied the effect of CO on the ATP-level and the rate of mitosis in eggs of the sea urchin, *Strongylocentrotus purpuratus*. The ATP level was determined with the aid of the firefly-luminescence technique. Epel found that when respiration was inhibited by CO treatments in the dark, both the ATP level and the rate of mitosis decreased. A complete inhibition of mitosis was obtained when the ATP level dropped below 50 per cent of the normal level. By using various degrees of CO inhibition, Epel was able to show that the rate of mitosis was closely related to the resultant ATP level. He also found that mitosis could be blocked at any stage, provided that the inhibition was applied at the appropriate time before that stage, a result which disagrees with previous reports that cells in mitosis are insensitive to inhibitors of energy metabolism. Similar results were obtained with other inhibitors of oxidative phosphorylation, such as azide and DNP. With DNP, inhibition was obtained at concentrations which stimulated respiration, suggesting that ATP is the important respiratory product.

Epel was able to show that the disagreement between his results and those of Swann (see above) was due to an insufficient inhibition of ATP synthesis in Swann's experiments. Swann used CO as a respiratory inhibitor in the presence of green light, whereas Epel's experiments were performed in darkness. A comparison between the two types of experiments revealed that the inhibition of ATP synthesis was not complete in green light, the ATP level being reduced to only about 75 per cent of the normal level. At this ATP level mitosis is slowed down but does proceed (Fig. 7-6).

Amoore (1961a, b, 1962a, b, 1963a) has studied the effects of partial and complete anoxia, CO, and hydrogen cyanide on mitosis, respiration, and ATP level in excised pea (*Pisum sativum*) root tips. In agreement with Epel, Amoore found that cell division actually in progress could be arrested by lack of oxygen or by inhibitors of heavy metal-containing enzymes. All stages of cell division in pea root tips depended upon the presence of oxygen, but the visible stages were less dependent than the stage of entering mitosis. In contrast to Epel, Amoore could not find any correlation between the rate of mitosis, on the one hand, and

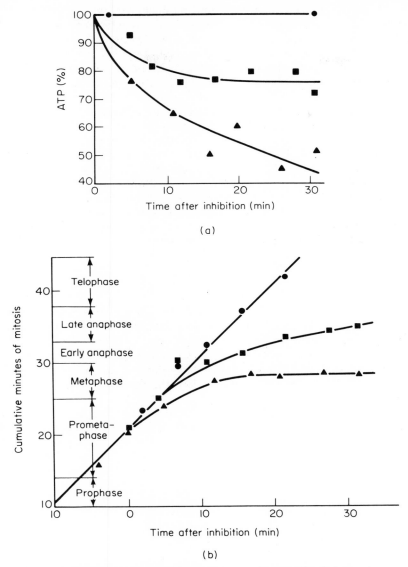

Fig. 7–6. ATP levels (a) and relative progress of mitosis (b) during various types of CO inhibition. *Circles*—control; *squares*—CO in green light; *triangles* —CO in total darkness. (Epel, 1963. Reprinted by permission of the Rocke-feller Institute Press, Inc., from J. Cell Biol., May, 1963, Vol. 17, No. 2, pp. 315–319.)

the rate of respiration and the ATP level, on the other. Thus, he found that a far higher degree of anaerobiosis was required to arrest mitosis than to stop respiration. In the absence of respiration, the ATP level was about 1.5 per cent of the normal value in air, which, according to Amoore, ". . . corresponded closely to the expected rate of ATP regeneration from known anaerobic sources of energy." (Amoore, 1963a.) At this ATP level, mitosis could continue, although at a reduced rate.

Amoore concludes that in root tips there must exist a nonrespiratory mitotic ferrous complex (MFH) which he believes to be ". . . an indispensable participant in the mitotic process" (Amoore, 1963b). For mitosis to proceed, MFH must be oxygenated. Mitosis is inhibited when no oxygen is available or when MFH is complexed with CO or cyanide. In contrast to the cyanide inhibition of the cytochrome oxidase-dependent respiration, the inhibition of mitosis by cyanide proved to be reversed by strong light. The inhibitory effect of CO on both mitosis and respiration is reversed by light. The relative affinities of MFH for oxygen, CO, and HCN, as well as the position of its absorption bands, suggest that it belongs to the class of phaeohaemins (Amoore, 1963b), and is closely related to, but clearly distinct from, cytochrome oxidase. Amoore suggests that the MFH should be called *mitohaem*.

C. Summary

Since DNA synthesis and oxidative phosphorylation are, as a rule, required for cell division, inhibition of these processes generally results in inhibition of mitosis. Thus, substances such as FUdR, AdR, cytosine arabinoside, and aminopterin, which strongly (and in most cases also specifically) inhibit DNA synthesis, have proved to be potent mitotic inhibitors. Cell division is resumed when the block of DNA synthesis is removed.

Suppression of cell division may also be obtained with respiratory inhibitors (e.g., carbon monoxide, cyanide) and with uncoupling agents (e.g., DNP). At least in sea urchin eggs, the rate of mitosis appears to be closely related to the level of ATP maintained by oxidative phosphorylation.

Inhibition of Cell Division II:
Effects on Stages of Active Division

A. Inhibition of Spindle Function

When spindle function is inhibited, both cell division and nuclear division are, as a rule, prevented, but the chromosomes reproduce and divide to form separate daughter chromosomes. As a result, the number of chromosomes per cell will be doubled for each mitotic cycle in the presence of the inhibitor.

Today, a large number of agents with ability to suppress spindle function are known. However, the first of these agents to be discovered, colchicine, is still the most commonly used, because it combines a high effectivity with a low toxicity. When this aspect of mitotic inhibition is discussed, therefore, it seems reasonable to concentrate on the effect of colchicine itself. For a comprehensive account of inhibitors of spindle function, or "metaphase poisons," as they frequently are called, the reader is referred to the review by Biesele (1958a). Eigsti and Dustin (1955) have written an extensive review on colchicine and its effects.

Studies on the cytological effect of colchicine were stimulated by the discovery of Blakeslee and Avery (1937) that colchicine is able to induce chromosome doubling in plants. The first to recognize the colchicine effect as an inhibition of spindle function with an accumulation of arrested mitoses as a result, was probably Ludford (1936), who worked with animal cells *in vitro* and *in vivo*. Early cytological studies on the effect of colchicine in plant material are those by Gavaudan and Gavaudan (1937), Dustin et al. (1937), Eigsti (1938), and Nebel and Ruttle (1938). Among the now classical papers dealing with the colchicine effect in plants is also that of Levan (1938) on "The Effect of Colchicine on Root Mitoses in *Allium*," a study which, together with the cinemicrographic analysis by Molé-Bajer (1958) of the colchicine effect in endosperm of *Haemanthus katharinae,* has served as a basis for the description given below.

According to Levan, the modification of mitotic behavior induced by colchicine, which he refers to as "c-mitosis," consists of ". . . an inactivation of the spindle apparatus connected with a delay of the division of the centromere" (Levan, 1938). As mentioned above, the reproduction of chromosomes and their splitting into chromatids are not affected by colchicine, nor are the processes of chromosome condensation at prophase. However, the clear zone (compare Chap. 6), which during the normal course of mitosis is formed around the prophase nucleus, may not be present in c-mitosis. If present, it has a tendency to decrease before, and to increase after, the breakdown of the nuclear membrane, whereas the opposite is true for the normal course of mitosis (Molé-Bajer, 1958).

The presence of a clear zone appears to be a necessary condition for the occurrence of the mitotic contraction stage. If a clear zone is formed, the contraction stage takes place after the disruption of the nuclear membrane in c-mitosis, just as it does in the normal course of mitosis. During the contraction stage, the chromosomes are pushed towards the center of the nucleus. In the normal mitosis, the next stage would be the attachment of the centromeres to the spindle and the arrangement of the chromosomes into an equatorial plate. Under the influence of colchicine these processes do not happen. In the normal mitosis, the chromosome movements are the result of the interaction between the centromere and the spindle. In c-mitosis there is no such interaction, and the few movements that do occur appear to be a result of "(a) the strong tendency of the chromosomes to straighten, (b) the shortening of the chromosomes, (c) the oscillations of the chromosomes, and (d) the uncoiling of daughter chromatids" (Molé-Bajer, 1958). When the nuclear membrane breaks down, the daughter or sister chromatids are coiled around each other in a relational spiral which then slowly uncoils by a process resembling the terminalization of chiasmata during diakinesis (Fig. 8-1). At the same time, there is a further shortening of the chromosomes. When these processes are finished, the sister chromatids of each chromosome are held together only at the region adjacent to the centromere in characteristic cross-shaped pairs, often referred to as "c-pairs" (Levan, 1938) (Fig. 8-2). A result of the movements mentioned above is that the chromosomes of the full c-metaphase are scattered over the cell. The behaviors of the chromosomes during c-mitosis in the cinemicrographic studies of Molé-Bajer indicates ". . . that they bear an electric charge in the period from metaphase to early interphase."

In the normal mitosis, division of the most proximal regions on both sides of the centromere takes place as soon as the chromosomes have been assembled in the equatorial plate. In the colchicine-treated cell, where the chromosomes are not arranged into a metaphase plate as a result of the lack of centromere activity and a functioning spindle, the division of the centromeric regions is delayed for several hours. It is

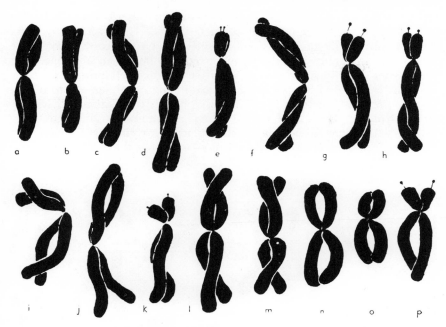

Fig. 8–1. The development of C-pairs in *Allium cepa*. (Levan, 1938; Hereditas 24, p. 472. Courtesy of A. Levan.)

this extension of the period between the disruption of the nuclear membrane and the division of the regions adjacent to the centromere which is responsible for the increased frequency of mitotic cells observed after treatments with colchicine. The stage delayed by colchicine corresponds

Fig. 8–2. C-pairs in *Allium fistulosum*. (Levan, 1938; Hereditas 24, p. 473. Courtesy of A. Levan.)

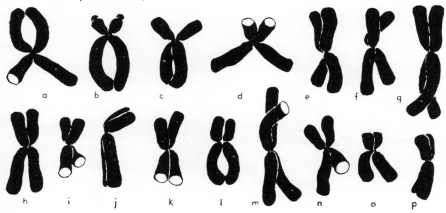

to the metaphase of the normal mitosis, and for this reason colchicine is said to cause an "accumulation of metaphases." However, if by metaphase is meant the stage of equilibrium between the convergent movements of prometaphase and the divergent movements of anaphase, then there is no such stage as metaphase after colchicine treatments.

Nor is there, of course, an anaphase in the usual sense. During the stage corresponding to anaphase (c-anaphase), the regions adjacent to the centromere divide and the daughter chromosomes fall apart (Fig. 8-3). The divisions do not always take place quite simultaneously within all the chromosomes in the cell, which indicates that they are desynchronized, as well as delayed (Levan, 1938).

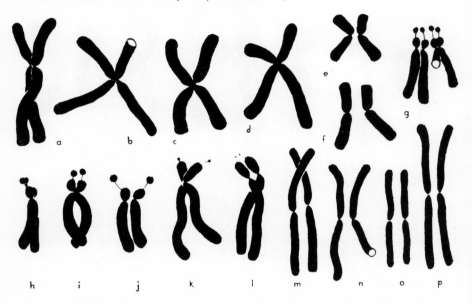

Fig. 8–3. The division of the centromere within C-pairs of *Allium cepa* (a–b, k–l) and *Allium fistulosum* (c–j, m–p). (Levan, 1938; Hereditas 24, p. 474. Courtesy of A. Levan.)

In the stage corresponding to telophase (c-telophase), the chromosomes are drawn together and all of them are included in one nucleus, which, consequently, will contain twice as many chromosomes as before c-mitosis. Occasionally, the chromosomes of colchicine-treated plant cells may pass directly from c-metaphase to c-telophase, the division of the centromeric regions in these cases taking place at interphase (Levan, 1954).

The failure of the centromeric regions to divide before c-telophase, which is an exception in plants, appears to be the rule in animal cells (Levan, 1954). It is, therefore, possible to distinguish between a plant and an animal type of c-mitosis on the basis of whether or not the centromeric regions divide before c-telophase sets in. However, just as the animal type of c-mitosis may occur in plants, occasional cases of the plant type of c-mitosis have been observed in animal material (Levan, 1954).

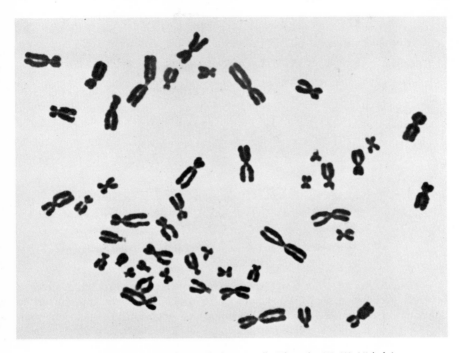

Fig. 8–4. C-mitosis in a human leukocyte cell. (Photo by W. W. Nichols.)

Other differences between the ways plant and animal cells respond to colchicine are the more frequent occurrence of multinucleate cells in colchicine-treated mammalian cells, and the fact that plant cells appear to be about 1000 times more resistant to colchicine than are mammalian cells. Levan (1954) found the lowest concentration which induced c-mitosis in mouse ascites tumor cells to be of the order of 10^{-7}M, the corresponding concentration for *Allium* being somewhat higher than 10^{-4}M (Fig. 8-5). The multinucleate mammalian cells are the result of widely scattered c-pairs in a cell forming separate nuclei when they enter c-telophase. Apparently, the micronuclei thus formed fuse during interphase or early prophase, because multinucleate prophases are rare. In animal tissues, as in plant tissues, c-mitosis results in doubling of the chromosome number.

In root tips of *Allium cepa* Levan (1938) observed a very high degree of polyploidy after prolonged treatments with colchicine. Thus, a 72 hour treatment gave rise to cells containing as many as 256 chromosomes, which is 16 times the diploid number ($2n = 16$). At the same time, the root meristem always contains cells with the diploid chromosome number, particularly in regions close to the tip. After removal of colchicine, selection operates in favor of these diploid cells which become the predominant cell type of the meristem in a few generations. In mammalian cells too, a reversal to the chromosome number characteristic of the particular cell type used takes place after the colchicine concentration has dropped below the threshold for c-mitotic action (Levan, 1954).

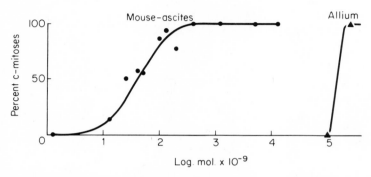

Fig. 8–5. The threshold regions for the colchicine effect of mouse ascites and of *Allium cepa*. (Levan, 1954; Hereditas 40, p. 12. Courtesy of A. Levan.)

The studies of Levan in *Allium* showed that the colchicine effect is reversible. Twelve to 24 hours after the roots had been transferred to colchicine-free water, the spindle began to regenerate. Between complete c-mitosis and normal mitosis there is a transition period, during which multipolar divisions are frequent. By the multipolar divisions more than two groups of chromosomes are separated from each other, and at telophase they form separate nuclei. Since cell walls frequently are formed between these nuclei, the multipolar divisions result in a reduction of the chromosome number.

The drug colchicine was isolated for the first time from the bulbous plant *Colchicum autumnale*. Since the tissues of this plant contain up to one per cent of colchicine, one would expect the mitoses of *Colchicum* to be resistant to the c-mitotic action of colchicine. On the other hand, there is no reason to expect that other, chemically unrelated, c-mitotic substances should be inactive in *Colchicum*. Levan (1940) has performed a comparative study of the effects of colchicine and acenaphtene on mitosis in *Allium cepa* and *Colchicum autumnale*. As expected, *Colchicum* was found to be completely resistant to colchicine, but almost as sensitive as *Allium* to the c-mitotic action of acenaphtene. These results were subsequently confirmed by Levan and Steinegger (1947). In this second study, chloroform was used as a c-mitotic agent in addition to colchicine and acenaphtene. In the chloroform experiments, the threshold concentration for c-mitotic activity was found to be the same in *Colchicum* as in *Allium*.

The relationship between c-mitotic activity and chemical structure of colchicine and its derivatives was studied by Steinegger and Levan (1947, 1948), who found that the c-mitotic activity was very sensitive to modifications of the colchicine molecule.

Colchicine is the methyl ether of colchiceine. Some colchiceine exists in two tautomeric forms (Figs. 8-6(a) and (b)), methylation of the OH-group in the C-ring of colchiceine results in two isomeric methyl ethers, colchicine (Fig. 8-6(c)) and isocolchicine (Fig. 8-6(d)). In

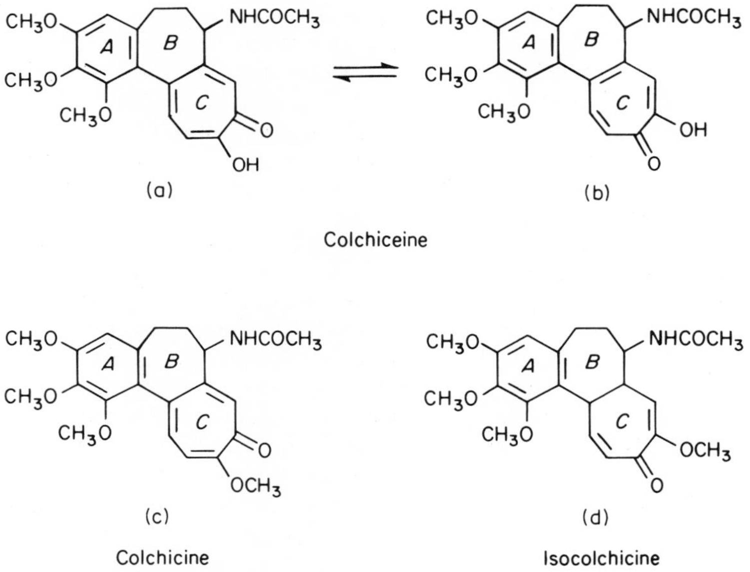

(a)   (b)

Colchiceine

(c)   (d)

Colchicine   Isocolchicine

Fig. 8–6. The chemical structural formulae of the two tautomeric forms of colchiceine (a) and (b), of colchicine (c) and of isocolchicine (d).

the experiments of Steinegger and Levan (1947) isocolchicine was about 100 times less effective than colchicine as an inducer of c-mitosis in *Allium cepa*. Since merely an interchange of the methoxy- and oxo-groups in the C-ring resulted in such a drastic reduction of the c-mitotic activity, it is not surprising that colchiceine, in which the methoxy-group in the C-ring is replaced by a hydroxy-group, was found to be almost inactive in *Allium* (Steinegger and Levan, 1948).

Replacement of substituents in other rings appears to be less fatal to the c-mitotic activity. Thus, the replacement of the acetylamido-group on ring D with a methylamino-group results in the compound colcemid or demecolchicine, which has been reported to be equally effective but less toxic than colchicine in mammalian cells (for references on colcemid, see Gelfant, 1963). In experiments with mammalian cells colcemid is, therefore, frequently preferred to colchicine.

The ability to induce c-mitosis is not restricted to colchicine and some of its derivatives. We have already mentioned two c-mitotic agents of rather different types, viz., acenaphtene and chloroform. The studies of Simonet, Gavaudan, and their collaborators in France, Schmuck and collaborators in the U.S.S.R., Östergren and Levan in Sweden, and of others have shown that the number of agents possessing c-mitotic activity is very large. The agents reported to be active belong to the most different groups of organic compounds, and there appears to be no correlation between the chemical properties of the agents and their c-mitotic activity. On the other hand, attempts to relate the activity of the c-mitotic agents to their physical properties have been more successful. Thus Levan and Östergren (1943), studying the effects of naphthalene derivatives, and Östergren (1944), studying benzene derivatives, found a positive correlation between water solubility and threshold concentration for c-mitotic activity; i.e., the c-mitotic activity of the members of the naphthalene and benzene series increased when their water solubility decreased. However, the decisive factor was believed to be the concentration of the c-mitotic substances in the lipid phase, rather than in the water phase, of the cell. Since within the naphthalene and benzene series, there is an inverse correlation between the solubilities in water and lipids, compounds with a high activity were those having a high solubility in lipids. The authors point out the similarity between their hypothesis that the c-mitotic activity of a compound is determined by its concentration in the lipid phase of the cell, and the Meyer-Overton lipid theory of narcosis. In fact, Levan and Östergren interpret c-mitosis as a *narcotized* mitosis. According to Östergren (1944), the intracellular lipid phase of significance in c-mitosis are the lipophilic side chains of the spindle proteins. By associating with these side chains, the c-mitotic agents would induce a folding of the polypeptide chains with a concomitant transition of the fibrous spindle proteins into more globular forms which are incompatible with spindle structure and function.

Although the activities of acenaphtene, chloroform, isocolchicine, and the great majority of the c-mitotic agents appear to be dependent on a physical property such as the relative lipid solubility, there are exceptions to this rule. The most noteworthy of these exceptions is colchicine itself, which combines a high activity with a good water solubility. This fact, as well as the finding that only a slight modification of the colchicine molecule drastically reduces its c-mitotic activity suggest that colchicine acts more specifically by a chemical mechanism, rather than by a physical mechanism.

By introducing the concept "thermodynamic activity" into toxicology, Ferguson (1939) has shown how it may be possible to distinguish between poisons acting by an unspecific physical mechanism and poisons which have a specific chemical effect. The thermodynamic activity of a compound may be roughly expressed as the relation between its lowest active concentration and its solubility in water. According to Ferguson, compounds which have a thermodynamic activity above 0.05 can be regarded as acting by a physical mechanism, whereas compounds with a thermodynamic activity below 0.05 are likely to act by a chemical mechanism. If the thermodynamic activities of colchicine and isocolchicine are calculated, the values obtained are <0.0003 and 0.28, respectively (Steinegger and Levan, 1947). Thus, it is evident that these two closely related compounds have different mechanisms of action; ". . . colchicine with its low thermodynamic activity is a typical representative of the chemically acting substances, while iso-colchicine with its 900 times higher thermodynamic activity belongs to the type of unspecifically acting substances" (Steinegger and Levan, 1947).

Although it is generally agreed that colchicine inhibits spindle function by a chemical mechanism, the nature of this mechanism has remained obscure. For a review of the various hypotheses on the mechanism of colchicine action, the reader is referred to Biesele (1958a).

It is also not quite clear what kind of changes in spindle structure the c-mitotic agents produce. Perhaps different agents induce different changes, which have in common only that they result in an inhibition of spindle and centromere function.

The effect of colchicine on the microscopic and submicroscopic structure of the spindle in the egg of the marine annelid worm, *Chaetopterus pergamentaceous*, has been studied by Inoué (1952) with the aid of the polarization microscope. Colchicine treatments were found to disorganize the orientation of the micelles in the astral rays and spindle fibers.

In Mazia's laboratory, attempts have been made to isolate the spindle from sea urchin eggs, in which mitosis was blocked at metaphase by colchicine. The idea behind this experiment was that ". . . if colchicine actually prevents the formation of the spindle, no spindle can be isolated, but if it creates some abnormality, that abnormality may be studied best in isolation" (Mazia, 1955). It was found that a spindle could be isolated but that it consisted of ". . . an amorphous mass of gel showing no microscopic fibers." The conclusion was that the formation of the spindle could be separated into two processes. The first of these is the formation of the shapeless gel by a polymerization process. This process, which involves the formation of intermolecular S-S bonds, is not affected by colchicine. The second process consists of a secondary bonding and orientation of the gelated spindle protein into the fiber system of the normal mitotic apparatus. The colchicine effect would consist of an inhibition of this secondary bonding which Mazia attributes to the action of the mitotic centers and the centromeres of the chromosomes.

B. Inhibition of Cell Plate Formation in Plants

Agents which suppress cell plate formation inhibit cell division without affecting chromosome or nuclear division. The result of the first division in the presence of these agents is a binucleate cell. Multinucleate cells are formed when repeated divisions occur in the presence of an inhibitor of cell plate formation.

This type of effect has been reported for several types of cyclic organic compounds, such as halogenated derivatives of benzene and toluene (Simonet and Guinochet, 1939), hydrazino-tropone compounds (Wada, 1952), and aminopyrine (Östergren et al., 1953; Fourcade et al., 1963).

However, so far as the present author is aware, in no other case is the inhibition of cell plate formation combined with such a low toxic effect as it is for methylated oxypurines, such as caffeine, theophylline, and theobromine. The ability of these compounds to suppress cell plate formation and to induce the formation of binucleate and multinucleate cells in plant root tips has been described by Shigenaga (1937), Gosselin (1940), Mangenot and Carpentier (1944), and Kihlman and Levan (1949). In a subsequent study on the cytological effect of 15 purine derivatives in root tips of *Allium cepa*, Kihlman (1949) found the ability to suppress cell plate formation to be a property common to all alkylated oxypurines tested.

In the study of Kihlman and Levan (1949) the threshold concentration for the inhibitory effect of caffeine, theophylline, and theobromine on cell plate formation was found to be 0.02 to 0.04 per cent $(1 - 2 \times 10^{-3}M)$. The effect could be observed as early as 30 minutes after the beginning of the treatment and gradually involved all dividing cells.

The rate of mitosis was not appreciably affected by concentrations just above the threshold concentration, and prolonged treatments with caffeine, theophylline, and theobromine drastically changed the appearance of the root meristem. Since the nuclei of binucleate or multinucleate cells often fuse during mitosis, it is not only the number of nuclei per cell which varies as a result of these treatments, but also the number of chromosome sets per nucleus. Another striking abnormality produced by the treatments is that the direction of the spindle axis frequently does not correspond with the direction of the root axis. Stickiness of chromosomes and chromosome structural changes, which are produced by higher concentrations of caffeine, theophylline, and theobromine, were found to be rare, or entirely absent at concentrations just above the threshold for inhibition of cell plate formation. The effect is easily reversible; about 30 minutes after removal of the inhibition, cell plates are formed again.

Figure 8-7 shows the production of a binucleate cell through inhibition of cell plate formation as a result of treatment with theophylline and the behavior of such binucleate cells during a subsequent mitotic cycle in the absence of the inhibitor.

The two daughter nuclei, which as a result of an unimpaired chromosome movement during anaphase, at the beginning of interphase are separated from each other by a distance corresponding roughly to the length of the spindle axis, gradually approach each other and usually are very close together by middle interphase. Since those sides of the

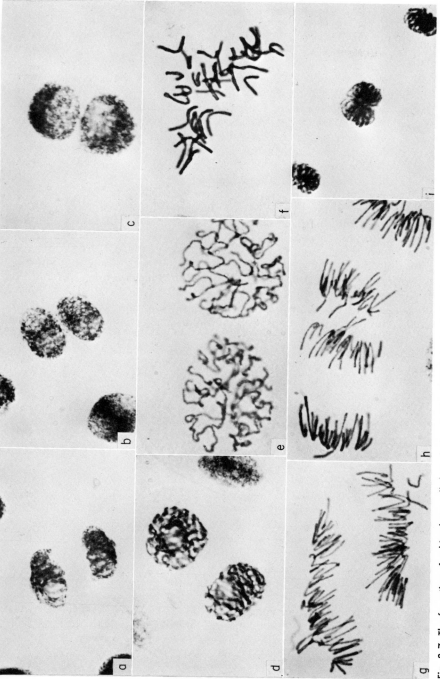

Fig. 8-7. The formation of a binucleate cell through theophylline inhibition of cell plate formation and the behavior of such binucleate cells during a subsequent mitotic cycle in the absence of the inhibitor.

two nuclei which are facing each other often are flattened, one gets the impression that the two nuclei are pressed together. So long as the nuclear membrane is intact, they do not fuse, however, but remain separated by a narrow slit.

In connection with chromosome condensation during prophase, the nuclei move apart some distance. If this distance is short or if the nuclei lie side by side in the middle of the cell, the two spindles, and, consequently, the chromosomes of the two metaphase plates will mix partially or wholly (Fig. 8-7f). Since the poles of the two parallel spindles either have fused or are very close together on either side of the equatorial plane of the cell, the chromosomes of the two nuclei make their anaphase movements together (Fig. 8-7g). The result of this type of binucleate cell division is two cells with tetraploid nuclei.

Frequently, however, at the end of prophase the two nuclei are situated at some distance from each other on either side of the equatorial plane of the cell. In this case no spindle fusion or mixing of chromosomes will occur at metaphase, and at anaphase there are four groups of daughter chromosomes arranged in tandem (Fig. 8-7h). The two groups in the middle are pushed together from both sides and will usually form one telophase nucleus (Fig. 8-7i). The result of this type of division will be three cells, one tetraploid and two diploid.

Since so little is known about cell plate formation (see Chap. 6), it is not surprising that the mechanism of its suppression by methylated oxypurines should be obscure. Without a better understanding of the biochemical aspects of cell plate formation, there is little hope of solving the problem. However, it ought to be possible to obtain valuable information by using living endosperm (Bajer, 1955) as experimental material and the cinemicrographic technique, preferably in combination with a polarizing microscope. An electron microscopic study would also be desirable, since it would be likely to show whether the phase of cell plate formation inhibited by alkylated oxypurines is that involving the vesicles produced by the Golgi apparatus (Whaley and Mollenhauer, 1963; compare Chap. 6).

Since the process of cytokinesis is so different in plant and animal cells (compare Chap. 6), it is not to be expected that agents suppressing cytokinesis in plants should have a similar effect in animal cells. It is true that Druckrey has reported that caffeine inhibits cell division of sea urchin eggs at concentrations which do not affect nuclear division (Druckrey and Schreiber, 1938), with the formation of multinuclear cells as a result, but since caffeine in sea urchin eggs shared this effect with a variety of different agents, including hormones, colchicine, peptone, benzoic acid, narcotics, acids, bases, and hypotonic solutions (Druckrey, 1938), it is probably here the question of a much less specific effect of caffeine which only has the end result, the production of multinucleate cells, in common with the caffeine effect on cell plate formation in plants.

The Production of Chromosomal Aberrations by Chemicals

A. Types of Aberrations and Hypotheses on Their Formation

The chromosome-breaking agents and their cytological effects cannot be profitably discussed until we have described and defined the various types of chromosomal aberrations which can be obtained and until we have mentioned the two main hypotheses for their formation.

According to the general or *breakage-first* hypothesis, the primary event produced by the chromosome-breaking agent is a chromatid or a chromosome break in a continuous interphase chromosome. It is assumed that as a rule the ends in the breakage point rejoin to restore the original configuration (restitution). However, the ends may also remain open or they may rejoin with ends from other breaks, provided that the latter have occurred close enough in space and time. The results of such illegitimate fusion of ends from different breaks are the union of sister-chromatids in an isochromatid break (SU = sister-union) and the various types of exchanges. Which of the alternatives—open breaks, restitution, or illegitimate fusion—that will occur is usually determined within one hour.

According to the *exchange* hypothesis proposed by Revell (1955, 1959), the primary event is not a break, but some other kind of lesion in the chromosome. This lesion decays with time, i.e., reverts to normal or to another state incapable of taking part in exchange formation. When two primary events are close enough in space and time, they may be succeeded by another stage, called exchange "initiation stage" by Revell. This stage is stable and can be of considerable duration. No genetic changes have yet occurred at the exchange initiation stage. Only during subsequent stages of chromosome development is it transformed into a real chromatid exchange. According to Revell's hypothesis, all types of chromatid aberrations arise as a result of an exchange process. The so-called isochromatid break is one of four possible types of chromatid intrachange (Fig. 9-1), and the chromatid break is an incomplete intra-

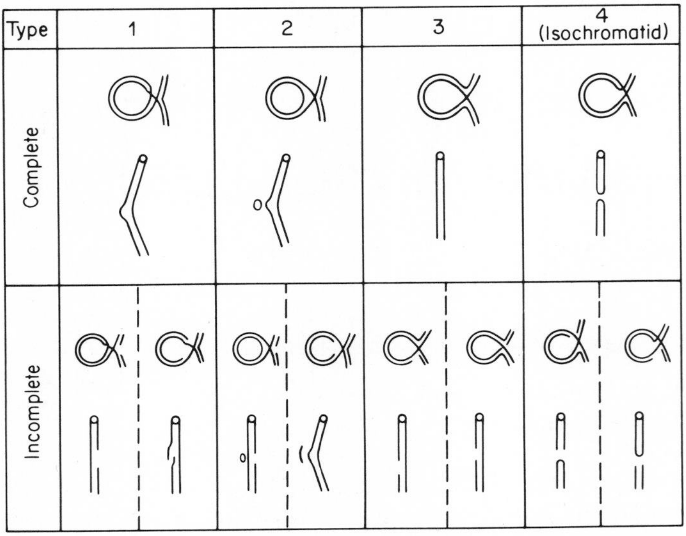

Fig. 9–1. The exchange hypothesis of Revell. Types of intra-arm chromatid intrachanges. Evans, 1962; Int. Rev. Cytol. 13:235. Reprinted by permission of Academic Press, Inc.)

change. According to the hypothesis, the true chromatid break is a comparatively rare type of aberration, occurring with a frequency only slightly more than twice as high as that of isochromatid breaks with proximal or distal sister-chromatid nonunion (NUp, NUd). The experimental data presented by Revell (e.g., Revell, 1959) are in good agreement with the hypothesis, and his results have been confirmed by Neary and Evans (1958) and Evans (1962). Evidently the majority of the aberrations scored as chromatid breaks by previous workers are not real breaks at all, but merely achromatic gaps in a continuous chromosome, and, therefore, they do not result in free fragments in anaphase.

During the last few years there has accumulated considerable evidence in favor of the exchange hypothesis. It has not only been demonstrated that all the different types of chromatid aberrations which occur after treatments with chromosome-breaking agents could have arisen as a result of chromatid intrachange and interchange, but there are also data from quantitative studies which convincingly show that the aberrations occur with the frequencies expected on the basis of the exchange hypothesis. Revell has worked out the exchange hypothesis only for chromatid aberrations, but there is no reason why it could not be applied just as well to aberrations of chromosome type.

The exchange hypothesis has many attractive features. One is that it may be easier to understand that an unreactive chemical is able to initiate an exchange process than that it is able to break such a complex structure as a chromosome. The chromosomes have a known capacity to exchange hereditary material. Normally the exchange process takes place under cellular control in the pachytene stage of meiosis. It is conceivable that the chromosome-breaking agents create a situation in the mitotic cell which leads to a similar kind of exchange process. Since the induced exchanges are not under cellular control, it is not surprising that they frequently are asymmetrical and usually occur between heterologous chromosomes. The similarity between the meiotic crossing-over process and the exchange process initiated by chromosome-breaking agents has been pointed out by several authors (e.g., Marquardt, 1950; Östergren and Wakonig, 1954).

Obviously, the terminology will be dependent on whether the aberrations are interpreted according to the general hypothesis or according to the exchange hypothesis. The discussion above has shown that there is much evidence in favor of the exchange hypothesis. When it nevertheless is decided to use the terminology of the general hypothesis, it is not because it is preferred to the exchange hypothesis, but because it is easier to understand what is meant by an isochromatid break with sister-union or with a chromatid break than by a complete chromatid intrachange, type 4, or by an incomplete chromatid intrachange, types 1, 2, or 3. For similar reasons, the terms "breakage" and "rejoining" will be used throughout this book.

The aberrations presented in Table 9-1 represent examples of the main types of aberrations produced by chromosome-breaking agents as they appear in metaphase and anaphase.

In a subchromatid aberration the unit of breakage is probably a half-chromatid. In any case it is smaller than a single chromatid. Subchromatid aberrations are induced in prophase by ionizing radiation and by certain chromosome breaking chemicals. When the unit of breakage is the single chromatid, the aberration is said to be of the chromatid type. This type of aberration is induced in the S and G_2 stages of interphase. In an aberration of chromosome type, the two chromatids of a chromosome are broken or exchanged at the same loci. The chromosome type aberration is believed to be induced in G_1, i.e. before duplication when the chromosomes still are single.

The exchanges can be subdivided into many different types depending on whether they are inter-arm or intra-arm, symmetrical or asymmetrical, polarized or nonpolarized, complete or incomplete. In addition to the SU (= sister-chromatid union) isochromatid break shown in the table, three other types are known, which it is customary to describe as NUp, NUd, and $NUpd$, depending on whether sister-union has failed to occur proximally (NUp), distally (NUd), or on both sides of the break

TABLE 9–1.

THE MAIN TYPES OF CHROMOSOMAL ABERRATIONS PRODUCED BY CHEMICALS.

Types of aberrations	Subchromatid exchange (intrachromosomal)		Chromatid aberrations			Exchange		Chromosome aberrations		Exchange
	U-type	X-type	Gap	Break	Isochromatid break SU-type	inter (asymm, complete)	intra (symm, complete)	Break	inter (asymm, complete)	intra (asymm. complete)
Metaphase configuration										
Anaphase configuration										

120

(*NUpd*). For a detailed discussion of the various types of aberrations and their formation, the reader is referred to the excellent review by Evans (1962).

B. Guiding Principles in the Study of Aberration Production by Chemicals

When the chromosome-breaking effect of chemicals is studied, it may be useful to try to answer the following questions: (1) How soon after the beginning of the treatment does the effect appear (can it be classified as delayed or as nondelayed)? (2) Are the aberrations only of the chromatid type or are aberrations of the chromosome or of the subchromatid type produced as well? (3) Do exchanges and sister-union occur or does the effect consist mainly of a fragmentation of the chromosomes? (4) Are the aberrations localized in certain chromosomes or chromosome regions, or are they randomly distributed? (5) Is the chromosome-breaking effect influenced by oxygen or by oxidative metabolism?

Although the answers to these questions are not sufficient to explain the mode of action of the chemicals, they are likely to give us useful information and to help us in the task of classifying the chromosome-breaking agents. Let us, therefore, examine the implications of these questions a little more in detail.

When the average duration of the cell cycle is 16 to 22 hours, as it is in root tips of many plants, including *Vicia faba,* and in tissue cultures of several mammalian cells, the effect is said to be nondelayed if chromatid aberrations begin to appear in metaphase at least three hours after the beginning of the treatment and occur with a maximum frequency at four to ten hours. The effect is delayed if it does not begin to appear until about eight hours after the treatment and the aberrations occur with a maximum frequency at 24 to 48 hours. Since, as we have seen in Chap. 5, the postsynthetic period G_2 is assumed to last in *Vicia* on the average five hours and prophase at least one hour, agents with nondelayed effects seem to be able to produce aberrations in cells which have completed their DNA-synthesis, whereas agents with delayed effect appear to be unable to do so.

The possibility of using the time between the beginning of the treatment and the appearance of the aberrations in metaphase as an indicator of the sensitive interphase stage has been questioned (Evans, 1963; Wolff, 1963) on the ground that the delayed appearance of the aberrations could be a result of the mitotic delay which most of the chromosome-breaking agents produce. It is true that only radioautographic experiments with labeled DNA precursors (e.g., H^3-thymidine) can tell whether the cell had finished its DNA synthesis when exposed to the chromosome-breaking agent, but there is reason to believe that in most cases time can be used as an indicator of stage sensitivity. Although the mitotic delay produced by chromosome-breaking chemicals may be considerable, prophase and G_2 cells appear to be comparatively little affected. As a matter of fact, lack of an inhibitory effect on prophase and G_2 cells appears to be a characteristic particularly of agents such as maleic hydrazide and nitrogen mustard, the chromosome-breaking effect of which is classified as delayed (Evans and Scott, 1964; Scott and Evans, 1964). A much more pronounced inhibition of G_2 cells is produced by 8-ethoxycaffeine, which has a typical nondelayed effect.

Cells of experimental materials such as tissue cultures or root-tips, divide asynchronously. In order to be able to determine stage sensitivity accurately it is necessary to synchronize the cell population or, alternatively, to label the cells at a particular stage of the mitotic cycle.

In tissue cultures of mammalian cells, and to a certain degree also in plant roots, a partial synchronization of cell division can be obtained by exposure of the material first to an inhibitor of thymidylic acid synthesis, such as FUdR, and then to thymidine (e.g., Hsu et al. 1964; Taylor, 1963b). As a result of the thymidylic acid deficiency produced by FUdR, DNA synthesis is inhibited. Cells in S are arrested at this stage, while cells in G_2, mitosis and G_1 advance to the beginning of S where they stop. By the addition of thymidine the block of DNA synthesis, and hence of cell division, is removed. The cells now proceed to division as a partially synchronized population.

Several methods for labeling of cells have been devised. One is the labeling of cells in S by the use of a DNA precursor labeled with a radioactive isotope (e.g., P^{32}-phosphate, H^3-thymidine). (Quastler and Sherman, 1959; Evans and Savage, 1963). By this method it is possible to detect not only S-cells but also G_2-cells, since it is reasonable to assume that the unlabeled cells which reach division before the labeled S-cells represent G_2-cells.

Cells in division can be labeled by treatment with spindle poisons such as colchicine (Östergren and Wakonig, 1954; Van't Hof et al., 1960) or (in plant material) by inhibitors of cell plate formation such as methylated oxypurines (e.g., caffeine, theophylline, 8-ethoxycaffeine) (Kihlman, 1955a). Cells which enter division in the presence of colchicine acquire a double set of chromosomes. Thus, in this case labeling consists of a doubling of the chromosome number. As a result of treatments with methylated oxypurines binucleate cells are formed.

It is also possible to label cells in division with micronuclei (Revell, 1953). Acentric chromatid fragments produced as a result of treatments with chromosome-breaking chemicals are not transported to the spindle poles during anaphase and, as a rule, do not become incorporated in the daughter nuclei; instead they remain in the equatorial region of the cell, where they form so-called micronuclei.

Cells which were labeled during the stages of active division by one of the methods mentioned above can be used to study the effect of chromosome-breaking agents at various stages of interphase or for the determination of the duration of the mitotic cycle. In the former case, the usual procedure is to expose the labeled cells at various times after labeling to the chromosome-breaking agent in question. The labeled cells are fixed and analyzed when they reach division. By combining two of the labeling techniques the stage sensitivity can be determined with high accuracy.

When ionizing radiation is used as the chromosome-breaking agent, aberrations of chromosome type are induced in G_1 and aberrations of chromatid type in S and G_2 [and possibly in very late G_1 (Evans and Savage, 1963)]. Irradiation of prophase cells results in subchromatid exchanges. After treatment with most chromosome-breaking chemicals, only chromatid aberrations are obtained. Subchromatid exchanges and aberrations of chromosome type are produced by chemicals such as 8-ethoxycaffeine and streptonigrin.

If Revell's exchange hypothesis is accepted, all the aberrations shown in Table 9-1, with the exception of the gaps, have arisen as a result of complete or incomplete exchange, and also according to the general hypothesis, a large proportion of the aberrations would be classified as exchanges. It may, therefore, be justified to refer to this effect as the *exchange* type of effect. It has further been found that some chemical agents produce an effect which almost exclusively consists of gaps, chromatid breaks, and *NUpd* isochromatid breaks. This effect, which results in fragmentation but not in exchange of chromosome material, will be referred to in the following as the *fragment* type of effect.

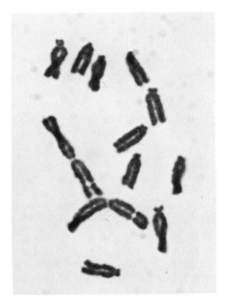

Fig. 9–2. The chromosomes of *Vicia faba* (2n= 12).

Although even after treatments with ionizing radiation, the aberrations are not completely randomly distributed between and within chromosomes, the nonrandomness is much more pronounced after treatments with chemical agents. Most of the available information on the distribution of breaks has been obtained with root tips of *Vicia faba* as experimental material. The chromosome complement in this plant consists of five pairs of nearly equally long chromosomes with subterminal centromer (S chromosomes) and one pair with median centromere (M chromosomes) (Fig. 9-2). In the M chromosomes a large satellite is separated from the rest of the chromosome by a nucleolar constriction. Since in metaphase an M chromosome is twice as long as an S chromosome, there is in a cell approximately 2.5 times more material from S chromosomes than from M chromosomes; if breaks occur at random, they should, therefore, be distributed between S and M chromosomes in the ratio of approximately 2.5 to 1. After treatments with chromosome-breaking chemicals, the ratios usually diverge greatly from 2.5:1. Under certain experimental conditions some chemicals have been found to produce an extreme localization to a particular segment in a particular chromosome.

In this connection it should be pointed out, however, that it is not so much the breaks themselves as the mechanisms by which they arise which we are interested in, since it is the mechanisms rather than the breaks which are likely to give the desired information about the structural organization and mode of reproduction of the chromosome. The mechanisms may be very different, although their end results, the breaks, appear the same. This applies also to the distribution of breaks. It has been found that different chemicals may produce an almost identical distribution of breaks (e.g., localization to heterochromatin), although the mechanisms by which the breaks are produced must be very different, indeed. It is only when a particular treatment produces a very strong localization of breaks to a particular chromosome, or, better still, a particular chromosome region, or when treatments at different stages of interphase with the same chemical result in a different distribution of breaks, that the distribution is likely to tell us something about the mechanism of action and thereby also about the organization and reproduction of the chromosome.

Other aspects of the cytological effect may be more valuable. Undoubtedly it is useful to know if the effect is delayed or not, what type of aberrations is produced, and whether or not the effect is influenced by the metabolism of the cell. But even in these cases it is necessary to be extremely careful. It is not possible to conclude that the biochemical mechanisms involved are the same just because the cytological effects of the chemicals in question are similar or similarly influenced by metabolism or external factors (oxygen tension, pH, temperature). On the other hand, if an identical cytological effect is produced by chemicals which have been selected because of their similar biochemical action and because they are known to be specific in their action, then, and only then, is it possible to conclude that the agents in question produce their cytological effect by a similar biochemical mechanism. This conclusion is strengthened if it can be shown that this particular type of cytological effect is not produced by agents which, although structurally related, have different biochemical effects.

It should be emphasized that it is, of course, the chemical, biochemical, or physicochemical action of the agents which is important for the cytological effect, and not their structure. The fact that two agents have a similar chemical structure does not necessarily mean that they have a similar cytological effect. On the other hand, a different chemical structure does not always mean a different cytological effect. Aminopterin, FUdR, and BUdR are good examples of this.

Aminopterin and FUdR have very different chemical structures, but they both are strong inhibitors of the biosynthesis of thymidylic acid. The cytological effect these two agents produce is almost identical.

FUdR and BUdR are structurally very similar, but biochemically they behave quite differently. The deoxyuridine analogue FUdR inhibits in phosphorylated form the formation of thymidylic acid, but is not incorporated into DNA. The thymidine analogue BUdR does not inhibit the thymidylate synthetase reaction, but is readily incorporated into DNA. As will appear in the following chapters, the cytological effect of these two 5-halogenated deoxyuridines is also very different.

Since this chapter has already become something of a practical guide, we may as well conclude it by making some suggestions which may be useful for those interested in studying the effects of chemicals on chromosome structure.

The various stages of interphase and active division are very differently affected both quantitatively and qualitatively by the chromosome-breaking chemicals. In order to be able to distinguish between these effects the following rules should be followed whenever possible.

1. The period of treatment should be kept as short as possible. The longer the duration of the mitotic cycle, the longer the period of treatment can be. One to two hours is a suitable treatment time when the mitotic cycle is 18 to 24 hours, which it is in most of the materials used for cytological studies. When it is necessary to use a longer period of treatment, it should be kept in mind that the cells fixed in metaphase represent a very heterogeneous population so far as their developmental stage at the time of treatment is concerned.

2. The dose should be as low as possible in order to avoid serious inhibition of cell division. In some cases, e.g., FUdR, this is not possible because very few aberrations are produced by doses low enough not to arrest mitosis.

3. Not only one but several fixation times should be used, and samples of the treated material should be fixed with short intervals and during a period long enough to cover at least one whole mitotic cycle.

4. As will appear in the following chapters, the 'effect of chemicals is frequently dependent on factors such as oxygen tension, treatment temperature, and pH of the solution. Therefore, it is important to have these factors under control. Use buffered solutions, which should be well aerated during treatment, and keep the temperature constant.

5. The chromosomal aberrations may be scored in metaphase or in anaphase. As a rule, it is preferable to score the aberrations in metaphase, since only by this method can the various types of aberrations be distinguished and a detailed analysis of the effect be made. In some cases—for instance, when fragmentation is excessive, as after treatments

with FUdR and AdR—the anaphase method may be more useful. When the aberrations are scored in metaphase, the material is usually treated with colchicine before fixation in order to collect metaphases and to facilitate the analysis. When plants are used as experimental material, a suitable treatment is to expose the roots for two to four hours to a well-aerated solution containing 0.05 to 0.1 per cent colchicine. Animal cells are more sensitive and a one and one-half hour treatment with 0.00004 per cent (10^{-6}M) colchicine is usually quite adequate.

The Chromosome-Breaking Chemicals

A. DNA Precursors and Related Compounds

Adenine. The purine derivative adenine (6-aminopurine) is one of the bases in DNA and RNA and occurs also in many prosthetic groups and coenzymes. It was found to produce chromosomal aberrations in plants (*Allium, Pisum, Vicia*) by Kihlman (1950, 1952a, 1961a) and in mammalian cells in tissue culture by Biesele et al. (1952b). The chromosome-breaking effect of adenine in plant root tips is rather weak and requires high concentrations of adenine ($\geqslant 2 \times 10^{-2}$M). The effect is delayed and the aberrations are always of the chromatid type. The predominant aberrations are *SU* isochromatid breaks and chromatid exchanges, which indicates that the breaks rejoin normally. The effect appears to be higher in the absence than in the presence of oxygen (Kihlman, 1961a). The mechanism responsible for the chromosome-breaking effect of adenine is not known, but it may be pertinent to mention that adenine has been found to inhibit strongly the purine synthesis in ascites tumor cells (Henderson, 1962). At concentrations which produce chromosomal aberrations in *Vicia faba* root tips adenine strongly inhibits the incorporation of P^{32} into the DNA and RNA fractions of excised roots of the same plant (Odmark and Kihlman, 1965). Adenine does also function as a chelating agent (Frieden and Alles, 1958; Harkins and Freiser, 1958).

Deoxyadenosine. The 2′-deoxyriboside of adenine, 2′-deoxyadenosine (AdR) has a cytological effect very different from that of adenine. A strong fragmentation of chromosomes is obtained in cells treated in late interphase with AdR at concentrations above 3×10^{-3}M. This nondelayed effect has been obtained both in the plant *Vicia faba* (Kihlman, 1963b) and in human leukocytes *in vitro* (Kihlman et al., 1963). The aberrations produced were mostly gaps and chromatid breaks. *SU* iso-

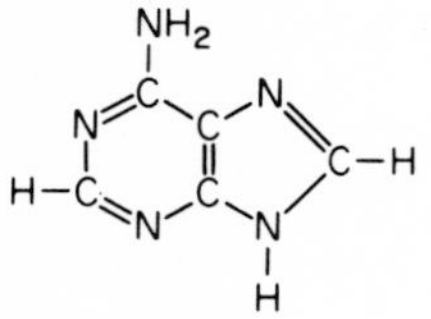

Adenine

Fig. 10–1.

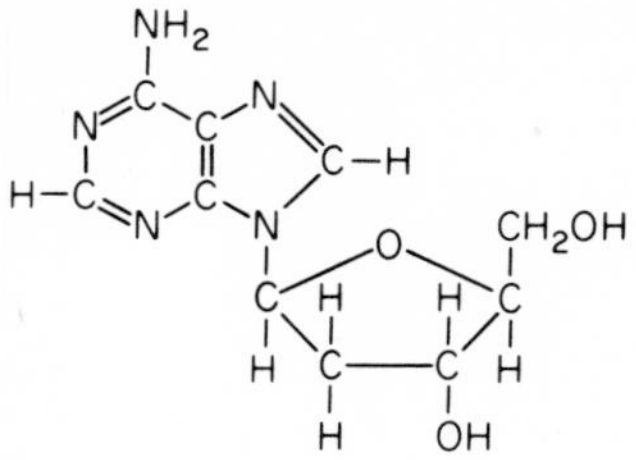

2′-Deoxyadenosine

Fig. 10–2.

chromatid breaks and interchanges were very rare, indicating that rejoining is inhibited. When plant cells were treated for 24 hours with lower concentrations of AdR (10^{-3}M) and then were allowed to recover for another 24 hours in AdR-free solution, the predominant type of aberration was chromatid exchanges localized in the nucleolar constriction. Aberrations of the chromosome type have not been observed. The effect of AdR is inhibited by anoxia and by inhibitors of oxidative phosphorylation. Adenosine and thymidine were found to reduce or to inhibit the AdR effect in *Vicia*. The chromosome-breaking effect of AdR is probably a result of its inhibitory action on deoxyribonucleotide synthesis. The 5′-triphosphate of AdR is known as a strong inhibitor of the reduction of ribonucleosidediphosphates to deoxyribonucleosidediphosphates. (Reichard et al., 1961).

Cytosine arabinoside. This compound is a structural isomer of cytidine, from which it differs by the configuration at carbon 2 in the pentose sugar. CA is inactive in *Vicia* (Kihlman, unpublished) but induces in human leukocytes at concentrations $\geqslant 10^{-6}$M nondelayed chromosome breakage of the same type as that produced by AdR (Kihlman et al., 1963). Thus extensive breakage is obtained with little or no rejoining.

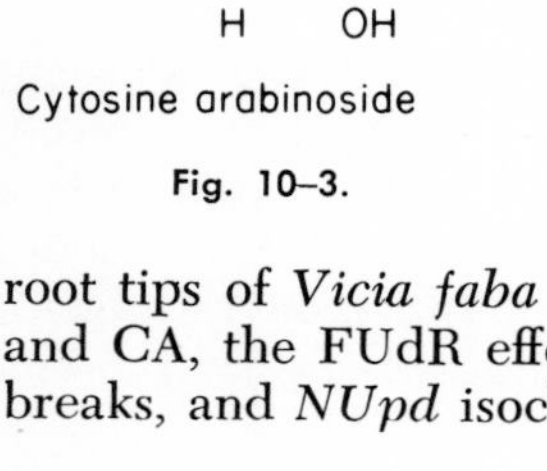

Cytosine arabinoside

Fig. 10–3.

The influence of oxygen and oxidative metabolism on the CA effect has not yet been tested. The similarity between the cytological effect of CA and AdR is not surprising, since, like AdR, CA inhibits the formation of deoxyribonucleotides. However, CA acts more specifically, since apparently it is only the formation of deoxycytidine diphosphate from cytidine diphosphate which is inhibited by CA (Chu and Fischer, 1962).

5-Fluorodeoxyuridine. The chromosome-breaking effect of 5-fluorodeoxyuridine (FUdR) was discovered by Taylor et al. (1962), using root tips of *Vicia faba* as experimental material. Like the effect of AdR and CA, the FUdR effect is nondelayed and consists of gaps, chromatid breaks, and *NUpd* isochromatid breaks. *SU* isochromatid breaks and exchanges are extremely rare in *Vicia* the first 10 hours after one hour treatments with FUdR at concentrations around 10^{-6}M. This type of effect, which is characterized by the lack of rejoining, was first observed after treatments with FUdR and subsequently found also after treatments with AdR and CA.

The FUdR effect is reduced by anoxia and by inhibitors of oxidative phosphorylation (Kihlman, 1962). When the roots are treated with a solution containing 10^{-4}M of thymidine or of a thymidine analogue such as BUdR at the same time as or after they are exposed to 10^{-6}M of FUdR, no aberrations are produced.

FUdR has a strong inhibitory effect on mitosis. In plants, the treatments used for the production of chromosome breakage (i.e., 10^{-6}M for 1 to 4 hours) result within ten hours in a complete inhibition of mitosis. In a FUdR-free medium, the roots usually recover from the mitotic inhibition within a day or two. In the cells dividing after the mitosis-free period, a low frequency of aberrations is found. These aberrations are of the type characteristic of agents with delayed effects, i.e., *SU* isochromatid breaks and chromatid exchanges (Kihlman, 1962).

Hsu et al. (1964) have studied the effect of FUdR on Chinese hamster cells and on mouse cells in tissue culture. In both types of cell cultures, FUdR produced shattering of chromosomes and mitotic inhibition. But whereas the mouse L-M cells were more sensitive than the Chinese hamster cells to the mitotic inhibition produced by FUdR, the opposite was true for the sensitivity of these two cell types to the chromosome-breaking effect of FUdR. The mitotic inhibition and the inhibition of DNA synthesis produced by FUdR was reversed by thymidine, when added at a concentration 100 times higher than that of FUdR. The chromosome-breaking effect of FUdR in mammalian cells was not reversed by thymidine under the experimental conditions employed.

When cells were treated with FUdR during the second half of interphase, the chromosomes most seriously fragmented were those known to replicate late, a fact which suggested a correlation between the damage and the DNA synthetic activity of the chromosomes.

FUdR resembles AdR and CA not only in its cytological effect but also in its biochemical action: the 5'-monophosphate of FUdR is an inhibitor of deoxyribonucleotide synthesis. The reaction inhibited by 5-fluorodeoxyuridylic acid (F-dUMP) is the methylation of deoxyuridylic acid to thymidylic acid, which is catalyzed by the enzyme thymidylate synthetase (Cohen et al., 1958). FUdR is not incorporated into DNA to any appreciable extent.

5-Bromodeoxyuridine. In spite of their both being 5-halogenated deoxyuridines, BUdR and FUdR have very different cytological and biochemical effects. In the plant *Vicia faba* BUdR does not produce any chromosome damage, but bean seedlings grown in the presence of BUdR are much more sensitive to chromosome breakage by X-rays (Kihlman, 1962, 1963a) than are seedlings not exposed to BUdR. Similar results have been obtained in *Vicia* with 5-chlorodeoxyuridine (CUdR) and

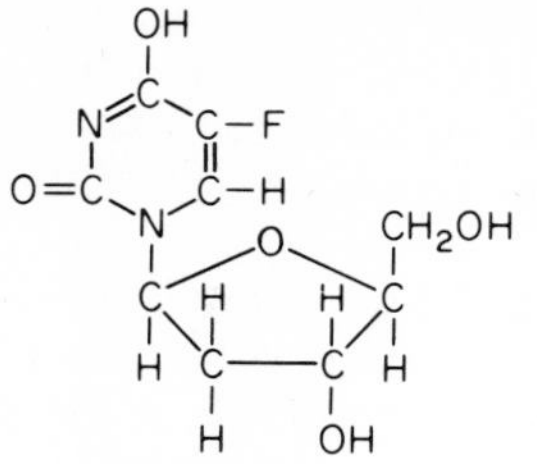

5-Fluorodeoxyuridine

Fig. 10–4.

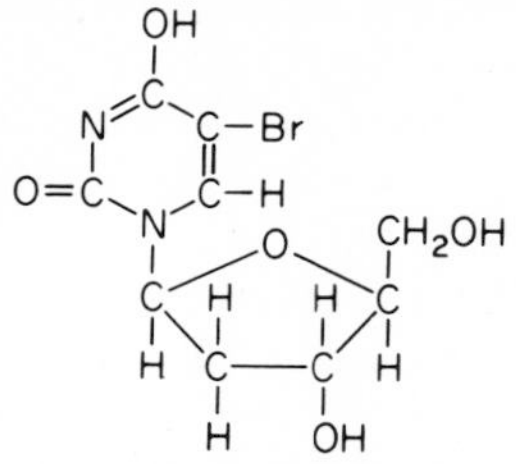

5-Bromodeoxyuridine

Fig. 10–5.

5-iododeoxyuridine (IUdR). In mammalian cells treatments with BUdR result in an increased frequency of chromosomal aberrations (Hsu and Somers, 1961; Somers and Hsu, 1962; Hsu, 1963). In contrast to the effect of FUdR, that of BUdR is only of the delayed type. In order to become effective, BUdR has to be incorporated into the DNA of the chromosomes (Somers and Hsu, 1962). Rejoining is not such an infrequent phenomenon as it is after treatments with FUdR. In Chinese hamster cells in tissue culture BUdR breaks preferentially chromosome ends (telomeres) and region 7 (Somers and Hsu, 1962) of chromosome No. 1.

The difference between the effects of FUdR and BUdR is just as great at the biochemical level as at the cytological level. In contrast to FUdR, BUdR does not inhibit the thymidylate synthetase reaction but is incorporated into the DNA of bacterial, plant, and animal cells, where it replaces thymidine. The fact that FUdR is a deoxyuridine analogue, whereas BUdR, CUdR, and IUdR are thymidine analogues is a consequence of the van der Waals radii of the halogen substituents. The radii of chlorine, bromine, and iodine correspond to the radius of the methyl group, whereas fluorine has a van der Waals radius which is more similar to that of hydrogen (Szybalski, 1962).

N-Methylated oxypurines. The chromosome-breaking effect of the naturally occurring methylated oxypurines caffeine, theophylline, and theobromine was described by Kihlman and Levan (1949), using roots of *Allium cepa* as experimental material. Subsequently, several other methylated oxypurines were synthesized and tested for chromosome-breaking activity in roots of *Allium cepa, Pisum sativum, and Vicia faba.* Of the purine derivatives studied, 8-ethoxycaffeine (EOC) and 1.3.7.9-tetramethyluric acid (TMU) combine a high activity with a reasonably good solubility in water (Kihlman, 1951, 1961b). The treatment periods used were usually one to four hours and the concentrations 2 to 10 $\times$ 10^{-3}M.

EOC and TMU have nondelayed effects. Exchanges and SU-isochromatid breaks occur with the same relative frequency as after X-irradiation, which indicates that rejoining is not inhibited. EOC induces subchromatid exchanges in cells treated during prophase and aberrations

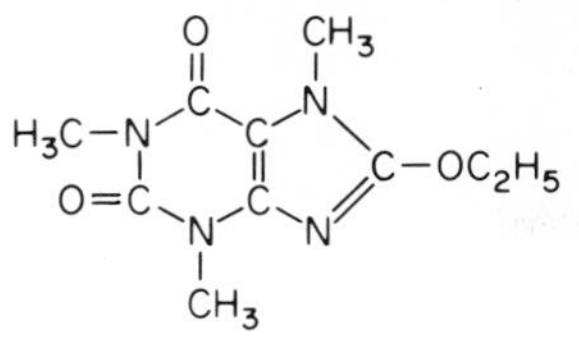

8-Ethoxycaffeine

Fig. 10–6.

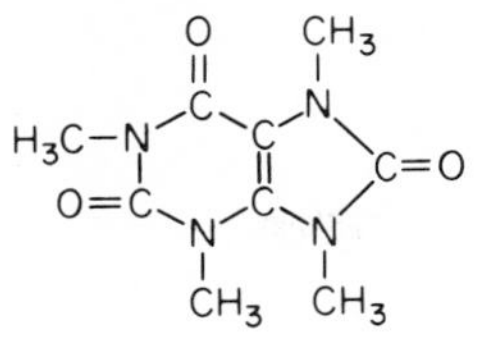

1.3.7.9.–Tetramethyluric acid

Fig. 10–7.

of the chromatid type in cells treated during G_2 and S. A low frequency of exchanges of the chromosome type are obtained in cells treated while in G_1. A high proportion (at low dosages close to 100 per cent) of the aberrations induced by EOC in S and in G_1 are localized in the nucleolar constriction (Kihlman and Levan, 1951; Kihlman, 1961b).

TMU proved to be active as a chromosome-breaking agent only during prophase, when subchromatid exchanges were induced, and during the G_2 period of interphase, when the aberrations induced were of the chromatid type (Kihlman, 1961b). Therefore, if expressed as the frequency of cells containing aberrations, the effect of TMU, in contrast to the effect of EOC, is dependent on the mitotic activity during the treatment: the larger the number of cells dividing during the period of treatment, the larger the number of cells containing structural chromosome changes. Since the inhibitory effect of TMU on mitosis increases with increasing concentration, the percentage of abnormal cells obtained after 24 hour treatments with TMU is inversely proportional to the concentration (Kihlman, 1961b). The number of aberrations per abnormal cell, on the other hand, is directly proportional to the concentration.

The different ability of TMU and EOC to affect cells in G_1 and S is correlated with their relative solubility in lipids (Kihlman, 1951) and may be due to the fact that only EOC is able to penetrate into the cell nucleus during early and middle interphase. Another possibility is that only EOC is capable of being adsorbed onto G_1 and S chromosomes (Kihlman, 1961b).

The effect of both EOC and TMU is completely suppressed by anoxia and by inhibitors of oxidative phosphorylation (Kihlman, 1955b). Low and high temperature reduces the effect of EOC, which is strongest around 12°C.

The methylated oxypurines have a low chemical reactivity, and judged by their ability to affect various enzymatic reactions (Kihlman, 1961b), they are also biochemically rather inert. They are not incorporated into DNA (Koch, 1956; Greer, 1958), but a temporal inhibition of DNA-synthesis has been reported to occur after caffeine treatments (Lieb, 1961). Both RNA synthesis and DNA synthesis are inhibited in *Vicia faba* root tips by EOC (Odmark and Kihlman, 1965). Like adenine, some of the methylated oxypurines are able to function as chelating agents. However, a requirement for chelating activity appears to be that position N7 in the purine molecule is not methylated (Giri and Rao, 1946) and the cytological effect is enhanced, rather than reduced, by N7 methylation.

The cytologically active methylated oxypurines are all effective solubilizing agents (Kihlman, 1952a). The solubilizing power is dependent on the ability of the purines to form molecular complexes (Weil-Malherbe, 1946), and this ability is correlated with their electron donor properties (Pullman and Pullman, 1958). As a consequence of these properties, the methylated oxypurines decrease the denaturation temperature of DNA (Ts'o et al., 1962).

B. Antibiotics

Azaserine. The antibiotic azaserine was isolated from the broth culture filtrate of a strain of *Streptomyces* by Bartz et al. (1954). Tanaka and Sugimura (1956) reported that azaserine produced chromosomal aberrations in root-tip cells of *Tradescantia paludosa*. Subsequently, the chromosome-breaking effect of azaserine in plants has been studied by several authors, including Davidson (quoted by Rieger and Michaelis, 1962), Taylor (personal communication), and Kihlman (1964 and unpublished work). In *Vicia faba* an effective treatment consists of one to two hours of 10^{-4}M azaserine. The chromosome-breaking effect of azaserine is delayed, the aberrations being only of the chromatid type. Rejoining is normal. The effect is completely suppressed by anoxia and by inhibitors of oxidative phosphorylation (Kihlman, 1964). Azaserine is an effective inhibitor of purine biosynthesis and causes disturbances of amino acid metabolism (Handschumacher and Welch, 1960). The possibility that azaserine may act as an alkylating agent has also been suggested (Freese, 1963).

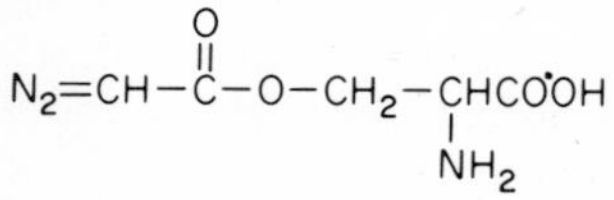

$$N_2=CH-\overset{\overset{\displaystyle O}{\|}}{C}-O-CH_2-\underset{\underset{\displaystyle NH_2}{|}}{CH}COOH$$

Azaserine

Fig. 10–8.

Mitomycin C. Like azaserine, the antibiotic mitomycin C is produced by a *Streptomyces* species. It was isolated in 1955 from *Streptomyces caespitosus* by Hata et al. (1956). Merz (1961) has studied the effect of mitomycin C on the root-tip chromosomes of *Vicia faba*. He observed a high frequency of chromosomal aberrations after one hour treatments with 0.001 per cent solutions of the antibiotic. The effect of mitomycin C is delayed, rejoining occurs, and the aberrations are of the chromatid type. The frequency of mitomycin C-induced aberrations is not reduced by anoxia or by inhibitors of oxidative phosphorylation (Merz, 1961; Kihlman, 1964), nor is the effect appreciably altered by changes in pH and temperature.

That mitomycin C is also an effective chromosome-breaking agent in human leukocyte cultures has been shown by Nowell (1964). Treatment of the leukocyte cells at the time of planting, when they were still mitotically inactive (in the G_0 stage of interphase), resulted in a high frequency of aberrations of the chromatid type, and the same type of aberrations was produced when the cells were treated during the G_1 or S periods of interphase. The frequency of aberrations produced by treatments during S was low. No aberrations were produced by treatments during G_2, which shows that the effect of mitomycin C in human leukocytes is of the delayed type. In agreement with this conclusion, exchanges of the chromosome type were extremely rare.

Mitomycin C produces inhibition of DNA synthesis and degradation of DNA in bacterial (Shiba et al., 1959; Reich et al., 1961) and mammalian cells (Shatkin et al., 1962). It has been suggested (Reich et al., 1961; Kersten, 1962) that a DNase is involved in the mitomycin C-induced degradation of DNA and that the antibiotic releases this enzyme from the ribosomes. Recent experiments (Iyer and Szybalski, 1963) have shown that mitomycin C cross-links complementary DNA strands. Schwartz et al. (1963) have suggested that mitomycin may act as an alkylating agent after it has been activated *in vivo*. The activation may possibly be a reduction which "unmasks" the potential activity of the fused aziridine ring.

Streptonigrin. This is the third *Streptomyces* antibiotic which has proved to have chromosome-breaking activity. Streptonigrin was isolated from *Streptomyces flocculus* (Rao, 1959). The effect of streptonigrin (SN) on human leukocytes *in vitro* was described by Cohen et al. (1963). They observed inhibition of mitosis and extensive chromosome breakage with 0.001 to 0.1 mg/liter streptonigrin. The fact that aberrations were observed when SN was added to the medium as late as two hours before harvest of the culture indicates that SN is able to break chromosomes in the G_2 period of interphase. However, according to Puck (1964), SN does not affect mammalian cells in which DNA synthesis is completed.

In root tips of *Vicia faba* chromosomal aberrations were produced by one hour treatments with 2 to 5 mg/liter streptonigrin (Kihlman, 1964). In contrast to azaserine and mitomycin C, streptonigrin has a nondelayed effect. Subchromatid exchanges are induced in early prophase cells, chromatid aberrations in cells which were in middle or late interphase (G_2 and S) during treatment and, possibly, exchanges of the chromosome type in early interphase (G_1). Like the effect of mitomycin C, that of SN was not suppressed by anoxia or by inhibitors of oxidative phosphorylation and very little influenced by changes in temperature and pH during treatment.

It has been reported that SN both inhibits the synthesis of bacterial DNA (Levine and Borthwick, 1963) and initiates a rapid degradation of the DNA of *Escherichia coli* (Radding, 1963).

The fact that streptonigrin has a nondelayed effect whereas mitomycin has only a delayed effect is rather remarkable, considering the fact that these two *Streptomyces* antibiotics appear to be chemically rather similar. Thus, Rao et al. (1963) have shown that they both con-

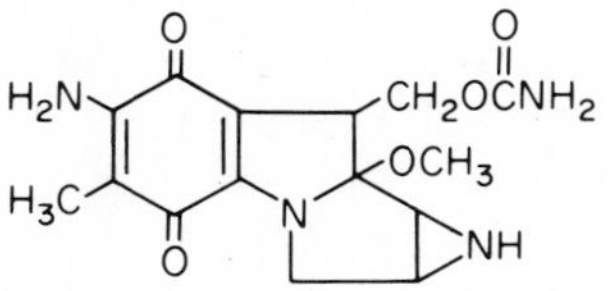

Mitomycin C

Fig. 10–9.

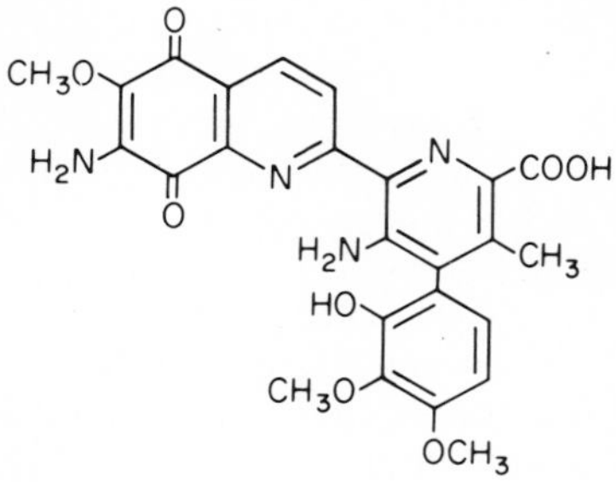

Streptonigrin

Fig. 10–10.

tain the same *o*-aminoquinone moiety. However, Iyer and Szybalski (1964) have pointed out that this chemical similarity may be only superficial, since the reactivity of streptonigrin with DNA *in vitro*, in contrast to that of mitomycin C, is not influenced by chemical reduction.

C. Alkylating Agents

Di(2-chloroethyl)methylamine or *nitrogen mustard*. The sulphur and nitrogen mustards were not only the first chemicals for which a mutagenic effect was demonstrated in *Drosophila*, but also the first chemicals analyzed for their chromosome-breaking effects on mitotic cells (Darlington and Koller, 1947). The effect of HN2 was studied more in detail by Ford (1949), using root tips of *Vicia faba* as experimental material. In Ford's experiments, which were performed at 20°C, the first aberrations appeared between eight and ten hours after a one-half hour treatment with 10^{-5}M HN2, which indicates that the effect is of the delayed type. Only aberrations of the chromatid type are produced by HN2, and the rejoining frequency is normal. In Ford's experiments, the breaks were distributed between the S and the M chromosomes of *Vicia* in the ratio of 24.8 to 1, which is far from a random distribution. The effect of HN2 is independent of the oxygen tension during the treatment (Kihlman, 1955*b*).

Di(2.3-epoxypropyl)ether. The chromosome-breaking effect of the epoxides were discovered by Loveless and Revell (1949). Owing to the studies of Revell (1953) the effect of di(2.3-epoxypropyl)ether (DEPE) is particularly well-known. Treatments of *Vicia* root tips with 2 to 10 × 10^{-4}M DEPE for one hour at 20°C result in few or no aberrations the first eight hours after the treatment (Revell, 1953; Kihlman, 1956). Ten to twelve hours after the treatment, structural chromosomal aberrations begin to appear, but the maximum effect is not obtained until 24 to 36 hours after the treatment. The effect of DEPE, like that of HN2, is delayed and the rejoining frequency is normal. The aberrations, which are of the chromatid type, appear to increase linearly with the dose. The breaks were distributed between S and M chromosomes in the ratio of 18.5:1. A heterochromatic segment in the middle of the long arm of the S chromosomes appeared to be particularly often affected by DEPE (Revell, 1953). The effect of DEPE increases strongly with temperature and is independent of the oxygen tension during treatment (Kihlman, 1956).

β-Propiolactone. The chromosome-breaking effect of β-propiolactone (BPL) was discovered by Smith and Srb (1951) and has subsequently been studied by Smith and Lotfy (1955) and by Swanson and Merz (1959). The effect of BPL is delayed; few aberrations are found in root tips of *Vicia faba* after 24 hours of recovery, the maximum effect being obtained at 48 hours. The aberrations induced by BPL are of the chromatid type and the rejoining frequency is high. The S chromosomes are much more frequently broken by BPL than expected on the basis of a random distribution of breaks between S and M chromosomes. The breaks are localized in heterochromatic segments in the middle of the long arm of the S chromosomes and on either side of the centromere in the M chromosomes. The BPL-induced frequency of aberrations is not affected by changes in pH or oxygen tension, but it increases with increasing temperature.

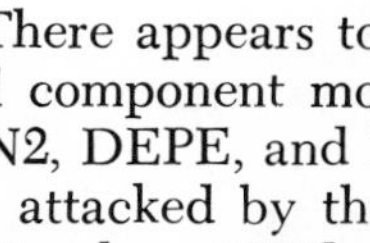

Di(2-chloroethyl)methylamine   Di(2,3-epoxypropyl)ether   β-Propiolactone

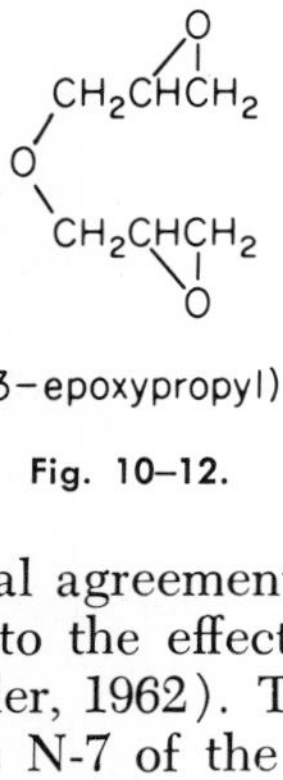

Fig. 10–11.   Fig. 10–12.   Fig. 10–13.

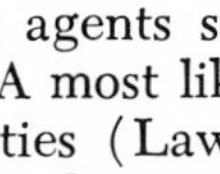

There appears to be a general agreement that DNA is the chromosomal component most sensitive to the effect of alkylating agents such as HN2, DEPE, and BPL (Wheeler, 1962). The site in DNA most likely to be attacked by these agents is N-7 of the guanine moieties (Lawley and Brookes, 1963b; Roberts and Warwick, 1963). The mechanism of action of the alkylating agents is discussed in Chap. 13, pp. 182–184.

D. Nitrosocompounds

N-Nitroso-N-methylurethan. The first nitrosocompound which proved to be able to produce chromosomal aberrations was N-nitroso-N-methylurethan (NMU) (Kihlman, 1960). When root tips of *Vicia faba* were treated with 10^{-4}M NMU for $\frac{3}{4}$ hour at 19°C, the aberrations began to appear 8 to 12 hours after the treatment and occurred with a maximum frequency at 24 to 48 hours. Thus, the NMU effect is delayed. The aberrations are of the chromatid type and the rejoining frequency is normal. The breaks were distributed between S and M chromosomes in the ratio of 2.2:1, which suggests a random distribution between the chromosomes. Within the chromosomes, the aberrations appear to be localized in heterochromatic segments (Kihlman, 1960). The frequency of NMU-induced aberrations increases with increasing temperature but is not affected by variations in the oxygen tension.

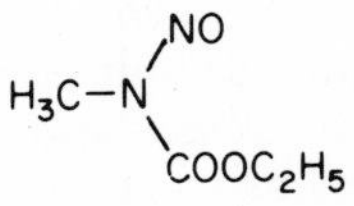

$$H_3C-N\begin{array}{l} \diagup NO \\ \diagdown COOC_2H_5 \end{array}$$

N-Nitroso-N-methyl urethan

Fig. 10–14.

The cytological effect of NMU does not differ very much from that of the alkylating agents HN2, DEPE, and BPL. This is not surprising, since it has been suggested (von Pechmann, 1895) and recently proved (Schoental, 1961) that NMU is converted *in vivo* into the alkylating agent diazomethane, which also is formed from NMU *in vitro* by treatments with alkali.

N-Methylphenylnitrosamine. When root tips of *Vicia faba* were treated in the presence of oxygen for one to two hours with 0.5 to 1×10^{-3}M N-methylphenylnitrosamine (MPNA), a high frequency of structural chromosome changes was obtained (Kihlman, 1961d). The aberrations produced by MPNA are of the chromatid type, the effect delayed, and the frequency of rejoining normal. The aberrations were distributed between S and M chromosomes in the ratio of 2.97:1, which is close to a random distribution. The frequency of MPNA-induced aberrations is not influenced by temperature during treatment, nor is it influenced by the pH of the treatment solution. MPNA is inactive in the absence of oxygen and in the presence of respiratory inhibitors. At 5 per cent oxygen in the gas phase, the effect of MPNA is about $\frac{1}{6}$, and at 20 per cent oxygen about $\frac{2}{3}$, of the effect at 100 per cent oxygen. 2.4-Dinitrophenol, which inhibits oxidative phosphorylation without reducing the rate of respiration, does not influence the chromosome-breaking effect of MPNA.

MPNA and several other nitrosamines are known as carcinogenic agents (Druckrey et al., 1961a, b, c). It seems that the presence of at least one alkyl group in the molecule is necessary for carcinogenic activity. Like the chromosome-breaking effect, the carcinogenic effect of nitrosamines requires the presence of oxygen (Magee and Vandekar, 1958; Brouwers and Emmelot, 1960). It is believed that the species responsible for the carcinogenic effect are alkylating agents, formed *in vivo* by an enzyme-catalyzed oxidative dealkylation (compare Chap. 13, sec. D). Such a mechanism would seem to provide a likely explanation also to the chromosome-breaking effect of MPNA, were it not for the fact that dimethylnitrosamine (DMNA) is inactive as a chromosome-breaking agent (Kihlman, 1961d), whereas cupferron, which has no alkyl group, under suitable experimental conditions can be quite effective a producer of chromosomal aberrations (Kihlman, 1957, 1959b, 1961d). On the other hand, it is true that the effect of cupferron may well be due to its chelating properties, or to a spontaneous decomposition of this nitrosamine to yield a phenylcarbonium ion.

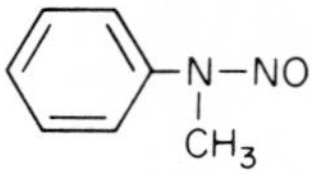

N-Methylphenylnitrosamine

Fig. 10–15.

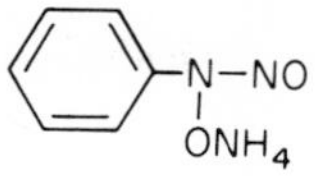

Cupferron

Fig. 10–16.

N-hydroxylphenylnitrosamine-ammonium or cupferron. The chromosome-breaking effect of cupferron was discovered in connection with a study on the effects of heavy metal complexing agents on chromosome structure in *Vicia faba* (Kihlman, 1957). In subsequent reports (Kihlman, 1959*b*, 1961*a*) the cupferron effect was described more in detail. Cupferron produces aberrations of the chromatid type, and its effect is delayed. The relative frequency of chromatid exchanges and SU isochromatid breaks is high, which indicates that rejoining is not prevented. At room temperatures and at pH values around and above 7, the effect is generally low, even when high concentrations of cupferron (10^{-3}M) are used. The frequency of cupferron-induced aberrations can be strongly increased by raising the temperature and by lowering the pH of the treatment solution. Unfortunately, the toxic effect of cupferron is also increased by these modifications of the experimental conditions, with the result that *Vicia* roots are frequently killed by treatments producing a maximum frequency of aberrations. Cupferron appears to be inactive in the absence of oxygen, but with from 1–100 per cent oxygen present in the gas phase, the effect is independent of oxygen tension.

Cupferron is a well-known chelating agent. Because of its ability to form complexes with ferrous and ferric iron and with copper, it is also an effective respiratory inhibitor (Kihlman, 1958). In aqueous solution, cupferron is instable at low pH. By raising the temperature, the rate of decomposition can be increased.

1-Methyl-3-nitro-1-nitrosoguanidine. The chromosome-breaking effect of 1-methyl-3-nitro-1-nitrosoguanidine (MNNG) was studied by Gichner et al. (1963), using root tips of *Vicia faba* as experimental material. The aberrations obtained were only of the chromatid type. The peak frequency of aberrations occurred between 24 and 48 hours after one hour treatments with 5×10^{-4}M MNNG, which shows that the effect of MNNG is of the delayed type. Both the toxic and the chromosome-breaking effects of MNNG are enhanced by

1-Methyl-3-nitro-1-nitroso-guanidine

Fig. 10–17.

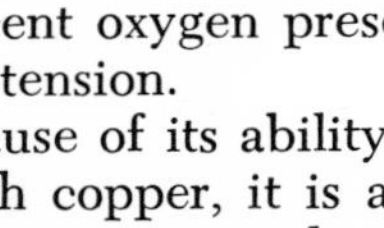

low pH. The frequency of MNNG-induced aberrations increases when the temperature is raised from 18 to 24°C. A further raise of temperature results in a decreased effect. The chromosome-breaking effect of MNNG is reduced by anoxia and by pretreatments with sodium azide. Uncoupling of phosphorylation from respiration by means of 2.4-dinitrophenol does not influence the chromosome-breaking effect of MNNG.

In aqueous solution MNNG decomposes readily, yielding nitrous acid under acid conditions and diazomethane under alkaline conditions.

E. Miscellaneous

Maleic hydrazide. Darlington and McLeish (1951) found that MH, or 1.2-dihydro-3.6-pyridazinedione, has a strong chromosome-breaking effect in the root tips of *Vicia faba*. A large proportion of the MH-induced aberrations in *Vicia* are localized in a heterochromatic segment close to the centromere in the nucleolar arm of the M chromosome (Darlington and McLeish, 1951; McLeish, 1953). The localization is more pronounced at low concentrations of MH. The first six to eight hours after MH treatments only normal cell divisions occur. The highest frequency of aberrations produced by a two hour treatment with 10^{-4}M MH at 20°C and pH 5.8, is obtained between 24 and 36 hours after the treatment. Thus, MH has only a delayed effect. Only aberrations of the chromatid type are produced by MH, and the rejoining is normal. These observations are supported by the results of the recent radioautographic experiments of Evans and Scott (1964). They found that cells exposed to MH while in G_2 were not delayed in their development to the first mitosis and did not contain any aberrations, whereas cells exposed to MH while in the S phase were considerably delayed and contained aberrations of the chromatid type. The same type of aberrations were also produced in G_1 cells.

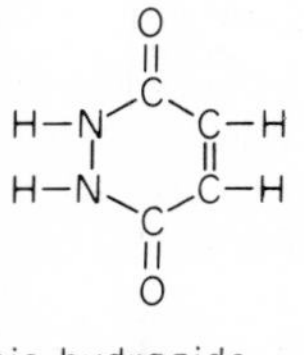

The frequency of MH-induced aberrations increases with temperature and is about four times higher at pH 4.7 than at pH 7.3 (Kihlman, 1956). The chromosome-breaking effect of MH is reduced by anoxia and by inhibitors of oxidative phosphorylation (Kihlman, 1956).

Maleic hydrazide

Fig. 10–18.

MH is a structural isomer of uracil (Loveless, 1953), but no conclusive evidence has been obtained in favor of the idea that MH produces chromosomal aberrations because it acts as an antimetabolite in nucleic acid synthesis. The biological activity of MH has also been attributed to the fact that it reacts with sulfhydryl groups in the cell (Muir and Hansch, 1953). It has been found that MH irreversibly inhibits certain enzymes requiring free sulfhydryl groups (Hughes and Spragg, 1958).

Potassium cyanide. Lilly and Thoday (1956) found that potassium cyanide (KCN) produces chromosomal aberrations in root-tips of *Vicia faba*. The aberrations are of the chromatid type, and the effect is delayed. A few *SU* isolocus breaks can be seen eight hours after one hour treatments with 4×10^{-4}M KCN, but the peak frequency of aberrations occur 24 to 36 hours after the treatments. Rejoining is normal. Like the effect of MPNA, the effect of KCN is independent of temperature during treatment (Kihlman, 1957). KCN is inactive in the absence of oxygen and has little effect at oxygen concentrations below 10 per cent. Above 10 per cent oxygen in the gas phase, the effect increases with increasing oxygen concentration. The frequency of KCN-induced aberrations in *Vicia* is not influenced by inhibitors of oxidative phosphorylation (Kihlman, 1957).

KCN reacts readily with heavy metals, and since aerobic respiration is catalyzed by enzymes containing heavy metals such as iron or copper (e.g., cytochromes), this ability makes KCN an effective respiratory inhibitor. Other heavy-metal-containing enzymes which are strongly inhibited by KCN are catalase and peroxidase.

The chromosome-breaking effect of KCN is believed to be a result of its inhibitory effect on heavy-metal-containing enzymes. Lilly and Thoday (1956) have suggested that the aberrations obtained after KCN treatments are produced by hydrogen peroxide, which is believed to accumulate in the cell in the presence of KCN. An increase of the H_2O_2 concentration would be expected as a result of the cyanide inhibition of the cytochrome oxidase, catalase, and peroxidase enzymes (Wyss et al., 1948).

Hydroxylamine (NH_2OH). Somers and Hsu (1962) have found that hydroxylamine (HA) produces chromosomal aberrations in *in vitro* cultures of Chinese hamster cells. Other effects of treatments with HA were the production of constrictions and despiralization of chromosomes. The aberrations observed were both of the chromatid and of the chromosome type, and exchanges were frequent. An unusually high frequency of HA-induced aberrations was localized in the centromeric regions of the chromosomes. Hydroxylamine is believed to react primarily with the cytosine moiety of DNA. That other reaction mechanisms are also possible is indicated by the recent results of Borenfreund et al. (1964). These authors studied the effect of hyponitrite, HA, and hydroxylamine derivatives in cultures of Chinese hamster cells and mouse embryo cells, and obtained high frequencies of chromatid aberrations. In chemical experiments, HA reacted as expected with the cytosine moiety of DNA, but prolonged treatments with hyponitrite under the same conditions were without measurable effect. However, all the tested chemicals were able to induce main chain cleavage in isolated DNA at sites which were believed to be peptide esters holding polynucleotide units together. The authors, therefore, suggest that the chromosomal aberrations induced by HA and its derivatives are the result of main chain scission of DNA rather than of a reaction with the cytosine in DNA.

HA has recently been reported to be active also in plant material (Cohn, 1964). Chromosome breakage and shattering was observed one to two days after treatments of *Vicia faba* and *Allium cepa* root tips for one-half to four hours with $10^{-3}M$ HA. Aberrations of exchange type were rare after these treatments. The percentage of cells containing aberrations was low, but the cells affected exhibited a relatively high frequency of breaks.

Acridine orange-visible light. In the acridine orange-visible light (AO-VL) system, the energy required for the production of chromosomal aberrations is provided by the physical component of the system, i.e., by visible light. Therefore, it would perhaps be more appropriate to discuss the effect of this system in connection with the biological effects of radiation. However, the fact that the type of effect seems to be determined by the chemical rather than by the physical component of the system would seem to justify a discussion of the chromosome-breaking effect of the AO-VL system under the heading "Effects of chemicals on dividing cells."

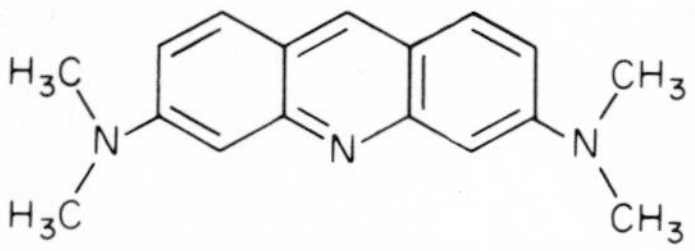

Acridine orange

Fig. 10–19.

When root tips of *Vicia faba* are grown in the dark for 20 hours in the presence of low concentrations of acridine orange ($4 \times 10^{-6}M$) and then exposed to visible light and oxygen, structural chromosome changes are produced (Kihlman, 1959a; Nuti-Ronchi and D'Amato, 1961). All three factors—acridine orange, visible light, and oxygen—have to be present; if either of them is missing, no aberrations are produced. A significant effect is not obtained until the gas phase contains more than 20 per cent oxygen. Only light of the wave lengths absorbed by acridine orange is effective. Treatments producing chromosomal aberrations also have strong toxic effects, which result in the blackening, bending, and, sometimes, killing of the roots. In contrast to ionizing radiations, but like most chromosome-breaking chemicals, the AO-VL system has only a delayed effect and the aberrations are of the chromatid type with normal rejoining. The effect is not influenced by respiratory inhibitors.

In subsequent studies (Kihlman, 1959e, 1961c) on the production of chromosomal aberrations by the AO-VL system, it was found that oxygen can be replaced by nitric oxide (NO) and by the phenylnitrosamines cupferron, methylphenylnitrosamine (MPNA) and diphenylnitrosamine (DPNA). Sodium nitrite was also effective in these experiments, although to a lesser degree. In addition to these compounds, 25 agents were tested for their ability to activate the AO-VL system. These agents included paramagnetic salts, chelating agents, respiratory inhibitors, radical scavengers, and the free radical ion potassium nitrosodisulphonate. None of these 25 agents were able to replace oxygen in the AO-VL system (Kihlman, 1961c). Furthermore, it is quite possible that NO and the phenylnitrosamines are able to replace oxygen only in connection with the chromosome-breaking effect of the AO-VL system. In the photodynamic inactivation of *E. coli* phage T3 by the AO-VL system, NO and cupferron were unable to replace oxygen (Kihlman, 1961c).

It should be pointed out that of the five agents which were able to replace oxygen, MPNA, cupferron, and nitric oxide are by themselves

TABLE 10–1.

THE INDUCTION OF CHROMOSOMAL ABERRATIONS IN *Vicia faba*
BY ACRIDINE ORANGE-VISIBLE LIGHT IN THE PRESENCE OF OXY-
GEN, METHYLPHENYLNITROSAMINE, DIPHENYLNITROSAMINE AND
CUPFERRON. (AFTER KIHLMAN, 1961*b;* ADVANCES. GENET. 10:19
AND KIHLMAN, 1961*c;* RADIAT. BOT. 1:39.)

Active Chemical Present (concentration in μM)	Pretreatment with Acridine Orange (+ or −)	Illumination (+ or −)	Abnormal Metaphases (per cent)	Isolocus Breaks and Exchanges Per 100 Cells
Oxygen (1300)	+	+	22	27
	−	+	0	0
	+	−	0	0
Methylphenylnitros-amine (400)	+	+	31	43
	−	+	1	1
	+	−	1	1
Diphenylnitros-amine (<40)	+	+	17	28
	−	+	0	0
	+	−	0	0
Cupferron (400)	+	+	47	78
	−	+	1	1
	+	−	0	0

chromosome-breaking agents. However, under the conditions employed in the AO-VL experiments, both cupferron and MPNA were quite inactive in the absence of either light or acridine orange (or both). This is only to be expected, since the chromosome-breaking effects of both cupferron and MPNA require the presence of oxygen, and in the AO-VL experiments no oxygen was present. It is then more surprising that the introduction of oxygen reduced the effect of cupferron and MPNA in the AO-VL system. However, this fact suggests that cupferron and MPNA do not produce aberrations by the same mechanism in the presence of the AO-VL system as in its absence. In contrast to cupferron and MPNA, NO produces chromosomal aberrations in the absence of oxygen. The chromosome-breaking effect of NO, and particularly the toxic effect of NO, were, as a rule, much lower in the absence than in the presence of the AO-VL system.

Previously, NO has been found to replace oxygen as an enhancer of X-ray sensitivity (Howard-Flanders, 1957). It has also been reported that NO enhances the production of chromosomal aberrations by X-rays in *Vicia faba* (Kihlman, 1959*d*). According to Howard-Flanders, the ability of oxygen and nitric oxide to enhance X-ray sensitivity may be caused by their affinity for organic radicals. The effect of O_2 and NO in the AO-VL system may have a similar explanation. It is further possible that the phenylnitrosamines and sodium nitrite are active in the AO-VL system because they function as a source of nitric oxide. Phenylnitrosamines are known to give off NO quantitatively when heated (Wieland, 1911). A light-activated production of NO from HNO_2 has been reported by Mukerji and Dhar (1925). The antagonism observed between oxygen and the phenylnitrosamines in the AO-VL system supports the hypothesis that NO is the active species. NO combines rapidly with oxygen to form N_2O_4 (NO_2) which hydrolyzes in water. The experimental results indicate that there are only two compounds able to activate the AO-VL system, i.e., oxygen and nitric oxide. These are the same agents which are able to enhance the X-ray sensitivity. Thus, the active species in the production of chromosomal aberrations by phenylnitrosamines, both when used alone and when used in combination with acridine orange-visible light, appears to be a decomposition product. This active decomposition product is probably different in the two cases, however. Whereas a carbonium ion is the most likely candidate in the production of chromosomal aberrations by phenylnitrosamines alone, the active species in the AO-VL system is probably nitric oxide.

The function of acridine orange in the AO-VL system is obviously to absorb light energy. The energy absorbed is then transferred to compounds in the cell which are combined or in contact with the dye, i.e., compounds such as nucleic acids, in which excited states and free radicals may be produced. *In vitro* experiments have shown that irradiation of DNA with visible light in the presence of acridine orange results in the breakage of chemical bonds in DNA. The requirements for this to occur are the presence of oxygen and binding of the dye to DNA (Freifelder et al., 1961).

The Cytological Effect of the Chromosome-Breaking Chemicals

A. Delayed and Nondelayed Effects

In experiments with *Vicia faba* it may be advisable, for both practical and theoretical reasons, to distinguish between the effect obtained 0 to 8 hours after a one to four hour exposure to the chemical agent and that obtained 8 to 48 hours after the treatment. The latter is usually referred to as the delayed effect and the former as the nondelayed effect. The terms are convenient, but since they frequently have been misunderstood, they are not an entirely happy choice. The 8 to 48 hour effect is delayed only in the sense that the appearance of the effect in metaphase is delayed in relation to the time of the treatment. It is not delayed as a result of a delay in mitosis, but only because it is produced in an earlier stage of interphase than the nondelayed effect.

Table 11-1 shows the types of aberrations characterizing the effects of various chromosome-breaking agents. No aberrations are found the first eight hours after treatments with the majority of the agents listed in the table. The delayed effect obtained between 8 and 48 hours after treatments with these agents is always of exchange type, the aberrations consisting mainly of chromatid exchanges and SU isochromatid breaks. Subchromatid exchanges and exchanges of the chromosome type do not occur.

The fact that the effect consists only of chromatid aberrations indicates that G_1 cannot be the stage when the aberrations are formed, because if they are produced at a stage when the chromosomes are unsplit, they would be of the chromosome type. The delayed appearance of the aberrations has indicated and radioautographic experiments with tritium-labeled thymidine have proved that cells in the postsynthetic in-

TABLE 11–1.

CHROMOSOMAL ABERRATIONS CHARACTERISTIC OF THE EFFECTS
OBTAINED 0–8 AND 8–48 HOURS AFTER 1–4 HOUR TREATMENTS
WITH VARIOUS CHROMOSOME-BREAKING CHEMICALS.

Type of Compound	Name of Compound	Abbreviation or Formula	Effects on Chromosomes — Hours After the Beginning of Treatment					
			0–8			8–48		
			None	Sub.ex. Ch'd ex.	Fragm.	Fragm.	Ch'd ex.	Ch'e ex.
DNA-precursor or closely related	Adenine	—	x				x	
	Deoxy-adenosine	AdR			x	x	x	
	Fluorodeoxy-uridine	FUdR			x	x	x	
	Ethoxy-caffeine	EOC	x				x	x
Antibiotic	Streptonigrin	SN		x			x	x
	Mitomycin C	MC	x				x	
	Azaserine	AS	x				x	
Alkylating agent	Nitrogen mustard	HN2	x				x	
	Diepoxy-propylether	DEPE	x				x	
	β-Propiolactone	BPL	x				x	
Nitroso-compound	Nitrosomethyl-urethan	NMU	x				x	
	Methylphenyl-nitrosamine	MPNA	x				x	
	Cupferron	CF	x				x	
	Methylnitro-nitrosoguanidine	MNNG	x				x	
Miscellaneous	Maleic hydrazide	MH	x				x	
	Potassium cyanide	KCN	x				x	
	Visible light–acridine orange	VL-AO	x				x	

Sub.ex. – subchromatid exchanges, Ch'd ex. – chromatid exchanges,
Ch'e ex. – chromosome exchanges, Fragm. – Fragmentation.

terphase stage G_2 are not affected. Thus, the interphase stage when chromosomal aberrations are formed or initiated in treatments with these agents appears to be S, the period of DNA synthesis. In the case of alkylating agents, the chemical reaction responsible for aberration production (e.g., alkylation of a DNA precursor) could, on the other hand, well have occurred in G_1, or during mitosis, or even during G_2 of the previous cell cycle, although chromosomal aberrations are not initiated by the product of the reaction until the cell is in S.

Nondelayed effects, i.e., effects obtained 0 to 8 hours after the beginning of the treatment, have the inhibitors of deoxyribonucleotide synthesis FUdR and AdR, the methylated oxypurine EOC and the antibiotic streptonigrin. As appears in the table, there are at least two types of nondelayed effects which have in common only the rapid appearance of aberrations. X-rays and other agents which have what we may call the typical nondelayed effect produce subchromatid exchanges in early prophase cells, chromatid aberrations of the exchange type in cells treated while in the G_2 and S stages of interphase, and chromosome-type exchanges in G_1 cells. The peak frequency of aberrations is obtained four to six hours after the beginning of the treatment. It is evident in the table that the aberrations obtained between 0 and 8 hours after treatments with EOC and streptonigrin consist mainly of subchromatid and chromatid exchanges and that exchanges of the chromosome type (Fig. 11-1) occur among the aberrations obtained between 8 and 48 hours.

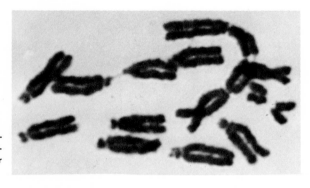

Fig. 11–1. 8-Ethoxycaffeine-induced chromosome type exchange in the nucleolar constriction, Vicia faba.

Thus, EOC and streptonigrin appear to have typical nondelayed effects. However, in comparison with the effects of EOC and X-rays, that produced by streptonigrin is characterized by a higher relative frequency of chromatid breaks and incomplete chromatid exchanges during the first five hours after the treatment and by the fact that the peak frequency of aberrations occurs at ten hours, rather than at four to six hours.

In Fig. 11-2 a comparison has been made between the frequencies of chromatid- and chromosome-type aberrations obtained 12 to 26 hours after treatments with EOC and X-rays.

TMU differs from agents having a typical nondelayed effect by not producing any aberrations in cells fixed 8 to 48 hours after treatment. Apparently, TMU does not affect cells in the S and G_1 stages of interphase. The aberrations produced by TMU in prophase and G_2, like those produced by EOC and streptonigrin in the same stages, consist mainly of subchromatid and chromatid exchanges and SU isochromatid breaks (exchange type of effect).

In contrast, the effect obtained 0 to 8 hours after exposure of cells to FUdR and AdR is characterized by the absence of exchanges. No subchromatid exchanges are produced in prophase, and the effect produced in late interphase consists mainly of gaps, chromatid breaks, and $NUpd$ isolocus breaks (fragment type of effect) (Figs. 11-3a and b). Frequently, the chromosomes are so badly fragmented that scoring is

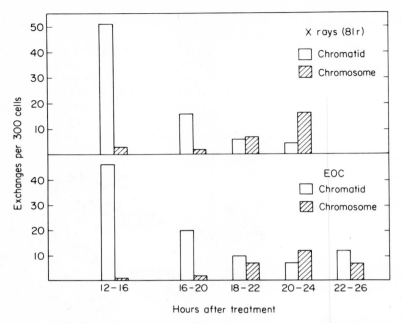

Fig. 11–2. Comparison between the frequencies of chromatid and chromosome type aberrations obtained 12–26 hours after treatment with X rays (81 r) and 8-ethoxycaffeine (EOC). Experimental material: root-tips of *Vicia faba*.

impossible (Figs. 11-3c and d). The mitotic inhibition is considerable and usually results in a complete suppression of cell division about ten hours after the beginning of the FUdR or AdR treatments. Removal of the inhibitor results in resumption of cell division, although the mitosis-free period, particularly after FUdR treatments, may last for several days. As a rule, some 10 to 30 per cent of the cells dividing after the mitosis-free period contain chromatid aberrations of the exchange type. Thus, FUdR and AdR have a nondelayed effect consisting of chromatid aberrations of fragment type and a delayed effect consisting of chromatid aberrations of the exchange type. The time between the beginning of treatment and the appearance of the effect, as well as results of radioautographic experiments, indicate that G_2 is the interphase stage when chromatid aberrations of fragment type are produced by FUdR and AdR (Kihlman, 1962; 1963b; Bell and Wolff, 1964). Results of similar experiments have shown that G_2 is the stage most sensitive to EOC and TMU (Kihlman, 1961b; Scott and Evans, 1964). Streptonigrin is effective in G_2, but the fact that there can be up to ten hours between the beginning of the treatment and the appearance of the maximum effect indicates that late S may be more sensitive than G_2 to streptonigrin.

As a summary of the discussion above, the following may be said: All the agents discussed, with the exception of TMU, have delayed

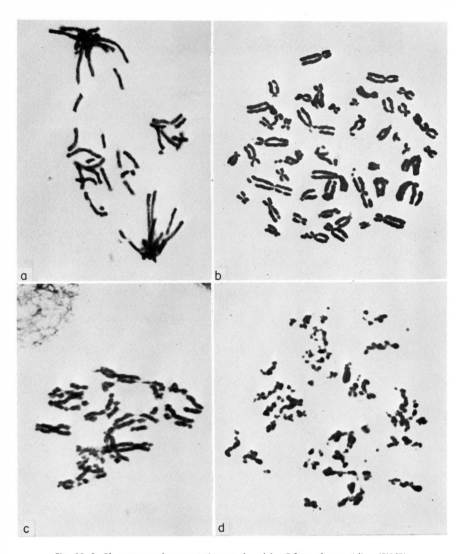

Fig. 11–3. Chromosome fragmentation produced by 5-fluorodeoxyuridine (FUdR) and deoxyadenosine (AdR). (a) Anaphase cell of Vicia faba fixed 4 hours after 1½-hour treatment with 0.5 μM FUdR. The aberrations consist of free and attached fragments but no bridges, which indicates that no rejoining of broken ends has taken place. (Kihlman, 1962; Caryologia 15, p. 264.) (b) Metaphase of a human leukocyte cell fixed 8 hours after the addition of AdR to the culture medium at a final concentration of 5 mM. Several gaps and chromatid breaks can be seen. (Kihlman et al., 1963; Hederitas 50, p. 140.) (c) Metaphase cell of Vicia faba with strongly fragmented chromosomes as a result of treatment with 5 mM AdR. Kihlman, 1963b; J. Cell Comp. Physiol., 62:269.) (d) Metaphase of a human leukocyte cell with strongly fragmented chromosomes as a result of treatment with 5mM AdR. (Kihlman et al., 1963; Hereditas 50, p. 140.)

effects, but only a few have also nondelayed effects. When there is no nondelayed effect, the delayed effect always consists of chromatid aberrations of the exchange type. The same type of delayed effect is produced by agents which have a nondelayed effect of the fragment type. When, on the other hand, the nondelayed effect consists of subchromatid and chromatid aberrations of the exchange type, the delayed effect is characterized by the occurrence of aberrations of the chromosome type.

B. Distribution of Aberrations Between and Within Chromosomes

As was already pointed out, the distribution of chemically induced aberrations between and within chromosomes as a rule is nonrandom. In root tips of *Vicia faba* chemicals such as EOC, AdR, and MH produce

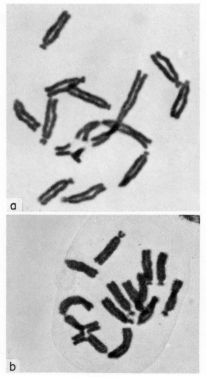

the most extreme localization. Under certain experimental conditions, the aberrations induced by these chemicals are almost exclusively confined to a certain locus, which is the nucleolar constriction in the case of EOC and AdR (Figs. 11-4a and b) and a heterochromatic segment close to the centromere in the nucleolar arm of the M chromosome in the case of MH. Aberrations induced in *Vicia* by alkylating agents tend to be concentrated in a heterochromatic segment situated in the middle of the long arm of the S chromosomes.

A nonrandom distribution of breaks between and within chromosomes has also been obtained in mammalian cells after treatments with chemical agents. Thus, Hsu and Somers (1961) found that chromosomal breaks induced by the thymidine analogue BUdR in cells of the Chinese hamster were nonrandomly distributed along chromosome No. 1, with more than 80 per cent of the total number of breaks concentrated to one region (= region 7). Other places that were broken more frequently than expected on the basis of a nonrandom distribution were the chromosome ends (Fig. 11-5). An-

Fig. 11–4. Chromatid exchanges localized in the nucleolar constriction of *Vicia faba* after treatments with 8-ethoxycaffeine (a) and deoxyadenosine (b). (Kihlman, 1963b; J. Cell Comp. Physiol., 62:269.)

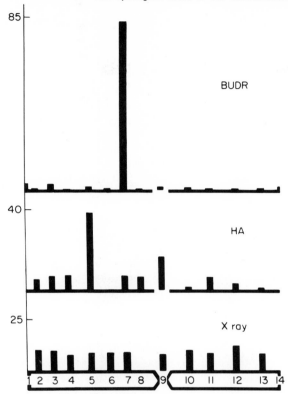

Fig. 11–5. Diagrammatic representation showing the relative frequencies of breaks produced by 5-bromodeoxyuridine (BUdR), hydroxylamine (HA) and X rays (250 rads) in the various regions of chromosome 1 of the Chinese hamster. (Somers and Hsu, 1962; Nat. Acad. Sci. (U.S.), Proc., 48:940. Courtesy of the authors.)

other chemical, hydroxylamine, produced a high frequency of breaks in the centromeric regions, but did not affect the regions sensitive to BUdR (Somers and Hsu, 1962). Kihlman et al. (1963) found that breaks induced by AdR and CA in the chromosomes of human leukocytes *in vitro* tended to be concentrated to chromosome ends. A nonrandom distribution of chromosomal damage induced by streptonigrin in human leukocytes was reported by Cohen et al. (1963). They found a deficiency of breaks in chromosomes Nos. 19, 20, 21, 22, and Y.

The reasons for the nonrandom distribution of chemically induced chromosomal aberrations may be several.

Thus, the nonrandom distribution of aberrations could be the result of an equally nonrandom distribution of the chromosome-breaking agent inside the nucleus. This possibility has been suggested as an explanation to the localization of EOC- and AdR-induced aberrations in the nucleolar constriction of the M chromosome in *Vicia* (Kihlman, 1952a, b; 1963b).

As a surface-active and lipid-soluble agent, EOC would be expected to be adsorbed mainly on well-developed interfaces, such as that between the nucleolus and the nuclear sap, and on structures containing high concentrations of lipids. Since the nucleolar constrictions of the M chromosomes of *Vicia* during interphase are in contact with the nucleolus (Fig. 11-6), and since these same structures are known to be particularly rich in lipids (Albuquerque and Serra, 1951; Zagury, 1957), the nucleolar constrictions would be exposed to higher concentrations of EOC than other parts of the chromosomes and hence would be broken more easily.

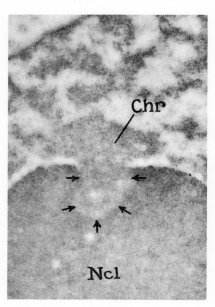

Fig. 11–6. Electron micrograph of an interphase nucleus of *Vicia faba* showing an intimate relationship between the nucleolus (*Ncl*) and a chromatid strand (*Chr*), which probably is the nucleolus-organizing region of the M chromosome. (Lafontaine, 1958b. Reprinted by permission of the Rockefeller Institute Press from J. Biophysic. Biochem. Cytol. November 25, 1958, Vol. 4, No. 6, pp. 777–784.)

Similarly, it has been suggested (Kihlman, 1963*b*) that AdR or dATP (the active agent produced from AdR by phosphorylation) may accumulate in the nucleolus and there reach a concentration high enough to suppress the synthesis of deoxyribonucleotides in adjacent chromosome structures. However, this hypothesis would seem to require that the reduction of ribonucleotides to deoxyribonucleotides occurs within the nucleus, along and in close contact with the chromosomes. Like EOC, AdR is a purine derivative. However, its physical properties are so different from those of EOC that the explanation to the possible accumulation of AdR or dATP in the nucleolus can hardly be the same as that suggested for the accumulation of EOC.

For the localization of EOC-induced aberrations to the nucleolar constriction there is another possibility which should be considered. Since EOC is effective only in the presence of a high intracellular (intranuclear) level of ATP, it is conceivable that it is intranuclear ATP, and not intranuclear EOC, which is concentrated in the nucleolus during the S and G_1 stages of interphase. This possibility would provide a better explanation to the fact that the EOC- and AdR-induced aberrations have an almost identical localization. ATP and dATP are chemically so closely related that a similar distribution of these two compounds within the nucleus is only to be expected.

It should be mentioned, however, that although the nucleolar constriction region is affected both by EOC and AdR treatments, the resulting aberrations are not exactly alike in the two cases. As appears in Table 11-2, 57 of 100 AdR-produced aberrations and 86 of 123 EOC-produced aberrations were in the nucleolar constriction (57 and 71 per

TABLE 11–2.

THE OCCURRENCE OF CHROMATID ABERRATIONS IN THE NUCLEO-LAR CONSTRICTION (NC) AFTER TREATMENTS WITH DEOXY-ADENOSINE, 8-ETHOXYCAFFEINE AND X RAYS. (KIHLMAN, 1963*b*; J. CELL COMP. PHYSIOL., 62:268.)

Treatment	Number of Meta-phases Analyzed	Abnormal Meta-phases %	Isochromatid Breaks			Chromatid Exchanges			Total Aber-rations	Aber-rations Per 100 Cells
			Total	in NC	in NC %	Total	in NC	in NC %		
24 hr. 1.5 mM deoxy-adenosine, 27 hr. recovery in water	300	29.3	43	7	16.3	57	50	87.7	100	33.3
5 hr. 10 mM 8-ethoxy-caffeine, 20 hr. recovery in water	300	35.7	103	81	78.6	20	5	25.0	123	41.0
54 r of x-rays (60 r/min.), 16 hr. recovery in water	300	34.3	72	0	0	51	0	0	123	41.0

cent, respectively). But whereas the ratio of exchanges to isolocus breaks was 50:7 for AdR, it was only 5:81 for EOC. Thus, whereas AdR induces mainly chromatid interchanges in the nucleolar constriction, EOC induces mainly isolocus breaks. Another difference is to be found in the precision of localization. Whereas the EOC-induced aberrations are always strictly within the constriction, those induced by AdR are sometimes situated outside the constriction itself, although very close to it.

Besides a nonrandom distribution of the chromosome-breaking agent inside the nucleus, there are several other possible explanations to the nonrandom distribution of aberrations obtained after treatments with chemicals. As was pointed out by several authors (e.g., McLeish, 1953; Revell, 1953; Evans and Bigger, 1961), one important factor influencing the distribution of aberrations is the organization of the interphase nucleus. Thus, there is probably a connection between the general tendency of aberrations to be concentrated into heterochromatin and the fact that heterochromatic segments tend to fuse into chromocenters in the interphase nucleus. Damaged chromatids or chromosomes can interact to form aberrations of exchange type only if they are in close association. This requirement appears to be fulfilled in chromocenters, and hence the high frequency of aberrations in heterochromatin. It should, perhaps, be recalled in this connection that chromatid and isochromatid breaks should be regarded as aberrations of exchange type, according to Revell (1959).

The nucleolus can also influence the frequency and distribution of aberrations in other ways than by providing a surface or a space where chemicals may accumulate. Evans and Bigger (1961) have found that the nucleolar arm of the M chromosome in *Vicia* is involved less frequently in chromatid exchange than the nonnucleolar arm. According to Evans and Bigger, the nucleolus acts as a physical barrier which reduces the possibility of contact between the nucleolar arm of the M chromosome and the other chromosomes of the complement.

The fusion of heterochromatin into chromocenters and the presence of the nucleolus as a physical barrier would, of course, affect the distribution of aberrations induced by all kinds of chromosome-breaking agents, and not only the distribution of chemically induced aberrations. A hypothesis applicable mainly to localized breakage produced by chemical agents is that the particular chemical composition or molecular organization of certain chromosome regions makes them either more capable of reacting with the chromosome-breaking chemical or more vulnerable to the result of the reaction. The explanation given by Somers and Hsu (1962) to the localized breakage produced by BUdR and hydroxylamine in Chinese hamster cells belongs to this category.

BUdR causes chromosome breakage only after incorporation into DNA. As a thymidine analogue, it replaces thymidine in the nucleic acid. It seems reasonable to assume that chromosome regions characterized by a particularly high BUdR content have a higher frequency of chromosomal aberrations than regions where the DNA is characterized by a low BUdR content. In addition to the degree of thymidine replacement, the BUdR concentration in a particular chromosome region may be expected to be dependent on the normal base composition of the DNA in that region. Since BUdR replaces thymidine, the BUdR concentration would be expected to be high in regions where the thymidine concentration is high, i.e., regions where the DNA is rich in adenine-thymine pairs. In Chinese hamster cells, telomeres and region 7 of chromosome No. 1 in particular are often broken as a result of BUdR treatments, and Somers and Hsu, therefore, conclude that these regions are particularly rich in adenine-thymine pairs. The broken ends in region 7 behave in a telomerelike way by being stable and by rarely combining with other broken ends. Hsu (1963) has suggested that the stability of broken ends in region 7, as well as that of normal chromosome ends (telomeres), is a consequence of their high adenine-thymine content.

Hydroxylamine is known to react with and to alter mainly the cytosine moieties of DNA. In the chromosomes of Chinese hamster cells, the centromeric regions are particularly often broken by HA, and the conclusion of Somers and Hsu (1962) is that these regions have a high content of guanine-cytosine pairs. However, attractive as it may be, the hypothesis of Somers and Hsu seems to be somewhat difficult to reconcile with the finding by Kihlman et al. (1963) that breaks induced by cytosine arabinoside in the chromosomes of human leukocytes tend to be concentrated in the chromosome ends. Cytosine arabinoside, which causes deficiency in cytosine deoxyribonucleotides, would be expected to affect mainly chromosome regions rich in guanine-cytosine pairs. Thus, in human chromosomes, the ends and not the centromeric regions would be rich in guanine-cytosine pairs, if it is true that the distribution of breaks is a reflection of the distribution of bases in chromosomal DNA. Although it is possible, of course, that corresponding chromosome regions may contain DNA of different base composition in different materials, this would in any case mean that Hsu's hypothesis on the connection between telomeric properties and a high adenine-thymine content is not tenable. The results of recent experiments by Borenfreund et al. (1964), which indicate that the effect of HA is due to main chain scission in DNA rather than to a reaction with the cytosine moiety in DNA, have also rendered the hypothesis less attractive.

There is, finally, one more reason for a nonrandom distribution of aberrations which should be mentioned.

In cases where the chromosome-breaking effect is believed to be the result of an inhibition of the synthesis of chromosome material, it is to be expected that the aberrations are localized in chromosome regions where synthesis took place at the time of treatment. By using tritium-labeled thymidine and the radioautographic technique, several workers have found that DNA is synthesized at different times in different chromosomes and chromosome regions. As a rule, heterochromatic chromosome regions appear to be late in synthesizing their DNA. In *Tradescantia*, Wimber (1961) has found that terminal portions of the chromosome arms continue to synthesize DNA at a time when other chromosome parts have ceased to synthesize. Therefore, if the chromosome-breaking effect of FUdR, AdR, and CA really is a result of their inhibitory action on deoxyribonucleotide and DNA synthesis, the distribution of aberrations induced by these inhibitors in a material where the DNA replication is markedly asynchronous, should reflect the distribution of chromosome regions where DNA synthesis took place at the time of treatment. Consequently, it should be possible to obtain different distributions of aberrations by varying the time between treatment and fixation. Preliminary studies on AdR-induced aberrations in human leukocytes indicate that this indeed is the case (chromosome ends and secondary constrictions being particularly affected by treatments at late interphase), but the evidence is far from conclusive as yet.

Hsu et al. (1964) have recently obtained evidence which indicates that when Chinese hamster cells are treated with FUdR during the second half of interphase, the chromosomes most seriously fragmented are those known to replicate late.

C. Distribution of Aberrations Between Nuclei

Not only the distribution of aberrations between and within chromosomes but also the distribution of aberrations between nuclei may be nonrandom. The fact that the frequency of X-ray-induced interchanges per cell does not always follow the anticipated Poisson distribution has recently been shown by several authors. In plant material, there was an excess of cells having one interchange and a deficiency of cells having more than one interchange (Atwood and Wolff, quoted by Wolff, 1961; Evans, 1961). In mammalian cell cultures, Mantel and Greenblatt (1962) found a surplus of cells with none or many aberrations in comparison with the expected frequency, assuming a Poisson variation. The explanation given for the lack of randomness observed in plant material is that there is only a limited number of sites within the nucleus where the chromosomes are sufficiently close to undergo exchange. The nonrandomness obtained in mammalian cells was believed to be the result of a ". . . varying radiation sensitivity of cells, in different portions of the growth cycle, in a mixed population."

As shown by Kihlman and Eriksson (1962), an even more marked deviation from the expected Poisson distribution of aberrations is obtained after treatments with certain chemical agents. In their experiments, root tips of *Vicia faba* were treated with EOC, methylphenylnitrosamine (MPNA), and N-nitroso-N-methylurethan (NMU). The frequencies and distributions of the resulting isolocus breaks and chromatid exchanges were determined and compared with the expected distribution, a Poisson distribution being assumed. In all three cases, the distributions of both types of aberrations did not fit the Poisson distribution, there being an excess of cells with none or many aberrations and a deficiency of cells having one aberration. Thus, the deviation from the expected Poisson distribution, which was particularly pronounced for interchanges produced by EOC and MPNA, was of the same type as that found after X-irradiation of mammalian cells. It is also quite possible that the causes for the nonrandom distribution are the same in the two cases. Cells fixed at a certain time after treatment represent a rather heterogeneous population so far as their developmental stage at the time of treatment is concerned, particularly if the roots have been treated before fixation for four hours with colchicine in order to collect metaphases, and this is usually the case. Therefore, since the sensitivity of the root-tip cells to the chromosome-breaking chemicals in question is different at different periods of interphase, a varying sensitivity in a mixed cell population could well be the explanation to the deviation from the expected Poisson distribution of the aberrations. EOC produces aberrations in root-tip cells of *Vicia* during all stages of interphase, but is highly effective only during a rather limited period of late interphase (three to four hours before metaphase). MPNA and NMU are inactive in late interphase, but the effects produced by these agents at other stages of interphase do not vary very much. In the EOC experiments, roots were fixed five hours after the treatment, whereas in the MPNA and NMU experiments the period between treatment and fixation was 26 hours.

Although the explanation discussed above seems to be the most likely one, others are also conceivable. One factor which should be considered in this connection is the distribution of the chemical within the root. The distribution of all chemical mutagens is dependent on penetration, a factor which, of course, is not limiting in the case of radiations such as gamma rays, 250 kvp X rays, and high-energy protons. It is possible that the chemicals penetrate some parts of the tissue more easily than others; in parts exposed to relatively high concentrations, the cells would contain more aberrations than in parts receiving only a low dosage. Relevant in this connection may be the fact that, in contrast to radiations, chemicals have a "threshold concentration," below which no aberrations are induced (e.g., Revell, 1953; Kihlman, 1955b).

In cases such as MPNA, where the active species apparently is not MPNA *per se*, but some decomposition product (carbonium ion) formed within the cell as a result of an enzymatic process, a nonrandom distribution of aberrations between cells could be the result of a nonrandom distribution of the enzyme involved in the decomposition process.

Recently Rieger and Michaelis (1964) have studied the distribution between nuclei of aberrations induced in *Vicia faba* root tips by the chemicals 4.4'-dibromodibutylether, di-2-chloroethylmethylamine oxide, *N.N*-(di-2-chloroethyl)*N.O*-trimethylenephosphordiamide, 2.4.6-triethylene-imino-1.3.5-triazine, and ethanol. In agreement with Kihlman and Eriksson, Rieger and Michaelis found that exchanges and isolocus breaks were similarly distributed, but in contrast to the former authors, their aberration data fitted the Poisson distribution.

D. Comparison with the Cytological Effects of X Rays: A Summary

When in the 1940's it was found that mutations and structural chromosome changes can be induced by chemical agents, it seemed natural to compare these effects of chemicals with the similar effects of ionizing radiation, which had been known for more than two decades. The chemical mutagens which were first discovered and studied in more detail were the sulphur and nitrogen mustards. Several striking differences soon appeared between the type of effects produced by these and other alkylating agents on the one hand, and X rays on the other.

Thus, as described above, the alkylating agents have only a delayed effect, whereas X-radiation has a nondelayed effect as well. The delayed effect of the alkylating agents consists exclusively of chromatid aberrations, whereas X rays induce subchromatid exchanges in prophase, chromatid aberrations in middle or late interphase, and aberrations of the chromosome type in early interphase. The aberrations induced by chemical treatment tend to be localized in heterochromatin (Fig. 11-7;

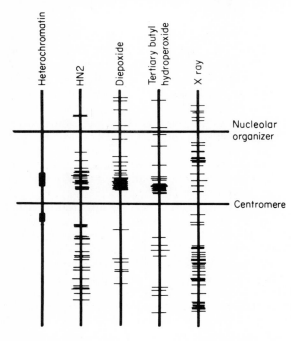

Fig. 11–7. The positions of two heterochromatic segments in the M chromosome of *Vicia faba* and the distribution of breaks induced by different agents. (Revell, 1953; Heredity 6 (Suppl.):112. Reprinted by permission of the Editor of Heredity.)

Revell, 1953), whereas X-ray-induced aberrations are more or less randomly distributed between and within the chromosomes. The distribution between nuclei may also be more nonrandom for chemically induced aberrations than for aberrations induced by X rays. To these differences may be added the fact that the effect of alkylating agents has been found to be independent of oxygen tension during treatment, whereas X-radiation is several times more effective in the presence than in the absence of oxygen. Also, other factors have been found to influence the effects of chemicals and radiation differently (see next chapter).

It was believed for some time that the cytological effect of the alkylating agents was typical for all chromosome-breaking chemicals, and thus that the same differences existed between X rays and all chromosome-breaking agents. That this was not so became clear when the chromosome-breaking effect of EOC was discovered and studied in detail. EOC has a nondelayed effect, and, like X rays, it induces subchromatid exchanges in prophase, chromatid aberrations in middle and late interphase, and aberrations of chromosome type in early interphase. Like the X-ray effect, that of EOC is dependent on oxygen tension. However, in contrast to the X-ray effect, the effect of EOC is nonrandomly distributed between and within chromosomes and between nuclei. When later more chromosome-breaking chemicals were discovered and studied, it was found that, although the majority had an effect of the same type as that produced by the alkylating agents, there were some which had an effect which in one or several respects was more similar to the effect of X-rays than to that of the alkylating agents. Typical for all chromosome-breaking chemicals appears to be, however, that the distribution of the aberrations they induce is more nonrandom than the distribution of X-ray-induced aberration. One possible reason for this could be a more nonrandom distribution within the tissue, cell, and nucleus of the chemical agent.

Physical and Chemical Factors Influencing the Production of Aberrations by Chemicals

A. The Influence of Oxygen and Oxidative Metabolism

Table 12-1 summarizes the influence of oxygen and oxidative metabolism on the effects of a number of chromosome-breaking chemicals. In the table the agents have also been classified according to the type of cytological effect they produce (whether delayed or nondelayed). It is evident that the chromosome-breaking effects of the various chemicals are very differently influenced by oxygen and oxidative metabolism. The effects of seven of the 17 chemicals listed in the table are not reduced by anaerobic conditions at the time of the treatment. These agents include three alkylating agents, i.e., HN2, DEPE, and BPL, the nitroso-compound NMU, which almost certainly also is an alkylating agent, the two antibiotics streptonigrin and mitomycin C, and the DNA-precursor adenine.

The fact that the effect of the alkylating agents is not reduced by anoxia is not surprising. Since they are small, neutral molecules, penetration should not be any problem and should occur without the aid of oxidative metabolism. They are all chemically very reactive agents, which produce chromosomal aberrations by alkylating a chromosomal constituent or precursor. Alkylation is a reaction which occurs independently of oxygen tension and oxidative metabolism.

Of the two antibiotics listed in this group, mitomycin C may also act as an alkylating agent after a reduction ". . . which 'unmasks' the potential activity of the fused aziridine ring" (Schwartz et al., 1963).

TABLE 12-1.

CLASSIFICATION OF CHROMOSOME-BREAKING CHEMICALS ACCORDING TO THE MODIFYING INFLUENCE OF OXYGEN AND OXIDATIVE METABOLISM ON THEIR EFFECTS AND ACCORDING TO THE CYTOLOGICAL EFFECT PRODUCED. (AFTER KIHLMAN, 1961b. ADVANCES GENET. 10:1–59, p. 41.) (FOR REFERENCES, SEE CHAPTER 10.)

Cytological Effect \ Influence of Oxygen and Oxidative Metabolism	Effect Inhibited by Anoxia			Effect Not Inhibited by Anoxia
	Effect Inhibited by Respiratory Inhibitors *		Effect Not Inhibited by Respiratory Inhibitors *	
	Effect Inhibited by Uncoupling Agents **	Effect Not Inhibited by Uncoupling Agents **		
Both Nondelayed and Delayed Effects — Nondelayed Effect of Fragment Type	5-Fluorodeoxy-uridine, Deoxyadenosine			
Nondelayed Effect of Exchange Type		8-Ethoxycaffeine, 1,3,7,9-Tetra-methyluric acid		Streptonigrin
Delayed Effects Only, Which Consist of Chromatid Aberrations of Exchange Type	Maleic hydrazide, Azaserine	N-Methylphenyl-nitrosamine, 1-Methyl-3-nitro-1-nitrosoguanidine	Acridine orange-visible light, Potassium cyanide	Nitrogen mustard, Di (2,3-epoxypropyl) ether, N-Nitroso-N-methyl-urethan, β-Propiolactone, Mitomycin C, Adenine

* e.g. cyanide, carbon monoxide, azide
** 2,4-dinitrophenol

159

The reduction would be expected to be favored by anoxia. An enhancement of the mitomycin C-effect by anoxia was not observed, however. On the other hand, both the effect of adenine and the effect of streptonigrin were markedly enhanced by anaerobic conditions. The mechanisms by which these two agents produce chromosomal aberrations is not known. Both are known as inhibitors of DNA-synthesis, but it is doubtful whether this is the explanation for their chromosome-breaking effect. For streptonigrin, a degradation of chromosomal DNA is a more likely explanation, and the chromosome-breaking effect of adenine may be connected with its chelating properties.

The effect of the other agents in the table is enhanced by oxygen. In most cases the agents are entirely inactive in the absence of oxygen, but maleic hydrazide is an exception. Although it is more effective in the presence of oxygen, MH also has a considerable effect under anaerobic conditions (Fig. 12-1).

Fig. 12–1. The influence of oxygen concentration on the frequencies of isolocus breaks and exchanges produced in *Vicia faba* by potassium cyanide (KCN), methylphenylnitrosamine (MPNA), 8-ethoxycaffeine (EOC) and maleic hydrazide (MH). (After Kihlman, 1961b; Advances Genet. 10:1–59, p. 33.)

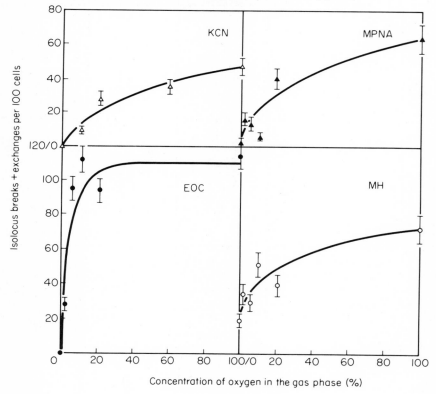

The slopes of the curves relating oxygen concentration and aberration yield are not always the same; for EOC the maximum effect is obtained at an oxygen concentration as low as 10 per cent in the gas phase, whereas for KCN, MPNA, and AO-VL, the effect increases with increasing oxygen concentration up to 100 per cent oxygen.

When the chromosome-breaking effect is reduced by anoxia, it is usually also reduced by respiratory inhibitors, which shows that the "oxygen effect" in the production of chromosomal aberrations by chemicals, in contrast to the oxygen effect known from experiments with X-rays, as a rule, operates over the respiratory chain. However, in two cases, potassium cyanide and the AO-VL system, the effect is not inhibited by respiratory inhibitors. It seems likely that oxygen influences the chromosome-breaking effect of the AO-VL system by reacting with free radicals which the system has produced in the cell. As an explanation for the oxygen dependence of the potassium cyanide effect, it has been suggested that the cyanide effect is mediated by peroxides, which are believed to accumulate in the cell as a result of the action of cyanide on cytochrome oxidase and peroxide-destroying enzymes.

An inhibition of the chromosome-breaking effect by respiratory inhibitors and by anoxia indicates either that oxidative phosphorylation is involved or that the chemical in question has to undergo an oxidative degradation in order to become active. When oxidative phosphorylation is involved, the effect should be inhibited by agents such as DNP which uncouple phosphorylation from respiration. Treatments with DNP do not influence the production of chromosomal aberrations by MPNA and MNNG. As will appear in the next chapter, the active species produced from these agents by an oxidative process is probably a carbonium ion, i.e., the same type of species which is involved in the production of aberrations by alkylating agents. Thus, MPNA and MNNG may be regarded as alkylating agents.

The effects of the remaining six compounds in Table 12-1 are all reduced, if not completely suppressed, by treatments with DNP. The reason why oxidative phosphorylation is required for the chromosome-breaking effect of FUdR and AdR is not difficult to understand, since these two agents are active only in phosphorylated form. The phosphorylation of FUdR and AdR to the active species F-dUMP and dATP, respectively, is catalyzed by kinase enzymes in the presence of ATP, and ATP is the product of oxidative phosphorylation.

Less clear is the role of oxidative phosphorylation in the effects of the remaining four agents. For azaserine and maleic hydrazide, which both have acid properties and are ionized at neutral pH, it could be the absorption of the agents which requires respiration energy (compare sec. B of this chapter and Chap. 1). This could not be the explanation for EOC (and TMU), since Fredga and Nyman (1961) have shown that tritium-labeled EOC is absorbed as rapidly under anaerobic as under aerobic conditions. The possibility that ATP is required for the transport of EOC into the nucleus cannot be excluded, however.

It is evident that oxidative phosphorylation may influence the production of chromosomal aberrations by chemicals in many different ways, the possibilities being by no means restricted to those suggested here. And it is not only the production of chromosomal aberrations which may be influenced by oxidative phosphorylation. As shown by Wolff and Luippold (1955), the repair of chromosomal damage is also dependent on oxidative metabolism, at least when X rays are the chromosome-breaking agent.

It has been known since the fundamental studies by Sax (1939, 1940, 1941) that the frequency of exchanges produced by a given dose of X rays is dependent on dose rate. When the duration of the period of irradiation is prolonged beyond a certain limit, the frequency of exchanges decreases. A similar decrease of the X-ray-induced exchanges can be obtained by giving the dose in two or several fractions separated from each other by a certain minimum time.

These dose-rate and fractionation effects are explained in the following way on the basis of the breakage-first hypothesis.

Exchanges can be formed between breaks that are close enough in time and space. Breaks remain open only for a relatively short time. At high dose-rates, all the breaks produced are open at the same time and are able to interact under exchange formation. At low dose-rates, breaks produced at the beginning of the irradiation period have had time to rejoin before irradiation is finished and are, consequently, unable to take part in exchanges with breaks produced towards the end of the irradiation period. Therefore, a higher frequency of exchanges is obtained at high dose-rates than at low dose-rates. Similarly, the decrease obtained by dose-fractionation is explained as being the result of the rejoining of breaks produced by the first fraction of the dose before the second fraction is given.

In the experiments of Wolff and Luippold referred to above, seeds of the broad bean, *Vicia faba,* were soaked for 18 to 24 hours and irradiated with X rays, the dose being given in two fractions. The time separating the two fractions, 75 minutes, was chosen in such a way that no interaction occurred between breaks produced by different fractions. The effect was studied in the first root-tip mitosis. The aberrations produced under these conditions were all of the chromosome type.

Wolff and Luippold found that when the soaked seeds were treated between the two dose fractions with respiratory inhibitors such as carbon monoxide (CO) in the dark and cyanide, or with the uncoupling agent DNP, the fractionation effect disappeared; i.e., the frequency of exchanges produced was as high as if the dose had been given in one fraction, indicating complete interaction of breaks produced by the two fractions. According to Wolff and Luippold, these results show that rejoining is a metabolic process which requires respiration energy. This interpretation was supported by the fact that the time necessary for rejoining of breaks was found to be shortened by the application of exogenous ATP. The requirement of ATP for rejoining indicates that the chemical bonds formed when breaks rejoin are strong covalent bonds (Wolff and Luippold, 1955).

It seems very likely that oxidative phosphorylation is involved in the repair of chromosomal damage produced by other chromosome-breaking agents as well, although, so far, it has been possible to demonstrate this for X-ray-induced aberrations only.

The finding of Allfrey et al. (1955b) that ATP may be formed inside the cell nucleus by an oxidative process has been described in a previous chapter. It would seem reasonable to assume that it is this intranuclear ATP-formation which is involved in the production and repair of chromosomal damage. It should be kept in mind, however, that the intranuclear system for an oxidative ATP-generation has been demonstrated only for mammalian cells, whereas plant cells have been the only material used in the studies on the relationship between oxidative phosphorylation and the production and repair of chromosomal aberrations. The fact that rejoining was inhibited by CO may argue against intranuclear ATP-formation as the oxidative phosphorylation process involved in the repair of chromosome damage. In contrast to the oxidative phosphorylation in mitochondria, nuclear phosphorylation is characterized by not being inhibited by carbon monoxide (McEwen et al., 1963a).

B. Temperature and Hydrogen Ion Concentration (pH)

As appears in Table 12-2, the chromosome-breaking agents may be divided into three groups on the basis of how their effects are influenced

TABLE 12–2.

CLASSIFICATION OF SOME CHROMOSOME-BREAKING AGENTS ON THE BASIS OF THE INFLUENCE OF TREATMENT TEMPERATURE ON THE EFFECT. (FOR REFERENCES, SEE CHAPTER 10.)

Effect not influenced by temperature	Effect increasing with increasing temperature	Effect first increasing then decreasing with temperature
Potassium cyanide Methylphenylnitros- amine Mitomycin C Streptonigrin	β-Propiolactone Diepoxypropylether Nitrosomethylurethan Maleic hydrazide Cupferron	Ethoxycaffeine Methylnitronitroso- guanidine

by the temperature during treatment. The effect of alkylating agents, maleic hydrazide, and cupferron increases with increasing temperature. The enhancement of the effect by temperature may be very marked. Thus, about seven times more aberrations are produced by the alkylating agent DEPE at 25°C than at 12°C, and maleic hydrazide is five times more effective at 25°C than at 3°C. Since both the absorption of the chemical and its possible reactions inside the cell would be facilitated by a rise of temperature, the observation that the effect increases with increasing temperature is not surprising. It is more difficult to explain that no effect of temperature was found in the experiments with KCN, MPNA, mitomycin C, and streptonigrin. Of these compounds, at least KCN, MPNA, and mitomycin C have in common that the chromosomal aberrations are produced by products of enzymatic reactions, rather than by the compounds themselves. But since we would also expect enzymatic reactions to be facilitated by a rise of temperature, the lack of a temperature effect in these cases remains obscure.

The influence of temperature on the effect of EOC and MNNG is particularly complex. MNNG was found to be more effective at 24°C than at 18°C or 30°C (Gichner et al., 1963). As shown by Fig. 12-2,

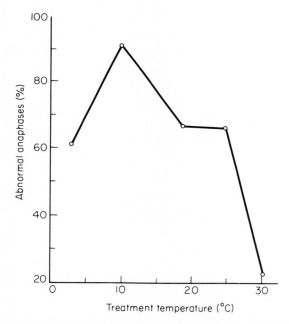

Fig. 12–2. The effect of treatment temperature on the frequencies of abnormal anaphases produced by 8-ethoxycaffeine in *Allium cepa*. (After Kihlman, 1951; Symb. Bot. Upsalienses 11 No. 2:1–39, p. 20.)

the frequency of EOC-induced aberrations increases with increasing temperature between 0 and 12°C. A further increase of temperature results in a decreased frequency of aberrations (Kihlman, 1951). It is possible that the relationship between temperature and effectiveness of EOC is a reflection of a similar relationship between temperature and intracellular (nuclear) ATP level. The effect of EOC is dependent on oxidative phosphorylation, and it is conceivable that the utilization of ATP is reduced more when the temperature is lowered from 25 to 12°C than is the formation of ATP, with a higher ATP level at 12°C as a result.

The effects of some chromosome-breaking agents have been found to be strongly influenced by the pH of the treatment solution. Two such chemicals are maleic hydrazide and cupferron. In both cases the effect is enhanced by low pH. The chromosome-breaking effect of MH was found to be four times stronger at pH 4.7 than at pH 7.3 (Kihlman, 1956) (Fig. 12-3), and the effect of cupferron three times stronger at pH 6.3

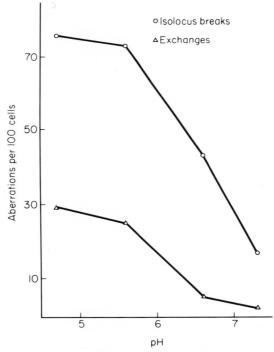

Fig. 12–3. The influence of the pH of the treatment solution on the frequencies of isolocus breaks and exchanges produced by maleic hydrazide in *Vicia faba*. (Kihlman, 1956. Reprinted by permission of the Rockefeller Institute Press from J. Biophys. Biochem. Cytol., September 25, 1956, Vol. 2, No. 5, pp. 543–555.)

than at pH 7.4 (Kihlman, 1959*b*). Maleic hydrazide is a weak acid, and cupferron is the ammonium salt of the acid N-nitrosophenylhydroxylamine. At low pH, a larger proportion of these acids would exist as undissociated molecules in aqueous solution. It is known that undissociated molecules penetrate the plasma membrane more easily than dissociated ones (compare Chap. 1), and it is, therefore, possible that

MH and cupferron are more effective at low pH because they enter the root-tip cells more easily under such conditions. Since, for cupferron, the active species may be a decomposition product, rather than the nitrosamine itself, the stronger effect at low pH could also be due to the fact that the decomposition of cupferron is facilitated by low pH. That the pH-dependence of the chromosome-breaking effect of cupferron has a connection with the acid properties of the nitrosophenylhydroxylamine molecule is indicated by the fact that the production of chromosomal aberrations by MPNA is not at all influenced by pH (Table 12-3). MPNA is closely related to cupferron, but is, in contrast to the latter, a neutral compound. In the AO-VL system the activity of cupferron

TABLE 12–3.

THE INFLUENCE OF THE pH OF THE TREATMENT SOLU-
TION ON THE FREQUENCIES OF CHROMATID ABERRATIONS
PRODUCED BY N-METHYLPHENYLNITROSAMINE AND CUP-
FERRON IN *Vicia faba*. (AFTER KIHLMAN, 1961d; RADIAT.
BOT. 1:43–50, P. 47.)

Nitrosamine	pH	Abnormal Metaphases (per cent)	Isolocus Breaks + Exchanges Per 100 Cells
MPNA	5.8	37	60
	7.4	43	60
Cupferron	6.3	25	36
	7.4	10	13

is influenced by pH in the same way as is the chromosome-breaking effect of cupferron alone. The activities in the AO-VL system of the closely related but neutral compounds MPNA and diphenylnitrosamine are unaffected by pH.

C. Comparison with the Effects of Modifying Factors on the Production of Chromosomal Aberrations by X rays

Although the effects of such a large and important group of chromosome-breaking chemicals as the alkylating agents are not markedly affected by variations in the oxygen tension, it is evident in Table 12-1 that independence of the oxygen tension is no more a characteristic of the production of chromosomal aberrations by chemicals than is dependence of oxygen a characteristic of the production of aberrations by radiations. Chemicals which have oxygen-dependent effects are EOC, AdR, MPNA, azaserine, and KCN, to mention only a few, whereas ultraviolet light and α-radiation are examples of radiations which have oxygen independent effects. It is also evident in Table 12-1 that there are many different kinds of oxygen effects involved in the production of aberrations by chemicals. In some cases (e.g., EOC, AdR, azaserine) oxidative phosphorylation seems to be required, and in other cases only respiration is required. Finally, there are cases (AO-VL, KCN) where neither phosphorylation nor respiration appear to be involved.

Among the radiations, oxygen dependence is a characteristic particularly of X rays (and γ-rays). A qualitatively and quantitatively similar enhancement of the X-ray effect is obtained with nitric oxide. Oxidative phosphorylation does not seem to be involved in the enhancement of the X-ray effect by oxygen.

It should be pointed out, however, that in organized tissues the relationship between oxygen concentration and yield of X-ray-induced aberrations is dependent on respiration. If roots are irradiated with a constant dose at various concentrations of oxygen, the effect at 5 per cent oxygen in the gas is about the same as that obtained in the absence of oxygen. A marked increase in the frequency of aberrations is obtained when the oxygen concentration is raised from 5 to 21 per cent, and at 50 per cent oxygen in the gas, the maximum effect has been reached; i.e., a further increase of oxygen concentration does not influence the effect (Kihlman, 1959c).

The number of aberrations produced at 50 per cent oxygen may be about seven times higher than that produced by the same dose in the absence of oxygen. The dose required to produce a given effect in the absence of oxygen is three to five times higher than the dose required to produce the same effect in the presence of 50 per cent oxygen.

If, in similar experiments, the roots are irradiated in the presence of a respiratory inhibitor (carbon monoxide, cupferron), an increase of the X-ray effect is obtained at oxygen concentrations as low as 0.1 per cent, and the maximum effect is obtained when the oxygen concentration in the gas phase has reached 2 per cent (Kihlman, 1959c, 1961e). When suspensions of single cells are irradiated, a relationship is obtained between X-ray effect and oxygen concentration which is similar to that observed in bean roots in the presence of a respiratory inhibitor (Howard-Flanders and Alper, 1957; Deschner and Gray, 1959). It has further been shown that when chromosomal aberrations are produced in microspores by irradiating inflorescences, the curve relating aberration-yield and oxygen concentration is similar to that obtained when *Vicia* roots are irradiated in the absence of respiratory inhibitors (Giles and Beatty, 1950). If, on the other hand, the microspores are irradiated outside the anther, as a monolayer of cells on agar, then the relationship between oxygen concentration and aberration-yield is similar to that obtained when suspension of single cells or root tips exposed to respiratory inhibitors are irradiated (Evans and Neary, 1959).

The interpretation of these results is that when the experimental material consists of organized tissues, such as root tips or anthers, the available oxygen is to a large extent consumed in the outermost cell layers as a result of their respiratory activity. In order to get oxygen into the central parts of such tissues, it will be necessary to use relatively high oxygen concentrations or to inhibit respiration.

The ability of oxygen and nitric oxide to increase the sensitivity to X-rays is believed to be due to the affinity of these gases for organic radicals produced by the radiation in the tissue (Howard-Flanders, 1957). Oxygen and nitric oxide owe their radical properties and affinity for carbon radicals to the fact that they possess unpaired electrons in the π molecular orbital. According to this hypothesis, the carbon radicals (which would be the result of the primary change induced by the radiation in the molecules of the target) have a very short lifetime, so that the original configuration of a radiation-affected molecule, as a rule, is restored within a fraction of a second. A prerequisite for permanent damage to arise is the reaction with another radical. The latter may be radiation-induced, such as an OH-radical produced in water, or it may be stable, such as oxygen and nitric oxide.

As we have seen, the effects of chemical agents are usually markedly influenced by temperature, and the rule is that the higher the temperature, the stronger the effect. Since the primary effects of radiation are independent of temperature, the number of damaged sites (breaks?) primarily producd by a given dose would be expected to be independent of temperature. Nevertheless, it was found that the yields of various kinds of chromosomal aberrations induced in *Tradescantia* microspores increased markedly with decreasing temperature, being at 3°C roughly four times higher than at 36°C (Sax and Enzmann, 1939; Catcheside et al., 1946). The first interpretation of these results was that the effect of temperature was on the recovery process, such that restitution is favored at high temperature and reunion is favored at low temperature. When the oxygen effect was discovered, the possibility was considered that the temperature effect was a result of the fact that oxygen is more soluble in water at low temperatures than at high temperatures. It was soon found, however, that the increased aberration-yield at low temperatures could not solely be accounted for by the increased solubility of oxygen (Giles et al., 1951). Deschner and Gray (1959) have suggested another explanation which is based on the fact that there exists an oxygen gradient within organized tissues as a result of the respiratory activity of the outermost cell layers. When the temperature is lowered, the consumption of oxygen through respiration is also reduced and more oxygen is able to diffuse into the central parts of the tissue, with a higher X-ray sensitivity as a result.

The possible reasons for the modifying effects of hydrogen ion concentration on the frequencies of aberrations produced by some chromosome-breaking chemicals were discussed in sec. B of this chapter. It was concluded that the process primarily affected by pH probably was the passage of the chemical through the cell membrane. Since permeability is not a limiting factor for the penetration of radiations, an effect of pH on the chromosome-breaking effects of radiations is not to be expected.

Chemical, Physicochemical,
and Biochemical Properties
of Chromosome-Breaking Agents
Likely to Be Responsible for
Their Cytological Effect

A. Inhibition of the Synthesis of DNA
and DNA Precursors

Of the chromosome-breaking agents discussed in the previous chapters, several have been found to suppress nucleic acid synthesis. The question is whether any relationship can be found between the inhibitory effect on nucleic acid synthesis of these agents and their effect on chromosome structure.

The search for such a relationship is more likely to be successful if the various inhibitors are divided into different categories according to the level on which nucleic acid synthesis is affected and the mechanism by which the inhibition is produced. It may also be easier to find a relationship if a distinction is made between different types of chromosome damage.

In Table 13-1 such a classification of the biochemical and cytological effects has been attempted for eight inhibitors of nucleic acid synthesis. The table is constructed on the basis of results obtained in root tips of the broad bean, *Vicia faba*. The incorporation of P^{32}-labeled phosphate into the DNA and RNA fractions of excised root tips was used as an indicator of nucleic acid synthesis.

TABLE 13–1.

BIOCHEMICAL AND CYTOLOGICAL EFFECTS OF 8 INHIBITORS OF DNA-SYNTHESIS.

Compound	Inhibition of Nucleic Acid Synthesis		Level At Which DNA-Synthesis Is Likely to Be Inhibited	Effects on Chromosomes — Hours After the Beginning of Treatment								
				0–8 (nondelayed)					8–48 (delayed)			
	RNA	DNA		None	Stickiness	Sub.ex.	Ch'd.ex.	Fragm.	None	Ch'd.ex.	Ch'e.ex.	Fragm.
Adenine	x	x	Purine biosynthesis	x						x		
Azaserine	x	x	"	x						x		
AdR	x	x	Deoxyribonucleotide synthesis							x		x
FUdR	x	x	"					x		x		x
EOC	x	x	DNA-polymerase reaction		x	x	x			x	x	
Actinomycin D	x	x	"		x	x			x			
Ethidium bromide	x	x	"		x				x			
Streptonigrin	x	x	"		x	x	x			x	x	

Sub.ex. - subchromatid exchanges, Ch'd ex. - chromatid exchanges,
Ch'e ex. - chromosome exchanges, Fragm. - Fragmentation.

Adenine and azaserine both inhibit early steps of nucleic acid synthesis, the most sensitive reaction probably being the formation of glycinamide ribonucleotide (adenine) and the amination of formylglycinamide ribonucleotide (azaserine). Since they act at the level of purine biosynthesis, not only DNA synthesis, but also the synthesis of RNA and purine-containing coenzymes is inhibited by adenine and azaserine.

The chromosome-breaking effects of adenine and azaserine are also rather similar. Thus, both agents have only a delayed effect which is of the exchange type.

The reaction steps inhibited by FUdR and AdR are situated between the products of purine and pyrimidine biosynthesis, i.e., inosinic and uridylic acid, and the deoxyriboside triphosphates which are the immediate precursors of DNA (compare Chaps. 4 and 10). Since DNA synthesis is inhibited by FUdR and AdR at a level where the syntheses of RNA and DNA follow separate pathways, an effect on RNA synthesis of these agents is not to be expected, and, as appears in the table, was not found.

Just as was the case for adenine and azaserine, the similar type of biochemical action is parallelled by an almost identical cytological effect. Both FUdR and AdR have nondelayed effects characterized by breaks without rejoining (fragmentation, shattering) and delayed effects consisting of isochromatid breaks with sister-union and chromatid exchanges.

The third type of inhibitors of nucleic acid synthesis is represented by agents, the inhibitory action of which is likely to be the result of complex formation between the inhibitor and primer DNA (e.g., Elliott, 1963; Reich, 1964; Waring, 1964), which may or may not involve an alteration of the physical state of DNA. Since DNA functions as a primer both in the DNA and RNA polymerase reactions, it is not surprising that the interaction between DNA and inhibitor was found to result in an inhibition of both DNA and RNA synthesis. The fact that the two polymerase reactions were not inhibited to the same extent (both ethidium bromide and actinomycin D are much more effective as inhibitors of RNA synthesis than of DNA synthesis) may be a result of different forms of DNA or different parts of the DNA molecule functioning as primers in the two cases.

The cytological effect produced by this type of inhibitor of DNA synthesis is less uniform than those observed after treatments with the other two types, but appears to be characterized by the ability to affect chromosomes in division stages. Actinomycin D, streptonigrin, and EOC produce subchromatid exchanges in prophase. A strong stickiness effect is observed after treatments of metaphase cells with EOC and ethidium bromide. In contrast to ethidium bromide and actinomycin D, EOC and streptonigrin are also able to affect chromosomes in interphase, the resulting changes being aberrations of chromatid and chromosome type.

Thus, there is some indication that, of the agents included in Table 13-1, those which act by a similar biochemical or physicochemical mechanism also have a similar type of cytological effect. However, if the chromosome damage in all eight cases was the result of an inhibited DNA synthesis, it seems rather odd that the cytological effect should be so different for different types of inhibitors. At least, the stickiness effect and the subchromatid exchanges produced by the third type of inhibitors can hardly be a result of an inhibited DNA synthesis, since the synthesis of DNA should have been finished before prophase. It seems more likely that the chromosomal changes and the inhibition of DNA synthesis are two different consequences of the changes produced in DNA by the agents. These changes could be an altered physical state of DNA and/or an altered ability of DNA to attract and form complexes with nucleic acids, and possibly with proteins and lipids.

The type of cytological effect produced by adenine and azaserine is the one most usually observed after treatments with chromosome-breaking agents. Thus, this type of effect is found after treatments with the various types of alkylating agents, such as mustards, epoxides, ethylenimines, sulfonic esters, alkylsulfates, and certain N-alkyl-N-nitroso compounds. It is also found after treatments with heavy metal-complexing agents, such as cupferron, cyanide, hydroxyquinoline, $\alpha.\alpha'$-dipyridyl, and diethyldithiocarbamate. Other chromosome-breaking agents which have only delayed effects consisting of chromatid aberrations of the exchange type are maleic hydrazide, mitomycin C, and nitric oxide, and with these agents, the list is still far from complete. Although most of these agents are known to produce changes in DNA and in DNA precursors, their ability to suppress DNA synthesis appears to be highly variable. In many cases no inhibition of DNA synthesis has been observed. On the other hand, there are inhibitors of purine nucleotide biosynthesis, such as cordycepin (Overgaard-Hansen, 1964; Rottman and Guarino, 1964) and hadacidin (Shigeura and Gordon, 1962a, b) which have only a weak chromosome-breaking effect, if any.

It is apparent from these considerations that the delayed exchange-type effect is not typical for, or necessarily produced by, inhibitors of purine nucleotide biosynthesis. Although it is possible that the inhibitory action of adenine and azaserine on nucleic acid synthesis may be responsible for their cytological effect, other mechanisms of action should also be considered for these agents. The possibility that azaserine acts as an alkylating agent has been suggested (Freese, 1963), and adenine is a rather effective chelator of certain bivalent metal ions, such as Cu, Ni, and Co (Albert, 1953; Harkins and Freiser, 1958; Frieden and Alles, 1958). The idea that it is the chelating properties of adenine, rather than its inhibitory effect on purine biosynthesis, which is responsible for its cytological effect is supported by the fact that adenosine is inactive both as a chelating and as a chromosome-breaking agent (Harkins and Freiser, 1958; Kihlman, 1950), but inhibits purine biosynthesis almost as effectively as does adenine (Henderson, 1962).

There remains now to discuss whether the cytological effect of FUdR and AdR is a consequence of or related to their inhibitory effect on DNA synthesis.

Since FUdR and AdR inhibit DNA synthesis because they suppress the formation of the substrates of the DNA polymerase reaction, i.e., the formation of deoxyribonucleoside triphosphates, the first task is to find out whether there is any connection between their inhibitory effect on deoxyribonucleotide synthesis and their chromosome-breaking effect.

In *in vitro* experiments, FUdR in the presence of ATP produces a 95 per cent inhibition of the thymidylate synthetase reaction at a concentration of 10^{-7}M (Hartmann and Heidelberger, 1961). A thymineless state is produced in *in vivo* experiments by even lower concentrations of FUdR.

In mammalian cells the inhibition of DNA synthesis is followed by an inhibition of nuclear RNA synthesis. Apparently, the latter is a feed-back inhibition caused by UdR or dUMP, which accumulate in the cell nucleus as a result of the FUdR inhibition of the tymidylate synthetase reaction (Studzinski and Love, 1963). Other physiological processes do not seem to be affected the first hours after treatment with low concentrations of FUdR. After prolonged treatments, synthesis of cytoplasmic RNA and, eventually, protein synthesis are also inhibited. When the concentration of FUdR is increased, its action becomes less specific. The considerable incorporation of 5-fluorouracil into RNA, which occurs at these concentrations, would be expected to have physiological consequences.

In excised *Vicia faba* root tips, the incorporation of P^{32} into the RNA fraction was not affected by a three hour treatment with 10^{-5}M FUdR. The same treatment reduced the incorporation of P^{32} into the DNA fraction by 80 per cent (Odmark and Kihlman, unpublished).

Chromosomal aberrations are produced in *Vicia faba* by FUdR at concentrations above 10^{-8}M. Since at this concentration level the only known immediate biochemical effect of FUdR is the inhibition of thymidylate synthetase, it seems reasonable to assume that the chromosomal damage is the result of the FUdR-induced thymidylic acid deficiency. This conclusion is supported by several findings.

In *Vicia* chromosome damage can be prevented or cured by post-treatments with thymidine or thymidine analogues, such as CUdR, BUdR, and IUdR. This is the result expected if the aberrations were caused by thymidine deficiency. It should be pointed out, however, that in *Vicia* the concentrations required to produce this reversal of FUdR-induced chromosome breakage are about 100 times higher than those required for reversal of the FUdR-inhibition of DNA synthesis (Bell and Wolff, 1964; Odmark and Kihlman, unpublished), and that attempts to reverse FUdR-induced chromosome breakage in mammalian cells with thymidine were unsuccessful (Hsu et al., 1964).

More convincing evidence is the finding that the cytological effects produced by agents known to inhibit DNA synthesis at the deoxyribonucleotide level are almost identical, independently of whether the inhibitors are structurally related or not.

In previous chapters it has been pointed out that the chromosomal damage produced by FUdR and AdR in late interphase cells of *Vicia faba* is of a very characteristic type, which is not often found in experiments with chromosome-breaking agents. The aberrations consist mainly of gaps and open breaks, exchange-type aberrations being extremely rare. It seems quite clear that the extreme fragmentation observed after treatments with FUdR and AdR in both plant and mammalian cells involves true breaks and not only large gaps caused by localized despiralization, as suggested by Bell and Wolff (1964).

This same type of effect is produced in mammalian cells by cytosine arabinoside (Kihlman et al., 1963) and in *Vicia* by aminopterin (Taylor, 1963*b*). Cytosine arabinoside, like AdR, inhibits, after phosphorylation, the cytidine diphosphate reductase reaction (compare Chaps. 4 and 10). Aminopterin inhibits the reduction of folic acid to tetrahydrofolic acid (THFA), and since a formyl derivative of THFA is required in the thymidylate synthetase reaction, aminopterin, like FUdR, blocks the synthesis of thymidylic acid, although by a different mechanism.

The fact that an identical cytological effect of a very unusual type is produced by two compounds as structurally unrelated as FUdR and aminopterin, which chemically have in common only the ability to inhibit the synthesis of thymidylic acid, suggests that this ability is responsible for the cytological effect of these compounds.

The hypothesis that the ability of FUdR and AdR to produce chromosomal aberrations is a result of their inhibitory effect on deoxyribonucleotide synthesis is further supported by the findings that the chromosome-breaking effect of these agents is suppressed by inhibitors of oxidative phosphorylation (Kihlman, 1962, 1963*b*), since FUdR has to be phosphorylated to F-dUMP in order to inhibit the thymidylate synthetase reaction and AdR acts as an inhibitor of the CDP-reductase reaction only after phosphorylation to dATP.

The fact that CUdR, BUdR, and IUdR in concentrations up to 1000 times higher than those effective in FUdR experiments do not produce chromosome fragmentation in *Vicia* also supports the hypothesis, since, in contrast to FUdR, these halogenated deoxyuridines do not inhibit the thymidylate synthetase reaction (Hartmann and Heidelberger, 1961).

There is, however, at least one fact which does not seem to agree with the hypothesis, and that is that adenine and azaserine produce a cytological effect which is of an entirely different type. And yet purine deoxyribonucleotide deficiency, as well as purine ribonucleotide deficiency, would be expected to be the result of the action of these two agents, which inhibit DNA synthesis at the level of purine biosynthesis. There is no definite answer to the question of why adenine and azaserine do not produce an effect of the FUdR type. A rather unlikely explanation would be that purine deoxyribonucleotide deficiency does not produce this effect, although it is obtained as a result of pyrimidine deoxyribonucleotide deficiency. Another possibility is that purine and pyrimidine biosynthesis is completed before G_2, i.e., the stage when the FUdR type of effect apparently is produced. At this stage of interphase, the only reaction steps of DNA synthesis still occurring would then be those between uridylic acid and inosinic acid on the one hand, and DNA on the other. Cells in S would be arrested until all DNA-precursors become available. When this happens, they complete their DNA synthesis and arrive at metaphase with undamaged chromosomes.

In order to be able to test this hypothesis, a more detailed knowledge of the localization in time and space of the various steps of DNA synthesis would be needed. However, the explanation does not seem to be a very likely one, because uridylic acid and inosinic acid are required not only for the synthesis of DNA, but also for the synthesis of RNA, and RNA synthesis apparently occurs at such a high rate during the G_2 stage of interphase (e.g., Taylor, 1960a; Woodard et al., 1961; Reiter and Littlefield, 1964) that purine and pyrimidine biosynthesis would have to occur in order to provide enough precursors. It is finally possible that the reason for the difference between the cytological effects of adenine and azaserine on the one hand and FUdR and AdR on the other may be sought in the fact that both deoxyribonucleotide and ribonucleotide synthesis is inhibited by the former compounds, whereas FUdR and AdR inhibit only the synthesis of deoxyribonucleotides.

However, although the reason for the different cytological effects of the two types of inhibitors of DNA synthesis at the present cannot be satisfactorily explained, the evidence in favor of the hypothesis that the chromosome-breaking effect of FUdR and AdR is a result of their inhibitory effect on the synthesis of deoxyribonucleotides, appears convincing.

The next question to be answered is whether the chromosomal aberrations and the inhibition of DNA synthesis are two independent effects of the same cause, i.e., inhibition of deoxyribonucleotide synthesis, or whether the aberrations are the result of the inhibited DNA synthesis.

Since it is rather difficult to imagine why the structural integrity of the chromosomes should be dependent on deoxyribonucleotide synthesis if DNA synthesis is not involved, the latter alternative appears to be the more likely one. Nevertheless, it has recently been seriously criticized by Bell and Wolff (1964). According to these authors, DNA synthesis cannot be involved, since the FUdR effect occurs in G_2 cells and under conditions that do not inhibit DNA synthesis.

Previously, Kihlman (1962) had pointed out that the chromosome fragmentation produced by FUdR could be observed in metaphase and anaphase so soon after the beginning of the treatment that either the affected cells must have been at a stage closer to prophase than S when exposed to FUdR, or else the estimation of the duration of G_2 which had been obtained in radioautographic experiments must have been erroneous. In *Tradescantia* root tips, Davies and Wimber (quoted by Bell and Wolff, 1964) obtained chromosome shattering with FUdR within one hour after the beginning of the treatment, which indicated that cells in the last half of G_2 were sensitive to FUdR.

In the experiments of Bell and Wolff, lateral roots of *Vicia faba* were first treated with tritiated thymidine to label cells in S and then exposed to FUdR to produce breaks. The radioautographs showed that the cells containing aberrations were unlabeled and, therefore, must have been in G_2 rather than in S when exposed to FUdR.

In contrast to these findings, which indicate that FUdR produces chromosomal aberrations in G_2, Taylor (1963a) found that the time between the beginning of the FUdR treatment and the appearance of the first metaphases and anaphases with shattered chromosomes agreed well with the time it took the first labeled cells to reach metaphase and anaphase after treatments with H^3-thymidine. In agreement with the hypothesis that FUdR is active during the S period of interphase is also the finding by Hsu et al. (1964) that when hamster cells were exposed to FUdR in late S, the chromosomes known to replicate late were more affected than the others.

However, even if it should be true that FUdR acts mainly, or exclusively, during G_2, it does not necessarily mean that DNA synthesis is not involved. After all, the radioautographic method is not a very sensitive one. It can easily be calculated that the number of thymidine molecules which have to be incorporated if the cell shall be classified as labeled is of the order of several millions.

To illustrate the point, we may use some data of Evans and his collaborators. These workers classify a cell as labeled if it has a minimum of 12 silver grains in the emulsion overlying the chromosomes, which is something like ten times the background count (Evans, personal communication). To activate one silver grain, about 200 disintegrations from tritium are believed to be required (for references, see Evans and Savage, 1963). Since the half life of tritium is 12.26 years and the exposure time was about 21 days, 7.4×10^5 H^3 atoms are required to obtain an average of 12 grains in the emulsion overlying the metaphase plate. The thymidine used was labeled only in the 5-methyl group, and its specific activity was 4.7 C/mM, which means that 16 per cent of the thymidine molecules in the treatment solution were labeled (Evans and Savage, 1963). From this it follows that 4.5×10^6 thymine bases have to be incorporated into the chromosomes of the metaphase plate if the cell shall be scored as labeled in the experiments of Evans and his collaborators.

On the other hand, if the gaps in the chromatids represent single-strand breaks in a DNA double helix, as suggested by Taylor et al. (1962), it is conceivable that a gap is produced whenever a replicative unit is unable to complete its DNA synthesis, even if the unfinished piece may involve only one or a few nucleotides. It is further possible that DNA synthesis in G_2 is not only quantitatively, but also qualitatively, different from that in S. Evidence has been presented for the occurrence of two different DNA polymerases in the nuclei of mammalian cells (Krakow et al., 1962; Keir et al., 1963b), called replicative and terminal nucleotidyl transferase, respectively. Perhaps chromosome replication is completed by a limited DNA synthesis of the terminal type, too small to be detected by radioautographic methods, which would take place in G_2

after the bulk of DNA synthesis occurring during S has been finished. The terminal nucleotidyl transferase is much more resistant to the inhibitory effect of actinomycin D (Keir et al., 1963a), which would explain why this antibiotic does not produce an effect of the FUdR type, although replicative DNA synthesis is inhibited.

Thus, the fact that FUdR produces aberrations in G_2, i.e., after the main period of DNA synthesis, does not prove that DNA synthesis is not involved in the FUdR effect.

The other serious objection of Bell and Wolff was that the chromosome-breaking effect of FUdR is not counteracted by thymidine concentrations which completely reverse the inhibition of DNA synthesis. Bell and Wolff found that treatment of bean roots with equimolar concentrations of FUdR and TdR had no effect on H^3-TdR incorporation into DNA, but produced the same frequency of chromosomal aberrations as treatments with FUdR alone. Reversal of the chromosome-breaking effect of FUdR was not obtained until the TdR concentration was 100 times higher than that of FUdR.

The fact that relatively high concentrations of TdR or TdR analogues were required for complete reversal of the FUdR effect appeared already in the studies of Taylor et al. (1962) and Kihlman (1962). The observation of Bell and Wolff that the FUdR inhibition of DNA synthesis is reversed by equimolar concentrations of TdR or TdR analogues has been confirmed by Odmark (unpublished). In Odmark's experiments, which were performed with excised root tips of *Vicia faba* as experimental material, DNA synthesis was estimated by measuring the incorporation of P^{32} into the DNA fraction of the roots. As appears in Table 13-2 the FUdR-inhibition of P^{32} incorporation was completely reversed by an equimolar concentration of CUdR and by TdR at a concentration three times higher than that of FUdR. BUdR and IUdR were somewhat less effective. This is to be contrasted with the 1:100 relationship between inhibitor and metabolite which is required for reversal of the chromosome-breaking effect.

TABLE 13–2.

REVERSAL BY THYMIDINE OR THYMIDINE ANALOGUES OF THE FUdR-INHIBITION OF P^{32}-INCORPORATION IN THE DNA-FRACTION OF EXCISED *Vicia faba* ROOT-TIPS. RESULTS EXPRESSED IN PER CENT OF UNTREATED CONTROL.

Pyrimidine–deoxy-ribonucleoside present in addition to 10^{-5} M FUdR	Concentration, M			
	0	10^{-5}	3×10^{-5}	10^{-4}
TdR	23	75	111	90
CUdR	9	116	98	87
BUdR	13	53	57	77
IUdR	17	41	66	56

These experiments indicate that the FUdR-induced chromosomal aberrations are not a result of the FUdR inhibition of DNA synthesis during S, which is easily reversed by supplying the product of the inhibited reaction, and which can be studied by radioautographic methods. Other results pointing in the same direction have been reported by Hsu et al. (1964). They found that mouse L cells were more sensitive to inhibition of DNA synthesis by FUdR than were hamster cells, but more resistant to the chromosome-breaking effect of FUdR. The inhibition of DNA synthesis could be reversed by TdR, but not the chromosome-breaking effect.

It is, therefore, concluded that the chromosome-breaking effect of FUdR and AdR is not a result of their inhibitory effect on the bulk of DNA synthesis occurring during S. If DNA synthesis is involved at all, it is of a quantitatively and qualitatively different type which occurs during G_2. On the other hand, it seems quite clear that the chromosome-breaking effect of FUdR and AdR is connected with their ability to suppress deoxyribonucleotide synthesis. Therefore, if it is conceivable that deoxyribonucleotides are important for the structural integrity of the chromosomes in some other way than as components of DNA, then such an interpretation is compatible with the experimental evidence.[1]

B. Degradation and Denaturation of DNA

For the majority of the chromosome-breaking agents, treatments have to be performed during S or G_1 in order to be effective. That some compounds are active also in late interphase, subsequent to S, is evident from the discussions in the previous section of this chapter. As Table 13-1 shows, there are finally some chemicals which are able to induce subchromatid exchanges in prophase. In this respect the effect of these chemicals is similar to that of ionizing radiation. The chemicals referred to are EOC, streptonigrin, and actinomycin D.

It is evident that in these cases the cytological effect can hardly be a result of an effect on the synthesis of DNA, which should be completed before prophase begins. If DNA is involved at all, it must be as a complete molecule with its associated protein, and the effect would be the result of an alteration of the state and properties of this DNA-protein complex.

Is there, then, any evidence for such an effect on DNA of these chemicals?

Actinomycin D is known to react with DNA under complex formation. As a result of this reaction, the physical properties of DNA are altered (Reich, 1964). It has been suggested (Reich, 1964) that the inhibition of DNA polymerase by actinomycin D is an indirect one, caused by the changed physical properties of the DNA template.

Streptonigrin initiates a rapid breakdown *in vivo* of the DNA of *Escherichia coli* (Radding, 1963). According to Radding (1963), 35 per cent of H^3-labeled DNA is rendered acid-soluble in two hours by treatments with streptonigrin. Previously, a similar effect has been observed after treatments with mitomycin C (e.g., Kersten, 1962), the cytological effect of which is entirely different, however (compare Chap. 10).

EOC, caffeine, and other methylated oxypurines are known as efficient solubilizing agents (Weil-Malherbe, 1946; Neish, 1948; Booth and Boyland, 1953). The solubilizing power of the methylated oxypurines is correlated with their ability to form molecular complexes (Weil-Malherbe, 1946), and is probably caused by their electron-donor properties (Pullman and Pullman, 1958). A comparison between the ability to produce chromosomal aberrations, on the one hand, and the solubilizing power, on the other, has shown that a very good correlation exists between these properties of methylated oxypurines (Kihlman, 1952a).

Complex formation has also been observed between different methylated oxypurines, as well as between methylated oxypurines and other purine derivatives (Kihlman, unpublished observations; Ts'o et al., 1962), with solubilization of the less soluble partner as a result.

No data are available for the interaction between EOC and DNA, but the mother substance of EOC, caffeine, has been found to combine with DNA and to alter its physical properties (Ts'o et al., 1962; Ts'o and Lu, 1964). In the experiments of Ts'o et al., the melting (denaturation) temperature of DNA was lowered by caffeine.

Webb and Kubitschek (1963) have suggested that the ability of caffeine to increase the mutation frequency in *Escherichia coli* is connected with its ability to decrease the temperature for denaturation of DNA. The increased localized melting of strands in the presence of caffeine would increase mutation from natural sources.

Thus it is clear that all three agents are able to react with DNA and to alter its physical properties. Streptonigrin causes a degradation of DNA, EOC probably a denaturation, and actinomycin D inhibits strand separation. It may be relevant that an alteration of the physical properties of DNA also is obtained with ionizing radiation, which, like the three chemicals discussed, is able to produce subchromatid exchanges in prophase cells.

The ability of EOC, streptonigrin, and actinomycin D to alter the state and properties of DNA and to induce chromosomal aberrations appears to be a result of their physical properties, rather than of their chemical properties. This does not mean that they should all act independently of cell metabolism. EOC, for instance, is entirely inactive in the absence of oxidative phosphorylation.

It may be concluded that although it seems likely that the ability of EOC, streptonigrin, and actinomycin D to cause chromosomal aberrations at least partly is the result of their ability to combine with DNA and/or to alter its physical properties, very little is known about the mechanism by which the aberrations are produced. Among the many questions which remain to be answered are why oxidative phosphorylation is required for the EOC effect and whether main chain breakage in

DNA molecules always is involved in the production of aberrations by these agents, or if mere separation of DNA strands or DNA-protein complexes may result in aberration production.

C. Removal of DNA-Bound Metals

The idea that metals occur as parts of the chromosome structure was suggested by Mazia (1954). The results of his studies on the effect of EDTA on chromosome structure led him to propose a particulate organization of the chromosome, where the units are linked end to end by bridges of divalent cations. Mazia assumed that the metals were calcium or magnesium, or both, and this assumption was supported by the finding of Steffensen (1953, 1955) that the frequency of spontaneous chromosomal aberrations in *Tradescantia* was increased if the plant was cultivated on Ca- and Mg-deficient medium. The radioautographic studies of Steffensen and Bergeron (1959) demonstrated the presence of calcium in the pollen tube nuclei of *Lilium longiflorum*.

The occurrence of metals as stabilizing factors in chromosomes was also suggested by the findings of Kihlman and co-workers, who studied the ability of heavy metal-complexing agents to induce chromosomal aberrations and to enhance X-ray-induced chromosome breakage in the root tips of *Vicia faba* (Kihlman, 1957; Kihlman et al., 1957).

It appeared in these studies that the chelating agents sodium diethyldithicarbamate (DIECA), cupferron, and 8-hydroxyquinoline have a low but quite significant chromosome-breaking effect of the delayed type. $\alpha.\alpha'$-Dipyridyl did not produce any aberrations in these studies, but was subsequently found by Cohn (1961) to be active in *Vicia*. Chromosomal aberrations are also produced by nitric oxide (NO) (Kihlman, 1959d), which is known to combine with salts of heavy metals. The observations of Lilly and Thoday (1956) that potassium cyanide is an efficient chromosome-breaking agent in the presence of oxygen and enhances the frequency of X-ray-induced aberrations under near-anaerobic conditions, was confirmed in the study of Kihlman, Merz, and Swanson (1957). Of the other heavy metal-complexing agents studied by Kihlman et al., only cupferron proved to be able to enhance the X-ray effect.

It was concluded that both the chromosome-breaking effect and the enhancement of X-ray sensitivity was a result of the ability of the agents studied to form complexes with metals. Since under the conditions employed neither of the agents would be expected to react with calcium or magnesium, but all formed complexes with iron and copper, it seemed reasonable to assume that the metal involved was either iron or copper, or both. Iron was chosen as the most likely candidate, because, in contrast to copper, it was known to occur in cell nuclei.

It was suggested that iron had a similar function as calcium and magnesium according to the hypothesis of Mazia and Steffensen, i.e., that it formed chelate bonds with terminal phosphate groups of different DNA species (Kihlman, 1957). Another possibility considered was that iron, by forming complexes with the nucleic acid bases, influences electron transfer within the chromosomes in the same way as iron is believed to affect electron transfer between the different oxidation-reduction elements of the electron transfer system in mitochondria.

The hypothesis that chromosomal aberrations may arise as a result of removal of DNA-bound heavy metals from the chromosomes was rendered less attractive when the enhancement of X-ray sensitivity produced by KCN and cupferron proved to be a result of their inhibitory effect on respiration, particularly since other explanations of the chromosome-breaking effects of KCN and cupferron were possible.

Thus, it has been suggested that the chromosome aberrations observed after treatments with KCN are produced by peroxides, which are believed to accumulate in the cell as a result of the inhibitory action of cyanide on cytochrome oxidase and on enzymes which destroy peroxides (Lilly and Thoday, 1956). That properties of cupferron other than the ability to form complexes with heavy metals might be responsible for its chromosome-breaking effect was indicated by the finding that the closely related but nonchelating compound methylphenylnitrosamine (MPNA) was even more effective than cupferron as a chromosome-breaking agent (Kihlman, 1961d). However, since the cytological effect of MPNA, in contrast to that of cupferron, was dependent on respiration, it was doubtful whether these effects were produced by the same mechanism. MPNA was believed to be decomposed by oxidative metabolism to yield a peroxide or a free radical which would react with the chromosomes in a way similar to that suggested for alkylating agents (see also the next section of this chapter).

The reason why the heavy-metal hypothesis has not been completely abandoned is that so far no other satisfactory explanation has been found for the chromosome-breaking effects of DIECA, 8-hydroxyquinoline, $\alpha.\alpha'$-dipyridyl, and nitric oxide. As mentioned in Chap. 2, a considerable body of evidence has accumulated which indicates that iron and copper occur in cell nuclei and nucleoproteins. Trivalent iron appears to be chelated to an interior site in DNA, whereas copper probably is bound to the phosphate groups (Eisinger et al., 1961). There is reason to believe that metal ions are involved in the stabilization of the DNA double helix (Eichhorn and Clark, 1965). It is, therefore, still reasonable to assume that metal ions play a significant role in the chromosomes, both in connection with energy transfer and in the stabilization, combination and structural relationships of protein and nucleic acid in the deoxyribonucleoprotein, and that chromosomal aberrations may arise as a result of removal of these metals.

A chromosome-breaking agent which, in addition to those already mentioned, may possibly act by this mechanism is adenine, which is known to form complexes with copper (Harkins and Freiser, 1958; Frieden and Alles, 1958).

All agents discussed in this section have only delayed effects, which suggests that the effect is induced during or before S. The aberrations produced consist mainly of isolocus breaks and exchanges of the chromatid type.

D. The Production of Abnormal DNA by Alkylation and/or Incorporation of Abnormal Precursors

The majority of the known chromosome-breaking agents are believed to act by one or the other of these mechanisms. The cytological effects produced by these agents are only of the delayed type, and the aberrations are mainly isolocus breaks and exchanges of the chromatid type.

We may distinguish between two main types of agents acting by these mechanisms, viz., alkylating agents and base analogues. However, as pointed out by Lorkiewics and Szybalski (1961), the mechanisms by which aberrations are produced by these two types of agents may not be so very different, after all.

A base analogue, such as the thymidine analogue BUdR, must be incorporated into the chromosomal DNA in order to be effective (Somers and Hsu, 1962). Accordingly, BUdR treatments are effective only when the cell is exposed during the S period of interphase. Chromosomes containing DNA which has part of its thymidine replaced by BUdR are believed to be fragile and, consequently, more easily subject to breakage from natural sources.

The data presented by Lorkiewics and Szybalski indicated that the alkylating agent triethylenemelamine (TEM) reacts primarily with phosphorylated precursors of DNA, most probably thymidylate. By this reaction a thymine analogue is produced which, like BUdR, exerts its chromosome-breaking effect while being incorporated into newly synthesized DNA.

Although supported by the observation that breakage by alkylating agents occurs during S (Scott and Evans, 1964), this interpretation of the mechanism of action of alkylating agents is not generally accepted. Most authors seem to favor the view that mutations and chromosomal aberrations are produced by an alkylation of DNA, rather than of DNA precursors. There appears to be a general agreement that DNA is the most sensitive material to alkylation within the cell and is probably also the primary site of alkylation (Wheeler, 1962).

However, if it is true that DNA, rather than DNA precursors, is the primary site of alkylation, why is it, then, that alkylating agents are effective only during S?

A restriction of the effect to S is conceivable for several reasons besides incorporation of abnormal precursors. Thus, it may be that alkylation of DNA is possible only during S, because at other stages of the mitotic cycle the DNA of the chromosomes is protected by other substances. It is also conceivable that although DNA may be alkylated at any stage, the alkylation results in chromosomal aberrations only in connection with DNA synthesis. Finally, there is the possibility that the direct cause of the aberrations is not the alkylation of DNA, but the inhibition of DNA synthesis which the alkylation has produced. An inhibited DNA synthesis could be the result both of the alkylated DNA having a reduced primer activity and of a competition for sites on the DNA polymerase between normal and alkylated deoxyribonucleotide triphosphates, if the later are unable to function as substrates in the polymerase reaction. The scheme in Fig. 13-1 illustrates these possibilities.

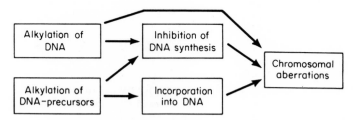

Fig. 13–1. Diagrammatic illustration of the possible sequences of events in the production of chromosomal aberrations by alkylating agents.

However, in sec. A of this chapter, it was already pointed out that inhibition of DNA synthesis is not a very likely cause of chromosomal aberrations. For alkylating agents, there appears to be no correlation between ability to inhibit DNA synthesis and ability to produce chromosomal aberrations (Wheeler, 1962).

If DNA is the primary site of alkylation, which is then the chief point of alkylation in DNA, and what kind of agents produce this effect?

During the last few years, facts have been obtained which indicate that alkylation of DNA may be obtained with a variety of different types of compounds in addition to such well-known alkylating agents as nitrogen and sulfur mustards, epoxides, ethyleneimines, sulfonic esters, alkylsulfates and diazoalkanes. Thus, alkylation of DNA results from treatments of cells with dimethylnitrosamine (Craddock and Magee, 1963) and has been suggested as the mechanism by which azaserine (Freese, 1963), mitomycin C (Schwartz et al., 1963), and the hepatotoxic pyrrolizidine alkaloids (Culvenor et al., 1962) act on cell nuclei.

The alkylating agents are chemically very reactive and combine readily with nucleophilic centers in other molecules. Sulfhydryl groups, ionized acid groups, and nonionized amino groups are nucleophilic in biological systems. The fact that the alkylating agents are electrophilic, i.e., have affinity toward nucleophilic groups, is a result of their ability to form positive carbonium ions in polar solvents, e.g.,

$$R_2NCH_2CH_2Cl \rightleftharpoons R_2NCH_2\overset{+}{C}H_2 + Cl^-$$

Some years ago, esterification of phosphate groups in DNA was regarded as the reaction most likely to be responsible for the genetical and cytological effects of alkylating agents (Stacey et al., 1958). Today, alkylation of heterocyclic nitrogen in DNA is believed to be more important, however. According to Lawley and Brookes (1963a, 1963b), the sites in RNA most reactive to alkylating agents are in order of decreasing reactivity: N-7 of guanine, N-1 of adenine, N-1 of cytosine, and N-3 of adenine. For DNA, the reactive sites are N-7 of guanine, N-3 of adenine, N-1 of adenine, and N-1 of cytosine. Denatured DNA behaves like RNA; i.e., the sites N-1 of cytosine and N-1 of adenine are more reactive than N-3 of adenine. The fact that DNA behaves differently from RNA and denatured DNA is ascribed to the involvement of N-1 of adenine and cytosine in H-bond formation in DNA. These sites are liberated by denaturation of DNA.

It was further found (Lawley and Brookes, 1963a) that after treatments with difunctional agents about 25 per cent of the alkylated guanine in DNA was cross-linked. This cross-linking of guanine moieties in DNA by difunctional alkylation, which may involve both adjacent guanines on the same strand and guanines on each of the twin strands, is believed to be important in connection with the production of chromosomal aberrations.

Following alkylation of DNA, the alkylated purines split off from the sugar-phosphate backbone. Fission of the sugar-phosphate chain in the depurinated DNA then follows at a slower rate.

The alkylation of nucleic acid and nucleic acid components by β-propiolactone has been studied by Roberts and Warwick (1963), who found the product of the reaction to be 7-(2-carboxyethyl)guanine.

The *in vivo* reaction of N-nitroso-N-methylurethan and diazoalkanes has been discussed by Emmelot et al. (1962). Apparently, the biological effects of NMU are due to diazomethane, which is formed *in vivo* from NMU (Schoental, 1961). In aqueous solution, diazomethane is converted into a diazonium ion, which either reacts directly with nucleophilic centers in other molecules or decomposes to yield nitrogen and a carbonium ion, the latter then reacting with nucleophilic centers, such as N-7 in the guanine moiety of DNA. As shown by Fig. 13-2, a diazonium ion can also be formed from NMU directly, without diazomethane as an intermediate.

Alkylating agents are also formed *in vivo* from alkylnitrosamines by an enzyme-catalyzed oxidative dealkylation process. As shown by Fig. 13-3a, the active agents resulting from the dealkylation of dimethylnitrosamine (DMNA) are the same as those formed from NMU. The corresponding reactions for methylphenylnitrosamine are shown in Fig. 13-3b.

As a result of the *in vivo* reactions of DMNA, DNA becomes rapidly methylated, the site of methylation being N-7 of guanine (Craddock and Magee, 1963).

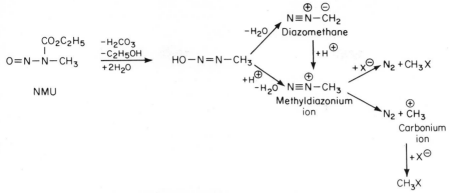

Fig. 13–2. Possible intermediates in conversion of NMU into an alkylating agent in aqueous medium and the mechanism of reaction with nucleophilic centers ($X^{\ominus}$) in other molecules (e.g., N-7 in the guanine moiety of DNA). (After Emmelot et al., 1962; Nature 193:1158–1161.)

E. Concluding Remarks

In this chapter various mechanisms by which chromosome-breaking agents may produce their cytological effects have been discussed. The conclusions arrived at are summarized in Table 13-3, where the agents discussed have been classified into four main categories on the basis of their most likely mode of action. The type of cytological effect produced has also been indicated in the table.

All the mechanisms discussed involve DNA. For aberrations produced by ionizing radiation Wolff (1960) has obtained evidence that protein, rather than DNA, is the chromosomal constituent involved in breakage. For chemicals, the bulk of evidence points to DNA as the material primarily affected.

Chemical, physicochemical, and biochemical mechanisms other than those discussed here have been suggested but not supported by sufficient facts. However, there are at least two additional mechanisms which ought to be mentioned.

On the basis of evidence obtained by Iyer and Szybalski (1963) and by Schwartz et al. (1963), mitomycin C has been classified above as an alkylating agent. According to another hypothesis, the degradation of DNA obtained after treatment with mitomycin C is an indirect effect which has been produced by DNase released from microsomes and from sRNA as a result of the action of mitomycin C (Kersten, 1962; Kersten et al., 1964). The experiments of Macgregor and Callan (1962) and of Gall (1963a) have shown that isolated lampbrush chromosomes are fragmented by DNase, and it would not be unreasonable to assume that the release of large amounts of DNase in the cell at a moment when the

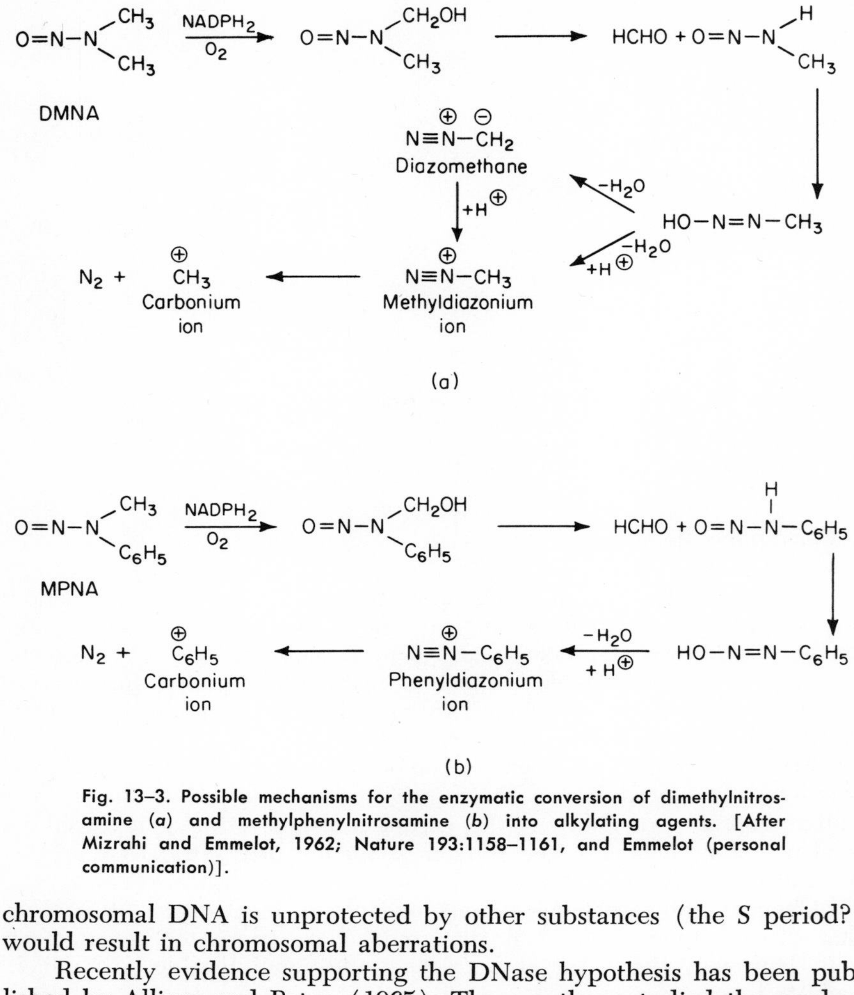

Fig. 13–3. Possible mechanisms for the enzymatic conversion of dimethylnitrosamine (a) and methylphenylnitrosamine (b) into alkylating agents. [After Mizrahi and Emmelot, 1962; Nature 193:1158–1161, and Emmelot (personal communication)].

chromosomal DNA is unprotected by other substances (the S period?) would result in chromosomal aberrations.

Recently evidence supporting the DNase hypothesis has been published by Allison and Paton (1965). These authors studied the production of chromosomal aberrations by visible light in the presence of various photosensitizing agents, using human diploid cells as experimental material. They found that the primary photosensitizing effects were on the lysosomes. In order to obtain chromosomal aberrations the photosensitizing agent had to be present in the lysosomes but its presence in the nucleus was not required. Allison and Paton conclude that damage to lysosomes can result in structural alterations in chromosomes and suggest that DNase released from lysosomes breaks "the DNA which is the backbone of the uncoiled interphase chromatid." They further suggest that other chemicals, such as alkylating agents and maleic hydrazide, also produce chromosomal aberrations by releasing DNase from lyso-

TABLE 13-3.

CLASSIFICATION OF CHROMOSOME BREAKING CHEMICALS ON THE BASIS OF THEIR CYTOLOGICAL EFFECT AND MOST LIKELY MECHANISM OF ACTION.

Chemical Action / Cytological Effect	Inhibition of Deoxyribonucleotide Synthesis	Denaturation or Degradation of DNA	The Production of Abnormal, Labile DNA by Chemical Reaction and/or Incorporation of Abnormal Precursors	Removal of DNA-bound Metals
Nondelayed Effect of Fragment Type	Deoxyadenosine Cytosine arabinoside 5-Fluorodeoxyuridine			
Nondelayed Effect of Exchange Type — Both Nondelayed and Delayed Effects		8-Ethoxycaffeine 1,3,7,9-Tetramethyl-uric acid Actinomycin D Streptonigrin		
Delayed Effects Only, Which Consist of Chromatid Aberrations of Exchange Type			Alkylating agents [mustards, epoxides, ethylene imines, sulfonic esters, alkyl sulfates, diazoalkanes, alkylnitrosamines, nitrosoalkylurethanes, β-propiolactone, mitomycin C (?) azaserine (?)] Acridine orange-visible light 5-Bromodeoxyuridine Maleic hydrazide	Potassium Cyanide Cupferron (?) α, α'-Dipyridyl Dieca 8-Hydroxyquinoline Adenine (?)

somes. However, if this were true, the cytological effect produced by these agents would be expected to be the same. As we have seen, this is not the case. Thus, the distribution of breaks between and within chromosomes is not the same after treatments with maleic hydrazide as after treatments with alkylating agents.

Another interesting hypothesis has been suggested by Borenfreund et al. (1964) on the basis of results obtained in a study of the effect of hyponitrite and hydroxylamine derivatives on isolated DNA in solution and on the chromosomes of Chinese hamster cells cultured *in vitro*. The chromosomal aberrations produced by the agents in question were believed to be the result of their ability to induce main chain cleavage in DNA. The isolated DNA was broken at sites which were believed to be peptide esters holding the polynucleotide units together (Bendich et al., 1963). These amino acid ester linkages would be equivalent to the R-linkers which, according to the chromosome model of Taylor (1963*a*, *b*), link the replicating units of the chromosomal DNA in a tandemlike fashion (compare Chaps. 3 and 5).

---

[1] Since this chapter was written, an interesting hypothesis has been suggested by Ahnström and Natarajan (1966). According to these authors chromosome breakage by FUdR and AdR is the result of a reversal of the DNA polymerase reaction caused by the deficiency of deoxyribonucleoside triphosphates.

DNA, Mutation and
Chromosomal Aberrations

A. DNA and Mutation

Owing to the brilliant studies by Benzer, Freese, Demerec, and others, we are now beginning to get some idea about the molecular mechanisms of mutation. Far less is known about the molecular mechanisms of chromosome breakage.

Among the many controversial questions in connection with the latter problem are the relationship between point mutation and structural chromosome changes, the nature of the chromosomal constituent(s) involved in breakage, and the chemical nature of the bonds involved.

In order to be able to discuss the first of these questions, it will be necessary to summarize briefly our present ideas about the mutation process. This summary is based mainly on an excellent review article by Freese (1963), to which the reader is referred for detailed information on the subject.

In 1932 Stadler (1932) pointed out that the so-called gene mutations were merely what was left after elimination of all those genetical changes which by cytological methods had been found to be caused by structural chromosome changes. The difference between gene mutation and chromosomal aberrations, therefore, may well be quantitative, rather than qualitative. Dobzhansky (1947) believed, however, that many mutations were caused by chemical changes within the gene molecule itself, since "It would be strange indeed if the hereditary materials possessed an eternally immutable chemical constitution." This conclusion has been borne out by recent analyses of the fine structure of the gene and of the mutation process in bacteria and phage. These analyses have also shown that mutations result from changes in the DNA component of the gene.

This is not surprising, considering the fact, now generally accepted, that DNA is the principal carrier of genetical information.

The changes appear to consist of alterations of the nature and number of bases in DNA. Of the various types of base alterations, the *replacements* appear to be most important, or at least best understood. Two kinds of replacements appear to be possible: *transitions* and *transversions*. In a transition, a purine is replaced by another purine or a pyrimidine by another pyrimidine. In a transversion, a purine is replaced by a pyrimidine, and vice versa.

For the purpose of studying the molecular mechanisms of mutation, Freese selected such agents as were known to react specifically and preferably with DNA. A further requirement was that the changes should involve only one or a few nucleotides. Preferably, the treatments should not produce breakage in the sugar-phosphate chain of the DNA molecule.

The chemicals used fall into two classes: (1) base analogues known to be incorporated into DNA, and (2) ". . . agents which alter resting DNA in such a way that mutations result in subsequent DNA replications" (Freese, 1959). Representatives of the first class of mutagens are 2-aminopurine (AP) and the thymine analogue 5-bromouracil (BU), representatives of the second, nitrous acid, the effect of which almost certainly is due to deamination of DNA bases, and hydroxylamine, which reacts preferably with the cytosine moiety in DNA. Since the deoxyriboside of BU, 5-bromodeoxyuridine or BUdR, is more easily incorporated into DNA and interferes less with RNA metabolism, it is frequently used in place of BU.

As a result of incorporation of BU and AP into DNA, an increased mutation rate is obtained. It is also true, however, that most genes do not mutate even when almost 100 per cent of the thymine in DNA has been replaced by BU. This indicates that the incorporation of the base analogue does not by itself constitute a mutation. The possibility that the mutant gene would be one containing a base analogue is unlikely also for the reason that such a gene could be duplicated only so long as the base analogue was available in the medium.

According to the hypothesis of Freese, mutations are the result of pairing mistakes, and base analogues induce mutations because they undergo such mistakes more frequently than normal bases.

The process is illustrated in Fig. 14-1 for BU. Normally BU, like thymine, would pair with adenine during DNA replication, but once in a while pairing would occur between BU and guanine. The mutation would be completed when guanine at the next replication pairs with its normal partner, cytosine. Thus, mutations which consist of the replacement of an adenine-thymine pair in the DNA molecule by a guanine-cytosine pair would require at least three replications to be established: the first when BU is incorporated, the second when BU by mistake pairs with guanine, and the third when guanine pairs with cytosine.

Mutation may also arise as a result of pairing mistakes at incorpora-

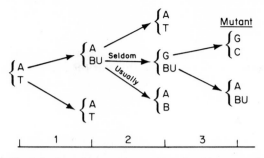

Fig. 14–1. The induction of base pair transitions by 5-bromouracil as a result of mistake in replication. A—adenine, G—guanine, T—thymine, C—cytosine, BU—5-bromouracil. (After Freese, 1963. In J. H. Taylor, ed., Molecular Genetics 207–269, p. 221.)

tion; i.e., BU may be incorporated in place of cytosine instead of in place of thymine.

We shall now turn to agents belonging to Freese's second category, i.e., agents such as nitrous acid (HNO_2) and hydroxylamine, which are believed to react with resting DNA.

There is good evidence indicating that HNO_2 acts by deaminating DNA bases. The deamination product of adenine is hypoxanthine, and that of guanine is xanthine, whereas deamination of cytosine gives uracil. The pairing properties of hypoxanthine is different from that of adenine but similar to the pairing properties of guanine. Uracil has the same pairing properties as thymine, which are different from those of cytosine. Therefore, during replication hypoxanthine will pair with cytosine, the ultimate change being the replacement of an adenine-thymine pair by a guanine-cytosine pair. Uracil pairs with adenine, and the ultimate result of the deamination of cytosine will be that a cytosine-guanine pair is replaced by a thymine-adenine pair.

Very likely, the mutagenic effect of hydroxylamine is the result of its ability to react with cytosine. As a result of the reaction, a hydroxyl-amino pyrimidine is produced which pairs with adenine, rather than with guanine. The ultimate change will be that a cytosine-guanine pair is replaced by a thymine-adenine pair.

Thus, the effects of base analogues, nitrous acid, and hydroxylamine appear to result from their ability to cause base-pair replacements of the type called transitions by Freese.

However, other mechanisms of mutation are also possible. Thus acridine dyes are believed to be ". . . intercalated between adjacent nucleotide pair layers by extension and unwinding of the deoxyribose-phosphate backbone" (Lerman, 1961). The actual mutation would consist of a deletion or insertion of one base pair in DNA and occur in connection with replication of the DNA-acridine dye complex.

As we have seen in the previous chapter, DNA can be altered in several different ways by alkylating agents. Thus, the phosphate groups of DNA can be alkylated to phosphate triesters, a reaction which results in breakage of the DNA backbone if the triester is hydrolyzed between the sugar and the phosphate. The bases in DNA are also alkylated, the chief point of alkylation being N-7 of guanine, followed by N-3 of adenine. The alkylated purine is easily split off from the sugar-phosphate backbone. As a result of this reaction, a depurinated DNA is produced. Depurination of DNA may also be obtained by low pH. Breaks of the sugar-phosphate chain occur with a much higher frequency in depurinated DNA than in normal DNA.

These various possibilities have been examined by Freese, who concludes that of the reactions mentioned, depurination is most likely to be responsible for the mutagenic effects of alkylating agents. During replication, any one of the four bases may get incorporated in the new complementary DNA strand at the point where the removed purine has left a gap in the template. If a purine is incorporated, a transversion will follow; if the wrong pyrimidine is incorporated, a transition will be the result; and if the gap is left out, the effect will be deletion of a base pair. According to this interpretation, breakage of the DNA backbone, which also is a result of treatment with alkylating agents, would not result in mutation but would be lethal to the organism.

B. DNA and Chromosome Breakage

Freese's attractive hypothesis has been supported by experimental results, and mutation may safely be regarded as changes within a small segment of the DNA component of the gene. For point mutations, these changes apparently consist of the replacement of one base pair by another, and do not involve breakage of the sugar-phosphate chain in DNA.

It is not easy to visualize that such replacements should result in structural chromosome changes. Very likely, therefore, point mutations and chromosome structural changes are qualitatively different and arise by different mechanisms. In agreement with this conclusion, BUdR and nitrous acid do not produce chromosomal aberrations in plants (Taylor et al., 1962; Kihlman, 1962, 1963a), whereas hydroxylamine has only a very weak effect (Cohn, 1964). No data appear to be available for the chromosome-breaking effect of AP in plants. As a further difference between mutagenic and chromosome-breaking agents, it may be mentioned that the rule of ethylating agents' being more effective than methylating agents, which appears to be valid for mutation-induction, does not seem to be applicable to the production of chromosomal aberration, although enough data are not available to warrant a definite conclusion on this point.

However, the situation is complicated by the fact that BUdR, hydroxylamine, and AP are quite efficient as producers of chromosomal aberrations in animal cells (Hsu and Somers, 1961; Somers and Hsu, 1962; Borenfreund et al., 1964; Biesele et al., 1952a). As is evident in

Table 15-1, it is also true that for several compounds, there is a better correlation between mutagenic effect and ability to produce chromosomal aberrations in animal cells than between their chromosome-breaking effects in plant and animal cells.

For these reasons, it is difficult to avoid the conclusion that, although the mechanisms by which point mutations and chromosomal aberrations are produced may be different, the chromosomal constituent involved must be the same, viz., DNA. The conclusion that DNA is involved in chromosome breakage was also arrived at in the previous chapter, where it appeared that the only property the chromosome-breaking agents discussed have in common is their ability to affect the synthesis, state, and structure of DNA.

The simplest explanation of the fact that chromosomal aberrations are produced by agents which act on DNA would be that the structural backbone of the chromosome is partly or wholly DNA. If this is true, it would seem reasonable to assume that chromosome breaks are breaks in DNA molecules, although it does not necessarily follow.

The structural organization of the chromosome was discussed in Chap. 3. It appeared in this discussion that good experimental evidence has been presented in favor of DNA's being necessary to maintain the structural integrity of the chromosome (e.g., Gall, 1963a and Macgregor and Callan, 1962), although, apparently, other material is also involved.

The observation that alkylating agents are able to produce main chain breakage in DNA (Lawley and Brookes, 1963b; Laurence, 1963) is compatible with the idea that chromosome breaks involve breaks in the DNA component of the chromosome, and so is the finding that chromosome fragmentation is produced by FUdR, AdR, and CA (Taylor et al., 1962; Kihlman et al., 1963), which inhibit the formation of the substrates of the DNA polymerase reaction. Evidence has been presented by Mennigmann and Szybalski (1962) that treatments with FUdR result in single-strand breaks in the DNA molecule. Degradation of DNA is reported to occur after treatments with the antibiotics mitomycin C and streptonigrin (Reich et al., 1961; Radding, 1963), which are highly effective as chromosome-breaking agents in both plant and animal cells, and main chain cleavage of isolated DNA has been observed after treatments with hyponitrite and hydroxylamine derivatives, which produce chromosomal aberrations in animal cells (Borenfreund et al., 1964). Chemical bonds in DNA are further broken after irradiation with visible light in the presence of acridine orange (Freifelder et al., 1961).

On the other hand, it is evident from the discussion in the preceding chapter that cleavage of the sugar-phosphate chain in DNA is not the most characteristic or most usual result of the reactions between alkylating agents and DNA, and that it has been questioned whether the FUdR effect on chromosome structure really is a result of its inhibitory effect on DNA synthesis. It should also be pointed out that hyponitrite and hydroxylamine apparently induce main chain cleavage in DNA at sites where polynucleotide units are linked together by peptide esters. The importance of protein in the formation of chromosomal aberrations is demonstrated by the finding of Wolff (1960) that protein synthesis is required for repair of X-ray-induced chromosome damage.

Thus, if the backbone of the chromosome consists of DNA molecules linked together by other substances, there certainly is the possibility of some agents acting on the linkers, rather than on DNA itself. Furthermore, when DNA is the chromosomal constituent affected by the chemical, the primary change does not necessarily have to be a break in the sugar-phosphate chain of DNA. It is also conceivable that some other, less drastic, alterations of the DNA make the chromosomes labile and/or liable to take part in exchange reactions during the processes of condensation and reorganization at late interphase and early prophase.

C. The Production of Chromosomal Aberrations as a Method for Studying Chromosome Structure

The purpose of studies on the effect of chromosome-breaking agents is obviously to explore the mode of action of these agents as well as the mechanisms by which chromosomal aberrations are formed. At the same time, it is hoped that these studies will provide information about the structural organization of the chromosome. Unfortunately, results obtained by this method are difficult to interpret, just because we know so little about the structure and organization of the interphase chromosome. Thus, workers in this field find themselves in some kind of a vicious circle: They use chromosome-breaking agents for studying the structural organization of the chromosome, but they cannot interpret the results obtained until they know more about the structural organization of the chromosome.

It was pointed out in Chap. 3 that our knowledge of the structure of the interphase chromosome is so restricted that we still do not know how many strands the chromatid is composed of, whether the structural backbone of the strand(s) may be regarded as a single molecule running from one end of the chromosome to the other, or if it is composed of smaller units linked end to end by bonds weaker than covalent bonds, nor do we know if the structural backbone of the chromosome is composed of DNA or of protein or of both.

The fact that most chromosome-breaking agents are known to affect the synthesis or structure of DNA suggests that the backbone is composed of DNA or, alternatively, DNA and protein. It may be recalled that according to Taylor et al. (1962), the nonstaining gaps produced by FUdR in the root-tip chromosomes of *Vicia* represent single-strand breaks in a DNA double helix, which is the essential structural component of the tandemly linked replicating units of the chromatid (compare Chaps. 3 and 5). This interpretation of the FUdR effect is supported by the results of the biochemical studies of Mennigmann and Szybalski (1962)

TABLE 14–1.

CHROMOSOME BREAKING AGENTS AND CHROMOSOME STRUCTURE.

Chromosome-Breaking Agent (s)	Number of Strands in a Chromatid	Time of Splitting into Chromatids, as Indicated by the Transition from Chromosome Type to Chromatid Type Aberrations	Chromosomal Components Involved in Maintaining the Structural Integrity of the Chromosome, as Indicated by the (Bio) Chemical Effects of the Chromosome Breaking Agents
EOC	At least two (induction of subchromatid exchanges in prophase)	The end of G_1 (induction of chromosome type aberrations in G_1, chromatid type aberrations in S and G_2)	DNA (inhibition of DNA synthesis; denaturation of DNA)
Streptonigrin			DNA (inhibition of DNA synthesis; degradation of DNA)
AdR, cytosine arabinoside	—	—	DNA (inhibition of deoxyribonucleotide and DNA synthesis)
FUdR	—	—	DNA (inhibition of deoxyribonucleotide and DNA synthesis, single strand breaks in DNA molecules)
BUdR	—	—	DNA (incorporation in DNA in place of thymidine)
Alkylating agents	—	—	DNA (alkylation of heterocyclic nitrogen in the DNA bases)
Hyponitrite, hydroxylamine derivatives	—	—	DNA (main chain cleavage in DNA)
Visible light-acridine orange	—	—	DNA (breakage of chemical bonds in DNA)
Chelating agents	—	—	Divalent cations and heavy metals (complex formation with metals)

which indicated that treatments with FUdR produce single-strand breaks in DNA.

The fact that calcium- and magnesium-deficiency causes chromosome breakage in *Tradescantia* (Steffensen, 1953, 1955), as well as the finding that chromosomal aberrations are produced by heavy-metal-complexing agents in *Vicia* (Kihlman, 1957; Cohn, 1961) indicate that metals occur as stabilizing factors in chromosomes. The results have been interpreted as evidence in favor of a particulate organization of the chromosome, where the units are linked together by bridges of metal ions.

That the prophase chromatid is at least bipartite is indicated by the fact that EOC, streptonigrin, and actinomycin D are able to induce subchromatid exchanges during prophase. This type of aberration has previously been observed and interpreted as a subchromatid exchange in X-ray experiments (e.g., LaCour and Rutishauser, 1954; Crouse, 1954).

The fact that ionizing radiation (and, possibly, chemicals such as EOC and streptonigrin) produces aberrations of the chromosome type in G_1 and chromatid-type aberrations in S and G_2 suggests that the splitting of chromosomes into chromatids occurs in late G_1 or, possibly, early S.

It may be concluded that although studies with chromosome-breaking chemicals have not been able to solve the problem of the structural organization of the chromosome, they nevertheless have provided some useful information about chromosome structure. Table 14-1 summarizes these results.

Comparison between the Effects of Chemicals on Animal and Plant Cells—Causes of Resistance

The experimental material in most of the studies described in the previous chapters belongs to two main categories, viz., root tips of plants and animal cells in tissue culture. These two categories have often been found to respond differently to the various cytological effects of the chemicals studied.

Thus, it appeared in Chap. 8 that the sensitivity of plant and animal cells to C-mitotic agents is markedly different, animal cells, as a rule, being much more sensitive to both the C-mitotic and toxic effects of these chemicals. The appearance of the C-mitotic effect proved also to be somewhat different in animal and plant cells.

The ability of a number of chemical compounds to produce chromosomal aberrations in plant root tips and in mammalian cells appears in Table 15-1. The third column in the table shows for which of these agents a mutagenic effect has been demonstrated without distinguishing between the experimental materials used, which may have been phage, bacteria, fungi, plants, or insects (*Drosophila*).

It is evident in the table that the fact that a compound is able to produce aberrations in mammalian cells does not necessarily mean that it is effective in root-tip cells, and vice versa. Thus, diaminopurine, purine riboside, BUdR, cytosine arabinoside, and hydroxylamine are all effective producers of chromosomal aberrations in mammalian cells in tissue culture (Biesele et al., 1952a; Biesele et al., 1955; Hsu and Somers, 1961; Kihlman et al., 1963; Somers and Hsu, 1962), but treatments of plant root tips with these agents produce few or no aberrations (Loveless, unpublished, quoted by Rieger and Michaelis, 1962; Taylor

TABLE 15–1.

COMPARISON BETWEEN CHROMOSOME-BREAKING AND MUTAGENIC
EFFECTS OF CHEMICALS IN PLANT AND ANIMAL MATERIALS.

| Compound | Chromosomal Aberrations | | Mutagenic Effect |
	Plant Root-tips	Mammalian Cells in Tissue Culture	
Adenine	+	+	+
2.6-Diaminopurine	-	+	+
Caffeine	+	±	+
8-Ethoxycaffeine	+	±	±
Purine riboside	-	+	+
Deoxyadenosine	+	+	No data
5-Fluorodeoxyuridine	+	+	No data
5-Bromodeoxyuridine	-	+	+
Cytosine arabinoside	-	+	No data
Maleic hydrazide	+	-	-
Azaserine	+	+	+
Streptonigrin	+	+	+
Mitomycin C	+	+	+
Hydroxylamine	±	+	+
Nitrogen mustard	+	+	+
Triethylenemelamine	+	+	+
Diepoxybutane	+	+	+

+ marked effect
− no effect
± effect very low, although just about significant

et al., 1962; Kihlman, 1962 and unpublished). Maleic hydrazide and 8-ethoxycaffeine, on the other hand, do not markedly increase the frequency of aberrations in mammalian cells (Barnes et al., 1957; Biesele et al., 1952b; Kihlman, unpublished), although they are highly effective in many plant cells (McLeish, 1953; Kihlman, 1955a, b). Of the 17 compounds listed in Table 15-1, six inhibitors of DNA synthesis, viz., adenine, azaserine, streptonigrin, mitomycin C, FUdR, and AdR, and three alkylating agents, viz., HN2, TEM, and diepoxybutane, have been found to be effective in both materials (Kihlman, 1950; Biesele et al., 1952b; Tanaka and Sugimura, 1956; Biesele, 1958b; Cohen et al., 1963; Kihlman, 1964; Merz, 1961; Nowell, 1964; Taylor et al., 1962; Hsu et al., 1964; Kihlman, 1963b; Kihlman et al., 1963; Ford, 1949; Koller and Casarini, 1952; Biesele et al., 1950; Biesele, 1954a; Loveless, 1951; Koller, 1953). The data in the table also indicate that as a rule there appears to be a good correlation between mutagenic effect and ability to induce chromosomal aberrations in mammalian cells.

The reason why plant and animal cells respond differently is sometimes rather obvious. Thus plant cells are surrounded by rigid cell walls and divide by the mechanism of cell plate formation, whereas animal cells, which lack cell walls, divide by constriction. It is, therefore, not surprising that agents which inhibit cytokinesis in animal cells frequently have no corresponding effect in plant cells, and vice versa.

In other cases, the reason for the different responses is less obvious.

Nothing indicates, however, that the mechanisms involved are fundamentally different from those responsible for the different effects of chemicals in different species of plants or animals, and in different cell lines of the same species. Thus, the question of why a chemical is inactive in animal cells although it is highly effective in plant cells, and vice versa, becomes a part of the more general problem: What are the causes of drug-resistance. This is a problem of utmost importance in connection with the chemotherapeutic treatment of diseases, since, obviously, the fact that the harmful cells (e.g., bacteria, cancer cells) may develop resistance towards a drug limits the usefulness of this drug as a chemotherapeutic agent.

Several mechanisms may be responsible for the development of resistance. One is that the cell develops an enzyme which destroys the drug. Thus, penicillin-resistant cells are characterized by a high penicillase activity, and DDT-resistant cells by a high dehydrochlorinase activity. Very likely, one of the mechanisms by which cells become resistant to methylated oxypurines is the development of a high demethylase activity (Henderson and Mazel, 1964). Other conceivable causes of resistance are decreased penetration of the chemical into the cell, loss of the enzyme catalyzing the transformation of the "inactive" drug into the inhibitor or reactive agent (e.g., FUdR into FdUMP, alkylnitrosamines into carbonium ions), increased formation of the enzyme affected by the drug (e.g., dihydrofolic acid reductase in the case of aminopterin resistance), increased production of metabolites which counteract the effect of the drug, and the development of an alternate metabolic pathway which by-passes the inhibited enzyme.

In the following we shall examine in more detail the mechanisms by which cells have become resistant to lethal, growth-inhibitory, and chromosome-breaking effects of some inhibitors of nucleotide biosynthesis.

In the majority of the cases studied, resistance to analogues of the nucleic acid bases and nucleosides appears to be the result of the loss of enzymes which convert the analogues to the corresponding nucleotides. Thus, the resistance of bacterial and tumor cells to the lethal and growth-inhibitory effects of the purine analogues 8-azaguanine, 6-mercaptopurine, and 2.6-diaminopurine involves the loss of nucleotide pyrophosphorylases, which catalyze the synthesis of purine nucleotides from purine bases and 5-phosphoribosyl-1-pyrophosphate (PRPP) (Brockman et al., 1959; Lieberman and Ove, 1960). Similarily, enzyme preparations from *Escherichia coli* resistant to the growth-inhibitory effect of 5-fluorouracil (FU) failed to catalyze the reaction of uracil and 5-fluorouracil with PRPP, in contrast to preparations from drug-sensitive strains, which catalyzed this reaction (Brockman et al., 1960). Kit et al. (1963) have found that a BUdR-resistant subline of L-M mouse fibroblast, called strain L-M (TK$^-$), is characterized by the deletion of the enzyme thymidine kinase, which catalyzes the phosphorylation of TdR and BUdR to dTMP and BdUMP, respectively.

The L-M (TK⁻) strain was derived from the BUdR-resistant strain L-M (BU 25), which has been described by Hsu and Somers (1962). Although the L-M (BU 25) cells incorporated BUdR in their chromosomes to the same extent as the cells in the sensitive parent strain (L-M), their growth capacity was not reduced and their frequency of chromosomal aberrations was not increased by BUdR treatments which in the L-M strain caused both extensive chromosomal damage and cell death.

In the fungus *Neurospora,* BUdR is inactive as a mutagen. Since *Neurospora* is unable to phosphorylate exogenous supplied thymidine (thymidine-kinase reaction), the resistance of *Neurospora* cells to the mutagenic effect of BUdR, like the resistance of the L-M (TK⁻) cells to the lethal, growth-inhibitory, and chromosome-breaking effect of BUdR, probably is the result of the lack or the inactivity of the enzyme thymidine kinase, which converts BUdR into BdUMP (Brockman and deSerres, 1963).

Although the thymidine kinase reaction may be an important "salvage" pathway, thymidylic acid is normally formed by methylation of deoxyuridylic acid. This normal pathway for *de novo* synthesis of dTMP is catalyzed by the enzyme thymidylate synthetase, which is strongly and specifically inhibited by 5-fluorodeoxyuridylic acid (FdUMP). Cells sensitive to FUdR contain an ATP-dependent kinase, which is capable of converting the noninhibitory FUdR into FdUMP (Hartmann and Heidelberger, 1961; Huennekens et al., 1963), and which apparently is identical with thymidine kinase (Okazaki and Kornberg, 1964). It would, therefore, seem reasonable to assume that FUdR resistance, like resistance to BUdR, is the result of a loss of thymidine kinase activity. That this is actually so is indicated by the studies of Dubbs and Kit (1964). These authors found that L-M cells were approximately 250 times more sensitive to FUdR than the thymidine kinase deficient L-M (TK⁻) cells. Both cell strains were equally sensitive to 5-fluorouracil, which is converted into FdUMP by a metabolic pathway not involving thymidine kinase (Fig. 15-1).

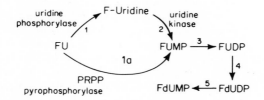

Fig. 15-1. Metabolic pathways by which 5-fluorouracil (FU) may be converted into 5-fluorodeoxyuridylic acid (FdUMP).

We have already mentioned the observation by Brockman et al. (1960) that FU-resistant bacteria fail to catalyze the reaction indicated by 1a in Fig. 15-1. It has further been shown by Reichard and his coworkers (Reichard et al. 1959; 1962; Sköld 1963) that uridine phosphorylase (reaction 1) and uridine kinase (reaction 2) activities are greatly reduced in tumor cells resistant to FU. Heidelberger et al.

(1960), on the other hand, came to the conclusion that FU-resistant cells of Ehrlich ascites tumor contained an altered thymidylate synthetase, which was not inhibited by FdUMP. Bloch and Hutchison (1964) studied the mechanism responsible for the resistance of four mutants of *Streptococcus faecalis* to the fluoropyrimidines 5-fluorouracil, 5-fluorouridine, 5-fluoro-2'-deoxyuridine and 5-fluoro-2'-deoxycytidine. They found that resistance in these cases depended upon the formation of increased amounts of the pyrimidine intermediates which counteracted the inhibitory action of the drugs. The potency of the fluoropyrimidines as growth inhibitors proved to be related to the relative ease by which they were converted to the active agent 5-fluoro-2'-deoxyuridylic acid.

When deoxyuridylic acid is methylated by N^5-N^{10}-methylene-tetrahydrofolic acid in the thymidylate synthetase reaction, thymidylic acid and dihydrofolic acid are formed (compare Chap. 4, Fig. 4-10). The first step in the reformation of methylene-tetrahydrofolic acid is the reduction of dihydrofolic acid (DHFA) by NADPH to tetrahydrofolic acid THFA, a reaction which is catalyzed by the enzyme DHFA-reductase. A new 1-carbon unit is then added to THFA to yield methylene-THFA. The DHFA-reductase reaction is strongly inhibited by the folic acid analogues aminopterin and amethopterin.

In connection with treatments of mammalian cells in tissue culture with aminopterin and amethopterin, resistant cell lines have been obtained. The most clearly demonstrable biochemical event accompanying resistance to the folic acid analogues is an increased formation of DHFA-reductase. In a comparative study of the DHFA-reductase activity in four amethopterin-resistant and two sensitive sublines of Sarcoma 180 cells, Hakala and Ishihara (1962) found that the reductase content increased with increasing resistance and was 300–400 times higher in the 3000-fold resistant cell line than in the sensitive parent cells.

An interesting mechanism of resistance to difunctional alkylating agents has recently been described by Lawley and Brookes (1965). They found that the initial effect of the agent, difunctional alkylation of guanine moieties in DNA, was the same in sensitive and resistant bacteria. "However, incubation of resistant bacteria in growth medium after alkylation results in excision of difunctionally alkylated guanine moieties from DNA."

The examples related above should be sufficient to give us an idea about the mechanisms which may be responsible for drug-resistance. If we now return to Table 15-1 with this information in mind, it seems to be a reasonable assumption that 2.6-diaminopurine, purine riboside, and cytosine arabinoside (CA) are unable to produce chromosomal aberrations in plant roots because the enzymes catalyzing the formation of nucleotides from these base-analogues and nucleoside-analogues are not present in the plant material used. The lack of chromosomal aberrations following treatments of plant roots with BUdR cannot be explained in this way, however, since we have reasons to believe that BUdR is incorporated in the DNA of plant-root chromosomes. Like the closely related compound IUdR, BUdR strongly enhances the frequency of X-ray-produced chromosomal aberrations in plant roots (Kihlman, 1963a). That IUdR is incorporated in the DNA of bean root chromosomes has convincingly been shown by Smith et al. (1963). Thus, the resistance of plant root cells to the chromosome-breaking effect of BUdR appears to be of the same type as that of the L-M (BU 25) mouse fibroblast cells to the lethal, growth-inhibitory and chromosome-breaking effect of BUdR. As mentioned above, Hsu and Somers (1962) found that incorporation of BUdR into the DNA of the L-M (BU 25) cells did not result in an increased frequency of chromosomal aberrations. The reason why the replacement of DNA thymine by BU results in chromosome breakage in some types of cells but not in others is not understood.

Since BUdR incorporation does not necessarily result in chromosome breakage, it is, of course, possible that the incorporation of other analogues (e.g., 2.6-diaminopurine) may also be tolerated by the chromosomes of plant root tips. In the case of cytosine arabinoside, it is not incorporation into DNA which is believed to be the cause of the chromosome-breaking effect, but inhibition of the synthesis of the DNA-precursor deoxycytidine phosphate. Therefore, for cytosine arabinoside, failure of formation of the inhibitory substance, probably a phosphorylated derivative of CA, or, possibly, degradation of CA seem to be the most plausible explanations of the inactivity of CA in plant roots.

The remaining three cases where the effect is strikingly different in animal and plant cells, viz., 8-ethoxycaffeine, maleic hydrazide, and hydroxylamine, are even more difficult to explain.

The mutagenic and chromosome-breaking effect of HA is believed to be the result of its ability to react with the cytosine moiety in DNA, or alternatively, with peptide esters linking polynucleotide units together in DNA. Why these reactions should occur more easily in phage and in mammalian cells than in plant cells is difficult to understand.

EOC is toxic in animal cells, but the frequency of chromosomal aberrations is only slightly increased (Biesele et al., 1952b). In plant cells, the highest frequency of aberrations is obtained when the treatments are performed around 12°C. A rise of temperature results not only in a decreased chromosome-breaking effect, but also in an increased toxic effect. Whether the chromosome-breaking and toxic effects of EOC in mammalian cells is influenced in a similar way by treatment temperature is not known. The experiments have generally been performed at 37°C. If plant cells are treated at 37°C a strong toxic effect and few chromosome aberrations are obtained.

The most likely explanation to the different effects of EOC in plant and mammalian cells is perhaps that EOC is more easily demethylated in mammalian cells. The chromosome-breaking activity of oxypurines is known to be dependent on the number and position of alkyloxy- and N-methyl groups in the molecule (Kihlman, 1952a). The effect increases with increasing N-methylation and is favored by the presence of an alkyloxy group at position 8 in the purine molecule. Demethylation would, therefore, be expected to reduce the chromosome-breaking effect, complete demethylation resulting in an inactive molecule. The presence in mammalian cells of enzyme systems capable of catalyzing a demethylation of purines has been demonstrated (Henderson and Mazel, 1964).

The chromosome-breaking effect of maleic hydrazide in plants appears to be dependent on the presence of heterochromatin. In *Vicia faba,* it is mainly a heterochromatic segment in the M chromosome which is broken (McLeish, 1953). In *Zea mays,* the frequency of structural chromosome changes is related to the number of heterochromatic "knobs" occurring in the corn varieties used; the larger the number of knobs, the more aberrations are produced (Graf, 1957). According to McLeish (1953), MH does not produce any aberrations in plants which lack visible heterochromatin (e.g., *Allium cepa, Hyacinthus orientalis*). Since in plants the chromosome-breaking effect of MH appears to be limited to particular chromosome regions in certain species, it is not possible to say that MH is inactive as a chromosome-breaking agent in mammalian cells, until its effect has been studied in a number of different materials.

A Summing Up: Oxidative Phosphorylation, DNA Synthesis, and Actions of Chemicals on Dividing Cells

In the preface, oxidative phosphorylation and DNA synthesis were mentioned as two major themes of the book besides the main theme: the disruptive actions of chemicals on dividing cells. It may, therefore, be appropriate to summarize some of the more important findings and conclusions discussed in the book with reference to these processes.

A. Oxidative Phosphorylation

The cytoplasmic organelles known as mitochondria function as centers for release of chemical energy by aerobic oxidation, and the conversion of this energy into the energy-rich phosphate bonds of ATP. This coupling of oxidation to synthesis has been called oxidative phosphorylation. Most of the energy required by the cell is provided by oxidative phosphorylation in mitochondria.

Recent studies by Allfrey, Mirsky, and others have indicated that the nucleus, at least in mammalian cells, ". . . can carry out oxidative reactions and that these reactions are coupled to ATP synthesis" (Allfrey, 1963). In contrast to the ATP production in mitochondria, nuclear ATP production is not inhibited by carbon monoxide.

Oxidative phosphorylation has been found to be involved in many ways in the disruptive effects of chemicals on cell division and chromosome structure. In some cases it appears to be the absorption of the chemical which is dependent on oxidative phosphorylation.

In order to produce its effects the chemical agent must penetrate into the interior of the cell. It has been found that different substances are taken up by different mechanisms, some by passive diffusion, others by active transport. When the transport is active, the energy requirement is usually provided by oxidative phosphorylation. Therefore, in these cases, inhibition of oxidative phosphorylation prevents or reduces the uptake of the chemical.

Inhibition of oxidative phosphorylation generally results in inhibition of cell division. This is because the development of the mitotic process requires energy, although not necessarily more than the synthetic processes during interphase. The studies of Epel (1963) have shown that the rate of mitosis in the sea urchin eggs is closely related to the ATP level. By inhibiting oxidative phosphorylation, the ATP level is reduced; when the level is below 50 per cent of that of the control, mitosis is completely inhibited.

Among the factors which have been found to influence the production of chromosomal aberrations by chemical agents, oxygen and oxidative metabolism are perhaps the most important ones. Whereas the effects of reactive chemicals such as the alkylating agents are independent of oxygen tension, the production of chromosomal aberrations by many other types of compounds has proved to be strongly influenced by the oxygen tension during treatment. The rule is that the effect decreases with decreasing oxygen tension, although there are exceptions, such as adenine and streptonigrin, which are more active in the absence than in the presence of oxygen.

When the effect is reduced by anoxia, it is usually also reduced by respiratory inhibitors. The inhibition of the chromosome-breaking effect by respiratory inhibitors as well as by anoxia indicates either that oxidative phosphorylation is involved or that the chemical in question has to undergo an oxidative degradation in order to be active. If oxidative phosphorylation is involved, the chromosome-breaking effect should be inhibited by DNP, which uncouples phosphorylation from respiration. The effects of methylphenylnitrosamine and methylnitronitrosoguanidine are not influenced by DNP, indicating that the active species are produced from these compounds by oxidative processes. DNP treatment partially or completely suppresses the effect of EOC, maleic hydrazide, FUdR, AdR, and azaserine. In cases such as maleic hydrazide and azaserine, it may be the uptake of the chemical which is dependent on oxidative phosphorylation. In the case of FUdR and AdR, ATP produced by oxidative phosphorylation is apparently required for the phosphorylation of these substances to the active compounds 5-fluorodeoxyuridylic acid and deoxyadenosine-5'-triphosphate.

As shown by Wolff and Luippold (1955), not only the production of chromosomal aberrations but also the repair of chromosomal damage are influenced by oxidative phosphorylation. Inhibition of oxidative metabolism by anoxia, carbon monoxide, or DNP results in an inhibition of the repair of chromosomal damage.

If cell nuclei are able to produce ATP by oxidative processes, it would seem reasonable to assume that it is this intranuclear ATP formation which is involved in the production and repair of chromosomal damage. However, this possibility is rendered less likely by the fact that the repair of chromosomal damage, in contrast to nuclear phosphorylation, is suppressed by carbon monoxide.

B. DNA Synthesis

The biosynthesis of DNA may be divided into three phases: (1) the synthesis of uridylic acid and inosinic acid, (2) the synthesis of the four deoxyribonucleoside triphosphates dATP, dGTP, dCTP, and dTTP which are the immediate precursors of DNA, and (3) the polymerization of these deoxyribonucleoside triphosphates in the presence of the enzyme DNA polymerase and a suitable DNA primer or template.

At least the polymerization process would be expected to occur within the cell nucleus. Accordingly, the presence in cell nuclei of the enzyme DNA polymerase has been demonstrated. Mazia and Hinegardner (1963) found a quantitative proportionality between the chromosome complement and the content of DNA polymerase in nuclei isolated from sea urchin embryos. They found no evidence for the presence of the enzyme outside the nucleus. According to Keir et al. (1963b), calf thymus nuclei contain both DNA polymerase and a physically distinct nucleotidyl-transferase which catalyzes the addition of one nucleotide residue only to the end of polydeoxyribonucleotide chains.

Radioautographic experiments have demonstrated that DNA synthesis occurs during the interphase of cell division and apparently coincides in time with chromosome duplication and with the splitting of chromosomes into chromatids. Since the work of Howard and Pelc (1953) it has become customary to distinguish between three interphase stages in the mitotic cell: (1) the S (-synthesis) period during which labeled precursors are incorporated into chromosomal DNA, (2) the postsynthesis period G_2 between S and prophase, and (3) the presynthesis period G_1 between telophase and the beginning of S.

For many chemical substances the inhibition of cell division and the production of chromosomal aberrations appear to be related to alterations induced by these agents in the structure or synthesis of DNA.

Doubling of DNA is not the only requirement for cell division, but, although there are exceptions, inhibition of DNA synthesis generally results in an inhibition of cell division. The suppression of cell division caused by FUdR, AdR, and cytosine arabinoside is almost certainly a result of the strong and specific inhibition of DNA synthesis produced by these agents. Also, when the primary effect of the substances is on DNA structure, the ultimate cause of the prevented mitosis may be an inhibited DNA synthesis. Chemical and physical alteration of DNA is likely to make it less suitable as a primer in the DNA polymerase reaction with an inhibited DNA synthesis as a result.

Most chromosome-breaking chemicals are active only during the S period of interphase, although some are able to induce aberrations in G_2 (EOC, FUdR, AdR, cytosine arabinoside, streptonigrin) and G_1 (EOC, streptonigrin) as well. Since DNA synthesis coincides in time with many other processes connected with chromosome duplication, the fact that a substance is active only during S must not necessarily mean that it produces chromosomal aberrations by interfering with DNA synthesis. Nevertheless, it seems to be true that the activities of most chromosome-breaking agents involve alterations in DNA structure or DNA metabolism. Four main categories of action mechanisms may be distinguished, viz., (1) inhibition of deoxyribonucleotide synthesis (FUdR, AdR, cytosine arabinoside), (2) denaturation or degradation of DNA (EOC, streptonigrin), (3) the production of abnormal, labile DNA by chemical reaction and/or incorporation of abnormal precursors (alkylating agents, BUdR), and (4) removal of DNA-bound metals (chelating agents).

The experimental studies of Freese and others have demonstrated that the mutation process consists of a change within the DNA component of the gene. Far less is known about the molecular mechanisms of chromosome breakage.

Since most chromosome-breaking agents appear to have in common only their ability to affect the synthesis, state, or structure of DNA, it is difficult to avoid the conclusion that the chromosome constituent involved is the same as for mutation, viz., DNA. However, we are not likely to be able to explain the mechanisms of chromosome breakage until we know more about the structure and organization of the interphase chromosome. In spite of the great advances in our basic knowledge about the cell and its substructures which have been made since the Second World War, we still know remarkably little about fundamental chromosome structure. Questions such as "How many strands are there in a chromatid?" and "Is the structural backbone of the chromosome composed of DNA or of protein or of both?" still remain unanswered. This is the more remarkable since the morphological appearance of the chromosomes during mitosis and their chemical composition has been known for some time.

The electron microscope, which has helped us to resolve so many substructures of the cell, has so far not been very useful as a tool for studying details of chromosome structure. However, the spreading technique of Kleinschmidt et al. (1962), which recently has been developed by Gall (1963b) for electron microscopic studies of interphase chromosomes appears to be much superior to the conventional sectioning techniques, and there is now hope that the question about the structural organization of the interphase chromosome shall be solved in the not-too-distant future. Once fundamental chromosome structure is understood, the damaging effects of chemicals will be more readily comprehensible, and all the pieces of the puzzle may then fall into place.

References

Abele, K., 1951. Über die Volumenabnahme des Zellkerns in die Plasmolyse und über das Zustandekommen der Kern-plasmarelation. Protoplasma 40:324–337.

Afzelius, B. A., 1955. The ultrastructure of the nuclear membrane of the sea urchin oocyte as studied with the electron microscope. Exp. Cell Res. 8:147–158.

Ahnström, G. and Natarajan, A. T., 1966. Mechanism of chromosome breakage—A new theory. Hereditas 54:379–388.

Albert, A., 1953. Quantitative studies of the avidity of naturally occurring substances for trace metals. I. Pteridines, riboflavin and purines. Biochem. J. 54:646–654.

Albuquerque, R. M. and Serra, J. A., 1951. Nucleolar composition and the nucleolar zones of the chromosomes. Portugaliae Acta Biol. 3:Pt. A, 187–193.

Alfert, M., 1955. Quantitative cytochemical studies on patterns of nuclear growth. Symp. on Fine Structure of Cells (Leiden) Int. U. Biol. Sci. Pub. B 21, pp. 157–163.

Allfrey, V. G., 1963. Studies of energy-yielding reactions in isolated cell nuclei. Exp. Cell Res. (Suppl. 9):418–429.

Allfrey, V. G. and Mirsky, A. E., 1957. Some aspects of ribonucleic acid synthesis in isolated cell nuclei. Nat. Acad. Sci. (U.S.), Proc., 43:821–826.

Allfrey, V. G., Mirsky, A. E., and Osawa, S., 1955a. Protein synthesis in isolated cell nuclei. Nature 176:1042–1049.

Allfrey, V. G., Mirsky, A. E., and Stern, H., 1955b. The chemistry of the cell nucleus. Advance. Enzymol. 16:411–500.

Allfrey, V. G., Stern, H., Mirsky, A. E., and Saetren, H., 1952. The isolation of cell nuclei in non-aqueous media. J. Gen. Physiol. 35:529–557.

Allison, A. C., and Paton, G. R., 1965. Chromosome damage in human diploid cells following activation of lysosomal enzymes. Nature 207:1170–1173.

Ambrose, E. J., and Gopal-Ayengar, A. R., 1953. Molecular orientation and chromosome breakage. Symposium on Chromosome Breakage. Heredity 6 (Suppl.): 277–292.

Amoore, J. E., 1961a. Arrest of mitosis in roots by oxygen-lack or cyanide. Roy. Soc. (London), Proc., B 154:95–108.

Amoore, J. E., 1961b. Dependence of mitosis and respiration in roots upon oxygen tension. Roy. Soc. (London), Proc., B. 154:109–129.

Amoore, J. E., 1962a. Oxygen tension and the rates of mitosis and interphase in roots. J. Cell Biol. 13:365–371.

Amoore, J. E., 1962b. Participation of a non-respiratory ferrous complex during mitosis in roots. J. Cell Biol. 13:373–381.

Amoore, J. E., 1963a. Non-identical mechanisms of mitotic arrest by respiratory inhibitors in pea root-tips and sea urchin eggs. J. Cell Biol. 18:555–567.

Amoore, J. E., 1963b. Action spectrum of mitotic ferrous complex. Nature 199:38–40.

Anderson, N. G., Fisher, W. D., and Bond, H. E., 1960. Cell division V. Molecular mechanisms. Ann. N.Y. Acad. Sci. 90:486–499.

Avanzi, S., Brunori, A., D'Amato, F., Nuti Ronchi, V., and Scarascia Mugnozza, G. T., 1963. Occurrence of 2 C (G_1) and 4 C (G_2) nuclei in the radicle meristems of dry seeds in *Triticum durum* Desf. Its implications in studies on chromosome breakage and on developmental processes. Caryologia 16:553–558.

Bahr, G. F., and Beermann, W., 1954. The fine structure of the nuclear membrane in the larval salivary gland and midgut of *Chironomus*. Exp. Cell Res. 6:519–522.

Bairati, A., and Lehmann, F. E., 1952. Über die submikroskopische Struktur der Kernmembran bei *Amoeba proteus*. Experientia 8:60–61.

Bajer, A., 1954. Cine-micrographic studies on mitosis in endosperm. I. Acta Soc. Bot. Poloniae 23:383–412.

Bajer, A., 1955. Living smears from endosperm. Experientia 11:221.

Bajer, A., 1957. Cine-micrographic studies on mitosis in endosperm. III. The origin of the mitotic spindle. Exp. Cell Res. 13:493–502.

Bajer, A., 1958. Cine-micrographic studies on mitosis in endosperm. IV. The mitotic contraction stage. Exp. Cell Res. 14:245–256.

Bajer, A., 1961. A note on the behaviour of spindle fibers at mitosis. Chromosoma 12:64–71.

Bajer, A., and Molè-Bajer, J., 1956. Cine-micrographic studies on mitosis in endosperm. II. Chromosome, cytoplasmic and Brownian movements. Chromosoma 7:558–607.

Baltus, E., 1954. Biochemical role of the nucleolus. Biochim. Biophys. Acta 15:263–267.

Baltus, E., and Brachet, J., 1963. Presence of deoxyribonucleic acid in the chloroplasts of *Acetabularia mediterrana*. Biochim. Biophys. Acta 76:490–492.

Barnes, J. M., Magee, P. N., Boyland, E., Haddow, A., Passey, R. D., Bullough, W. S., Cruickshank, C. N. D., Salaman, M. H., and Williams, R. T., 1957. The non-toxicity of maleic hydrazide for mammalian tissue. Nature 180:62–64.

Bartz, Q. R., Haskell, T. H., Elder, C. C., Johannessen, D. W., Frohardt, R. P., Ryder, A., and Fusari, S. A., 1954. Isolation and characterization of azaserine. Nature 173:72–73.

Bass, R., Bernick, S., and Saltman, P., 1957. The nucleus in the accumulation of iron by liver cell suspensions. Exp. Cell Res. 13:395–397.

Bass, R. L., and Saltman, P., 1959. The accumulation of iron by rat liver cell suspensions. Exp. Cell Res. 18:560–572.

Baud, C. A., 1948. A cytochemical study of the perinuclear lipidic layer in the liver cell. Nature 161:559.

Beadle, G. W., 1933. Polymitotic maize and the precocity hypothesis of chromosome conjugation. Cytologia 5:118–121.

Beevers, H., 1961. Respiratory Metabolism in Plants. 231 pp. Row, Peterson and Company, Evanston, Ill. and White Plains, N. Y., 1961.

Behki, R. M., and Schneider, W. C., 1962. Intracellular distribution of deoxyribosidic compounds in normal and regenerating liver and in Novikoff hepatoma. Biochim. Biophys. Acta 61:663–667.

Behki, R. M., and Schneider, W. C., 1963. Incorporation of tritiated thymidine into deoxyribonucleic acid by isolated nuclei. Biochim. Biophys. Acta 68:34–44.

Behrens, M., 1938. Über die Lokalisation der Hefenucleinsäure in pflanzlichen Zellen. Z. physiol. Chem. 253:185–192.

References

Bell, S., and Wolff, S., 1964. Studies on the mechanism of the effect of fluorodeoxy-uridine on chromosomes. Nat. Acad. Sci. (U.S.), Proc., 51:195–202.

Bendich, A., Borenfreund, E., Korngold, G. C., and Krim, M., 1963. Action of hydroxylamines on DNA and chromosomes. Fed. Proc. 22:582.

Bendich, A., and Brown, G. B., 1948. 2.6-Diaminopurine, a precursor of nucleic acid guanine. J. Biol. Chem. 176:1471–1472.

Bensch, K. G., and King, D. W., 1961. Incorporation of heterologous deoxyribonucleic acid into mammalian cells. Science 133:381–382.

Berg, N. O., 1951. A histological study of masked lipids. Stainability, distribution and functional variations. Acta Path. Microbiol. Scand. (Suppl. 90):1–192.

Bernstein, M. H., and Mazia, D., 1953. The deoxyribonucleoprotein of sea urchin sperm. I. Isolation and analysis. Biochim. et Biophys. Acta 10:600–606.

Bertani, L. E., Häggmark, A., and Reichard, P., 1963. Enzymatic synthesis of deoxyribonucleotides. II. Formation and interconversion of deoxyuridine phosphates. J. Biol. Chem. 238:3407–3413.

Bessman, M. J., 1963. The replication of DNA in cell-free systems, p. 1–64. In Molecular Genetics, Part 1, J. H. Taylor, ed.

Bessman, M. J., Lehman, I. R., Adler, J. Zimmerman, S. B., Simms, E. S., and Kornberg, A., 1958. Enzymatic synthesis of deoxyribonucleic acid. III. The incorporation of pyrimidine and purine analogues into deoxyribonucleic acid. Nat. Acad. Sci. (U.S.), Proc., 44:633–640.

Betel, I., and Klouwen, H. M., 1963. Adenosine triphosphate synthesis in isolated rat-thymus nuclei. Biochim. Biophys. Acta 76:327–329.

Bieber, S., Spence, J. A., and Hitchings, G. M., 1959. Nucleic acids and their derivatives and the development of Rana pipiens. Exp. Cell Res. 16:202–214.

Biesele, J. J., 1954a. Mitotic derangements in tissue culture caused by inhibitors of sarcoma growth in the mouse. Anat. Rec. 118:444.

Biesele, J. J., 1954b. Assay of carcinolytic and carcinostatic agents. Ann. N.Y. Acad. Sci. 58:1129–1145.

Biesele, J. J., 1958a. Mitotic Poisons and the Cancer Problem. 214 pp. Elsevier Publ. Co., Amsterdam, 1958.

Biesele, J. J., 1958b. Studies on mitosis in purine-treated tissue cultures. In Frontiers in Cytology (L. Palay, ed.), pp. 84–112. Yale University Press, New Haven, Conn., 1958.

Biesele, J. J., 1962. Experimental and therapeutic modification of mitosis. Cancer Res. 22:779–787.

Biesele, J. J., Berger, R. F., and Clarke, M., 1952a. Tissue culture screening of purines and purine nucleosides for selective damage to mouse sarcoma cells. Cancer Res. 12:399–406.

Biesele, J. J., Berger, R. F., Clarke, M., and Weiss, L., 1952b. Effects of purines and other chemotherapeutic agents on nuclear structure and function. Exp. Cell Res. (Suppl. 2):279–300.

Biesele, J. J., Clarke, M., and Margolis, M., 1955. Unsubstituted purine and its riboside as toxic antimetabolites in mouse tissue cultures. Cancer 8:87–96.

Biesele, J. J., Philips, F. S., Thiersch, J. B., Burchenal, J. H., Buckley, S. M., and Stock, C. C., 1950. Chromosome alteration and tumor inhibition by nitrogen mustards: the hypothesis of cross-linking alkylation. Nature 166:1112–1113.

Birnstiel, M. L., Chipchase, M. I. H., and Flamm, W. G., 1964. On the chemistry and organization of nucleolar proteins. Biochim. Biophys. Acta 87:111–122.

Birnstiel, M. L., Chipchase, M. I. H., and Hyde, B. B., 1963a. The nucleolus, a source of ribosomes. Biochim. Biophys. Acta **76**:454–462.

Birnstiel, M. L., Fleissner, E., and Borek, E., 1963b. Nucleolus: a center of RNA methylation. Science **142**:1577–1580.

Birnstiel, M. L., Sirlin, J. L., and Jacob, J., 1965. The nucleolus: a site of transfer ribonucleic acid synthesis. Biochem. J. **94**:10P–11P.

Birt, L. M. and Hird, F. J. R., 1956. The uptake of amino acids by carrot slices. Biochem. J. **64**:305–311.

Blakeslee, A. F. and Avery, A. G., 1937. Methods of inducing doubling of chromosomes in plants. J. Hered. **28**:393–411.

Bloch, A. and Hutchison, D. J., 1964. A mechanism of resistance to fluoropyrimidines. Cancer Res. **24**:433–439.

Bollum, F. J., 1963. "Primer" in DNA polymerase reactions. Progress in Nucleic Acid Research **1**:1–26.

Booth, J. and Boyland, E., 1953. The reaction of the carcinogenic dibenzcarbazoles and dibenzacridines with purines and nucleic acid. Biochim. Biophys. Acta **12**:75–87.

Borenfreund, E., Krim, M., and Bendich, A., 1964. Chromosomal aberrations induced by hyponitrite and hydroxylamine derivatives. J. Nat. Cancer Inst. **32**:667–679.

Brachet, J., 1940. La détection histochemique des acides pentosenucléiques. Compt. Rend. Soc. Biol. **133**:88–90.

Brachet, J., 1942. La localisation des acides pentosenucléiques dans les tissus animaux et les oeufs d'amphibiens en voie de développement. Arch. Biol. **53**:207–257.

Brachet, J., 1956. Cytoplasmic and nuclear structure in relation to metabolic activities. Ciba Foundation Symposium on Ionizing Radiations and Cell Metabolism:3–20. London, 1956.

Brandt, P. W., 1958. A study of the mechanism of pinocytosis. Exp. Cell Res. **15**:300–313.

Brockman, H. E. and de Serres, F. J., 1963. Induction of ad-3 mutants of *Neurospora crassa* by 2-aminopurine. Genetics **48**:597–604.

Brockman, R. W., Davis, J. M., and Stutts, P., 1960. Metabolism of uracil and 5-fluorouracil by drug-sensitive and by drug-resistant bacteria. Biochim. Biophys. Acta **40**:22–32.

Brockman, R. W., Sparks, C., Hutchison, D. J., and Skipper, H. E., 1959. A mechanism of resistance to 8-azaguanine. I. Microbiological studies on the metabolism of purines and 8-azapurines. Cancer Res. **19**:177–188.

Brouwers, J. A. J. and Emmelot, B., 1960. Microsomal N-demethylation and the effect of the hepatic carcinogen dimethylnitrosamine on amino acid incorporation into the proteins of rat livers and hepatomas. Exp. Cell Res. **19**:467–474.

Brown, G. L., Callan, H. G., and Leaf, G., 1950. Chemical nature of nuclear sap. Nature **165**:600.

Buchanan, J. M., 1960. Biosynthesis of purine nucleotides. *In* The Nucleic Acids, Vol. III, E. Chargaff and J. N. Davidson, eds., 304–322. Academic Press, New York, 1960.

Bullough, W. S., 1952. The energy relations of mitotic activity. Biol. Rev. **27**:133–168.

Burian, R., 1906. Chemie der Spermatozoen II. Ergeb. Physiol. **5**:768–846.

Busch, H., 1963. Summary of discussion on histones of tumor cells. Exp. Cell Res., Suppl. **9**:387–388.

References

Busch, H., Byvoet, P., and Adams, H. R., 1963. Chromatographic analysis of acid-soluble proteins obtained from the nuclear sap and deoxyribonucleoproteins. Exp. Cell Res. (Suppl. 9):376–386.

Buvat, R., 1963. Electron microscopy of plant protoplasm. Int. Rev. Cytol. 14:41–155.

Callaghan, J. J. and Grun, P., 1961. Incorporation of C^{14}-labeled maleic hydrazide into the root-tip cells of *Allium cernuum, Vicia faba,* and *Tradescantia paludosa.* J. Biophys. Biochem. Cytol. 10:567–575.

Callan, H. G., 1949. A physiological study of isolated nuclei and its implications regarding gene action. Proc. 8th Int. Congr. Genet. (Hereditas Suppl. Vol): 547–548.

Callan, H. G., 1956. Recent work on the structure of cell nuclei. Symposium on the Fine Structure of Cells (Leiden), Int. U. Biol. Sci. Pub. B 21, pp. 89–109.

Callan, H. G. and Macgregor, H. C., 1958. Action of deoxyribonuclease on lamp-brush chromosomes. Nature 181:1479–1480.

Callan, H. G. and Tomlin, S. G., 1950. Experimental studies on amphibian oocyte nuclei. I. Investigation of the structure of the nuclear membrane by means of the electron microscope. Roy. Soc. (London), Proc., B 137:367–378.

Carlson, J. G., 1954. Immediate effects on division, morphology, and viability of the cell. *In* Radiation Biology, Vol. 1, Part 2, A. Hollaender, ed., 763–824. McGraw-Hill, New York, 1954.

Caspersson, T., Farber, S., Foley, G. E., and Killander, D., 1963. Cytochemical observations on the nucleolus-ribosome system. Effects of actinomycin D and nitrogen mustard. Exp. Cell Res. 32:529–552.

Caspersson, T. and Schultz, J., 1939. Pentose nucleotides in the cytoplasm of growing tissues. Nature 143:602–603.

Caspersson, T. and Schultz, J., 1940. Ribonucleic acids in both nucleus and cytoplasm, and the function of the nucleolus. Nat. Acad. Sci. (U.S.), Proc., 26:507–515.

Caspersson, T. and Thorell, B., 1941. Der endozelluläre Eiweiss- und Nuklein-säurestoffwechsel in embryonalem Gewebe. Chromosoma 2:132–154.

Catcheside, D. G., Lea, D. E., and Thoday, J. M., 1946. The production of chromosome structural changes in *Tradescantia* microspores in relation to dosage, intensity and temperature. J. Genet. 47:137–149.

Cavalieri, L. and Rosenberg, B. H., 1961. The replication of DNA II. The number of polynucleotide strands in the conserved unit of DNA. Biophys. J. 1:323–336.

Chayen, J., LaCour, L. F., and Gahan, P. S., 1957. Uptake of benzpyrene by a chromosomal phospholipid. Nature 180:652–653.

Chipchase, M. I. H. and Birnstiel, M. L., 1963. The nature of nucleolar ribonucleic acid (RNA). Nat. Acad. Sci. (U.S.), Proc., 50:1101–1107.

Chorazy, M., Bendich, A., Borenfreund, E., and Hutchison, D. J., 1963a. Studies on the isolation of metaphase chromosomes. J. Cell Biol. 19:59–69.

Chorazy, M., Bendich, A., Borenfreund, E., Ittensohn, O. L., and Hutchison, D. J., 1963b. Uptake of mammalian chromosomes by mammalian cells. J. Cell Biol. 19:71–77.

Chu, M. Y. and Fischer, G. A., 1962. A proposed mechanism of action of 1-β-D-arabinofuranosyl-cytosine as an inhibitor of the growth of leukemic cells. Biochem. Pharmacol. 11:423–430.

Churney, L., 1941. Cytology, genetics, evolution. University of Pennsylvania Bicentennial Conf., Philadelphia, 1941. pp. 113–128.

References

Cocito, C., Prinzie, A., and DeSomer, P., 1962. Uptake by mammalian cells of nucleic acids combined with a basic protein. Experientia 18:218–220.

Cohen, M. M., Shaw, M. W., and Craig, A. P., 1963. The effects of streptonigrin on cultured human leukocytes. Nat. Acad. Sci. (U.S.), Proc., 50:16–24.

Cohen, S. S., Flaks, J. G., Barner, H. D., Loeb, M. R., and Lichtenstein, J., 1958. The mode of action of 5-fluorouracil and its derivatives. Nat. Acad. Sci. (U.S.), Proc., 44:1004–1012.

Cohn, N. S., 1961. The effect of chelation on the production of chromatid aberrations in Vicia faba. Exp. Cell Res. 24:596–599.

Cohn, N. S., 1964. Similar cytological effects of hydroxylamine and 5-FUdR, agents with different modes of action. Experientia 20:158–161.

Cole, A., 1962. A molecular model for biological contractility:implications in chromosome structure and function. Nature 196:211–214.

Collander, R. and Bärlund, H., 1933. Permeabilitätsstudien an Chara ceratophylla II. Die Permeabilität für Nichtelektrolyte. Acta Bot. Fenn. 11:1–114.

Craddock, V. M. and Magee, P. N., 1963. Reaction of the carcinogen dimethylnitrosamine with nucleic acids in vivo. Biochem. J. 89:32–37.

Creasey, W. A. and Stocken, L. A., 1959. The effect of ionizing radiation on nuclear phosphorylation in the radiosensitive tissues of the rat. Biochem. J. 72:519–523.

Crosbie, G. W., 1960. Biosynthesis of pyrimidine nucleotides, p. 323–348. In The Nucleic Acids, Vol. III, E. Chargaff and J. N. Davidson, eds.

Crouse, H. V., 1954. X-ray breakage of lily chromosomes at first meiotic metaphase. Science 119:485–487.

Culvenor, C. C. J., Dann, A. T., and Dick, A. T., 1962. Alkylation as the mechanism by which the hepatotoxic pyrrolizidine alkaloids act on cell nuclei. Nature 195:570–573.

Dalton, A. J. and Felix, M. D., 1957. Electron microscopy of mitochondria and the Golgi complex. Symp. Soc. Exp. Biol. 10:148–159.

D'Amato, F., 1949a. Preprophase inhibition of mitosis in root meristems. Caryologia 1:109–121.

D'Amato, F., 1949b. Prophase poisoning by chemical agents. Caryologia 1:327–328.

D'Amato, F., 1952. The cytological study of chemical mutagens. Genet. Iber. 4:3–20.

Danielli, J. F., 1954. The present position in the field of facilitated diffusion and selective active transport. In Recent Developments in Cell Physiology, J. A. Kitching, ed., pp. 1–14. Butterworths, London, 1954.

Darlington, C. D. 1937. Recent Advances in Cytology. 2nd ed. J. and A. Churchill Ltd. London, 1937, 671 p.

Darlington, C. D. and Koller, P. C., 1947. The chemical breakage of chromosomes. Heredity 1:187–221.

Darlington, C. D. and McLeish, J., 1951. Action of maleic hydrazide on the cell. Nature 167:407–408.

Das, N. K., 1962. Demonstration of a non-RNA nucleolar fraction by silver staining. Exp. Cell Res. 26:428–431.

Das, N. K., 1963. Chromosomal and nucleolar RNA synthesis in root-tips during mitosis. Science 140:1231–1233.

Davidson, D., 1964. RNA synthesis in roots of Vicia faba. Exp. Cell Res. 35:317–325.

References

Davidson, J. N. and McIndoe, W. M., 1949. Phosphorus compounds in the cell nucleus. Biochem. J. 45:xvi.

Deeley, E. M., Davies, H. G., and Chayen, J., 1957. The DNA content of cells in the root of *Vicia faba*. Exp. Cell Res. 12:582–591.

Deschner, E. E. and Gray, L. H., 1959. Influence of oxygen tension on X-ray-induced chromosomal damage in Ehrlich ascites tumor cells irradiated *in vitro* and *in vivo*. Radiat. Res. 11:115–146.

Dewey, W. C. and Humphrey, R. M., 1962. Relative radiosensitivity of different phases in the life cycle of L-P59 mouse fibroblasts and ascites tumor cells. Radiat. Res. 16:503–530.

Dobzhansky, T., 1947. Genetics and the Origin of Species. 446 pp. Columbia University Press, New York, 1947.

Dounce, A. L., 1943. Enzyme studies on isolated cell nuclei of rat liver. J. Biol. Chem. 147:685–698.

Dounce, A. L., 1952. The enzymes of isolated nuclei. Exp. Cell Res., Suppl. 2:103–119.

Dounce, A. L., 1954. The significance of enzyme studies on isolated cell nuclei. Int. Rev. Cytol. 3:199–223.

Dounce, A. L. and Beyer, G. T., 1948. The arginase activity of isolated cell nuclei. J. Biol. Chem. 174:859–872.

Dounce, A. L., Kay, E. R. M., and Pate, S., 1953. Cytochrome oxidase and succinic dehydrogenase of isolated liver cell nuclei. Fed. Proc. 12:198 (646).

Dounce, A. L. and Sarkar, N. K., 1960. Nucleoprotein organization in cell nuclei and its relationship to chromosomal structure, p. 206–210. *In* The Cell Nucleus, J. S. Mitchell, ed. Butterworths, London, 1960.

Dounce, A. L., Tishkoff, G. H., Barnett, S. R., and Freer, R. M., 1950. Free amino acids and nucleic acid content of cell nuclei isolated by a modification of Behrens' technique. J. Gen. Physiol. 33:629–642.

Druckrey, H., 1938. Experimentelle Beiträge zur Frage der Entstehung von Riesenzellen. Z. Krebsforsch. 47:13–16.

Druckrey, H., Preussmann, R., Schmähl, D., and Müller, M., 1961a. Chemische Konstitution und carcinogene Wirkung bei Nitrosaminen. Naturwissenschaften 48:134–135.

Druckrey, H., Preussmann, R., Schmähl, D., and Müller, M., 1961b. Erzeugung von Magenkrebs durch Nitrosamide an Ratten. Naturwissenschaften 48:165.

Druckrey, H., Preussmann, R., Schmähl, D., and Blum, G., 1961c. Carcinogene Wirkung von N-Methyl-N-nitrosoanilin. Naturwissenschaften 48:722–723.

Druckrey, H. and Schreiber, E., 1938. Die Wirkung des Coffeins auf die Zellteilung und das Wachstum. Arch. Exp. Pathol. Pharmacol. 188:208–214.

Dubbs, D. R. and Kit, S., 1964. Effect of halogenated pyrimidines and thymidine on growth of L-cells and subline lacking thymidine kinase. Exp. Cell Res. 33:19–28.

DuPraw, E. J., 1965. Macromolecular organization of nuclei and chromosomes: a folded fiber model based on whole-mount electron microscopy. Nature 206:338–343.

Dustin, A. P., Havas, L., and Lits, F., 1937. Action de la colchicine sur les divisions cellulaires chez las végétaux. Compt. Rend. Assoc. Anatom. 32:170–176.

Edmunds, L. N., 1964. Replication of DNA and cell division in synchronously dividing cultures of *Euglena gracilis*. Science 145:266–268.

Eichhorn, G. L. and Clark, P., 1965. Interactions of metal ions with polynucleotides and related compounds. V. The unwinding and rewinding of DNA strands under the influence of copper (II) ions. Nat. Acad. Sci. (U.S.), Proc., 53:586–593.

Eigsti, O., 1938. A cytological study of colchicine effects in the induction of polyploidy in plants. Nat. Acad. Sci. (U.S.), Proc., 24:56–63.

Eisinger, J., Shulman, R. G., and Blumberg, W. E., 1961. Relaxation enhancement by paramagnetic ion binding in deoxyribonucleic acid solutions. Nature 192:963–964.

Elliott, W. H., 1963. The effects of antimicrobial agents on deoxyribonucleic acid polymerase. Biochem. J. 86:562–567.

Emmelot, P., Mizrahi, I. J., and Kriek, E., 1962. Prevention by cysteamine of the inhibitory effect of carcinogenic N-nitrosodialkylamines on incorporation of amino acids in rat liver. Nature 193:1158–1161.

Epel, D., 1963. The effects of carbon monoxide inhibition on ATP level and the rate of mitosis in the sea urchin egg. J. Cell Biol. 17:315–319.

Erickson, R. O., 1947. Respiration of developing anthers. Nature 159:275–276.

Evans, H. J., 1961. Chromatid aberrations induced by gamma irradiation. I. The structure and frequency of chromatid interchanges in diploid and tetraploid cells of Vica faba. Genetics 46:257–275.

Evans, H. J., 1962. Chromosome aberrations induced by ionizing radiations. Int. Rev. Cytol. 13:221–231.

Evans, H. J., 1963. Chromosome aberrations and target theory, p.8-40. In Radiation-Induced Chromosome Aberrations, S. Wolff, ed. Columbia University Press, New York, 1963.

Evans, H. J., 1964. Uptake of ^{3}H-thymidine and patterns of DNA replication in nuclei and chromosomes of Vicia faba. Exp. Cell Res. 35:381–393.

Evans, H. J. and Bigger, T. R. L., 1961. Chromatid aberrations induced by gamma irradiation. II. Nonrandomness in the distribution of chromatid aberrations in relation to chromosome length in Vicia faba root-tip cells. Genetics 46:277–289.

Evans, H. J. and Neary, G. J., 1959. The influence of oxygen on the sensitivity of Tradescantia pollen tube chromosomes to X-rays. Radiat. Res. 11:636–641.

Evans, H. J. and Savage, J. R. K., 1963. The relation between DNA synthesis and chromosome structure as resolved by X-ray damage. J. Cell Biol. 18:525–540.

Evans, H. J. and Scott, D., 1964. Influence of DNA synthesis on the production of chromatid aberrations by X-rays and maleic hydrazide in Vicia faba. Genetics 49:17–38.

Feinendegen, L. E. and Bond, V. P., 1963. Nuclear ribonucleic acid (RNA) during mitosis in human cancer cells in culture (HeLa-S$_3$), studied with tritiated cytidine. Exp. Cell Res. 30:393–404.

Feldherr, C. M. and Feldherr, A. B., 1960. The nuclear membrane as a barrier to the free diffusion of proteins. Nature 185:250–251.

Felix, K., Fischer, H., and Krekels, A., 1956. Protamines and nucleoprotamines. Prog. Biophys. 6:2–23.

Ferguson, J., 1939. The use of chemical potentials as indices of toxicity. Roy. Soc. (London), Proc., B. 127:387–404.

Feulgen, R., Behrens, M., and Mahdihassan, S., 1937. Darstellung und Identifizierung der in pflanzlichen Zellkernen vorkommenden Nucleinsäure. Z. physiol. Chem. 246:203–211.

References

Feulgen, R. and Rossenbeck, H., 1924. Mikroskopisch-chemischer Nachweis einer Nucleinsäure vom Typus der Thymonucleinsäure und die darauf beruhende elektive Färbung von Zellkernen in mikroskopischen Präparaten. Z. physiol. Chem. **135**:203–248.

Finamore, F. J. and Volkin, E., 1958. Nucleotide and nucleic acid metabolism in developing amphibian embryos. Exp. Cell Res. **15**:405–411.

Flamm, W. G. and Birnstiel, M. L., 1964. Inhibition of DNA replication and its effect on histone synthesis. Exp. Cell Res. **33**:616–619.

Ford, C. E., 1949. Chromosome breakage in nitrogen mustard treated *Vicia faba* root tip cells. Proc. 8th Int. Congr. Genet. (Hereditas Suppl. Vol.):570–571.

Fourcade, M. F., Berger, C. A., and Witkus, E. R., 1963. Cytological effects of aminopyrine. Caryologia **16**:347–351.

Fraenkel-Conrat, H. and Ducay, E. D., 1951. The nucleic acid of egg white. Biochem. J. **49**:xxix.

Fredga, K. and Nyman, P. O., 1961. Study of the penetration of 8-ethoxycaffeine into roots of *Vicia faba*. Exp. Cell Res. **22**:146–150.

Freese, E., 1958. The arrangement of DNA in the chromosome. Cold Spring Harbor Symp. Quant. Biol. **23**:13–18.

Freese, E., 1959. On the molecular explanation of spontaneous and induced mutations. Brookhaven Symp. Biol. **12**:63–73.

Freese, E., 1963. Molecular mechanisms of mutations, p. 207–269. *In* Molecular Genetics, J. H. Taylor, ed. Academic Press, New York, 1963.

Freifelder, D., Davison, P. F., and Geiduschek, E. P., 1961. Damage by visible light to the acridine orange-DNA complex. Biophysic. J. **1**:389–400.

Frenster, J. H., Allfrey, V. G., and Mirsky, A. E., 1960. Metabolism and morphology of ribonucleoprotein particles from the cell nucleus of lymphocytes. Nat. Acad. Sci. (U.S.), Proc., **46**:432–444.

Frieden, E. and Alles J., 1958. Subtle interactions of cupric ion with nucleic acid components. J. Biol. Chem. **230**:797–804.

Gall, J. G., 1955. Problems of structure and function in the amphibian oocyte nucleus. Symp. Soc. Exp. Biol. **9**:358–370.

Gall, J. G., 1958. Chromosomal differentiation, p. 103–135. *In* Symp. on The Chemical Basis of Development, W. D. McElroy and B. Glass, eds. The Johns Hopkins Press, Baltimore, 1958.

Gall, J. G., 1963a. Kinetics of deoxyribonuclease action on chromosomes. Nature **198**:36–38.

Gall, J. G., 1963b. Chromosome fibers from an interphase nucleus. Science **139**:120–121.

Gartler, S. M., 1960. Demonstration of cellular uptake of polymerized DNA in mammalian cell cultures. Biochem. Biophys. Res. Commun. **3**:127–131.

Gavaudan, P. and Gavaudan, N., 1937. Modifications numériques et morphologiques des chromosomes, induites chez les végétaux par l'action de la colchicine. Compt. Rend. Soc. Biol. **126**:985–988.

Geitler, L., 1944. Über eine postmeiotische Teilungsanomalie und den Spiralbau der Chromosomen von *Paris quadrifolia*. Chromosoma **2**:519–530.

Gelfant, S., 1963. Inhibition of cell division: a critical and experimental analysis. Int. Rev. Cytol. **14**:1–39.

Gichner, T., Michaelis, A., and Rieger, R., 1963. Radiomimetic effects of 1-methyl-3-nitro-1-nitrosoguanidine. Biochem. Biophys. Res. Commun. **11**:120–124.

Giles, N. H. and Beatty, A. V., 1950. The effect of X-irradiation in oxygen and in hydrogen at normal and positive pressures on chromosome aberration frequency in *Tradescantia* microspores. Science 112:643–645.

Giles, N. H., Beatty, A. V., and Riley, H. P., 1951. The relationship between the effects of temperature and of oxygen on the frequency of X-ray induced chromosome aberrations in *Tradescantia* microspores. Genetics 36:552–553.

Gilson, G., 1892. On the affinity of nuclein for iron and other substances. Rep. Brit. Ass. Adv. Sci. 1892: 778–780.

Giri, K. V. and Rao, P. S., 1946. The inhibitors of enzymatic and cupric ion oxidation of vitamin C. Indian Acad. Sci., Proc., Sect. B. 24:264–278.

Gol'dshtein, B. I. and Gerasimova, V. V., 1963. Denaturation and fragmentation of deoxyribonucleic acid in cells of animal organisms. Ukr. Biokhim. Zh. 35(1):3–17.

Gosselin, A., 1940. Action, sur la mitose des végétaux, de deux alcaloides puriques. Compt. Rend. Acad. Sci. 210:544–546.

Graf, G. E., 1957. Chromosome breakage induced by X-rays, maleic hydrazide, and its derivatives in relation to knob number in maize. J. Hered. 48:155–159.

Green, D. E., 1964. The mitochondrion. Sci. Amer., Jan. 1964:63–74.

Greer, S. B., 1958. Growth inhibitors and their antagonists as mutagens and antimutagens in *Escherichia coli*. J. Gen. Microbiol. 18:543–564.

Grumbach, M. M., Morishima, A., and Taylor, J. H., 1963. Human sex chromosome abnormalities in relation to DNA replication and heterochromatinization. Nat. Acad. Sci. (U.S.), Proc., 49:581–589.

Grunberg-Manago, M., Ortiz, P., and Ochoa, S., 1955. Enzymatic synthesis of nucleic acid-like polynucleotides. Science 122:907–910.

Gulick, A., 1941. The chemistry of the chromosomes. Bot. Rev. 7:433–457.

Guttes, E. and Guttes, S., 1964. Thymidine incorporation by mitochondria in *Physarum polycephalum*. Science 145:1057–1058.

Hakala, M. T. and Ishihara, T., 1962. Chromosomal constitution and amethopterin resistance in cultured mouse cells. Cancer Res. 22:987–992.

Handschumacher, R. E. and Welch, A. D., 1960. Agents which influence nucleic acid metabolism, p. 453–526. *In* The Nucleic Acids, Vol. III, E. Chargaff and J. N. Davidson, eds. Academic Press Inc., New York, 1960.

Harkins, T. R. and Freiser, H., 1958. Adenine-metal complexes. J. Amer. Chem. Soc. 80:1132–1135.

Harris, H. and LaCour, L. F., 1963. Site of synthesis of cytoplasmic ribonucleic acid. Nature 200:227–229.

Harris, H. and Watts, J. W., 1962. The relationship between nuclear and cytoplasmic ribonucleic acid. Roy. Soc. (London), Proc., B 156:109–121.

Harris P. and James, T. W., 1952. Electron microscope study of the nuclear membrane of *Amoeba proteus* in thin section. Experientia 8:384–385.

Hartmann, K-U. and Heidelberger, C., 1961. Studies on fluorinated pyrimidines XIII. Inhibition of thymidylate synthetase. J. Biol. Chem. 236:3006–3013.

Hassenkamp, G., 1957. Der elektronenoptische Bau der pflanzlichen Kernmembran während der meiotischen Prophase. Naturwissenschaften 44:334–335.

Hata, T., Sano, Y., Sugawara, R., Matsumae, A., Kanamori, K., Shima, T., and Hoshi, T., 1956. Mitomycin, a new-antibiotic from *Streptomyces*. I. J. Antibiotics (Japan) 9 A:141–146.

References

Hauschka, T. S. and Levan, A., 1951. Characterization of five ascites tumors with respect to chromosome ploidy. Anat. Rec. 111:467.

Haven, F. L. and Levy, S. R., 1942. Phospholipids of tumor cells and nuclei. Cancer Res. 2:797–798.

Heidelberger, C., 1963. Biochemical mechanisms of action of fluorinated pyrimidines. Exp. Cell Res., Suppl. 9:462–471.

Heidelberger, C., Kaldor, G., Mukherjee, K. L., and Danneberg, P. B., 1960. Studies on fluorinated pyrimidines. XI In vitro studies on tumor resistance. Cancer Res. 20:903–909.

Henderson, J. F., 1962. Feedback inhibition of purine biosynthesis in ascites tumor cells. J. Biol. Chem. 237:2631–2635.

Henderson, J. F. and Mazel, P., 1964. Demethylation of purine analogs by microsomal enzymes from mouse liver. Biochem. Pharmacol. 13:207–210.

Hill, M., 1961. Uptake of deoxyribonucleic acid (DNA): a special property of the cell nucleus. Nature 189:916–917.

Hilmoe, R. J. and Heppel, L. A., 1957. Polynucleotide phosphorylase in liver nuclei. J. Amer. Chem. Soc. 79:4810–4811.

Hoff-Jørgensen, E. and Zeuthen, E., 1952. Evidence of cytoplasmic deoxyribosides in the frog's egg. Nature 169:245–246.

Hoffman-Ostenhof, O., 1963. Enzyme inhibition by quinones. In Metabolic Inhibitors, R. M. Hochster and J. H. Quastel, eds., II:145–159. Academic Press, New York, 1963.

Hogeboom, G. H. and Schneider, W. C., 1952. Synthesis of diphosphopyridine nucleotide by cell nuclei isolated in aqueous media. Nature 170:374.

Holter, H., 1961. The induction of pinocytosis, p. 77–86. In Biological Aspects of Cancer Chemotherapy, R. J. C. Harris, ed. Academic Press, New York.

Hoskins, G. C. and Montgomery, P. O'B., 1962. Nucleolar phagocytosis by HeLa and Chang liver cells in tissue culture as studied by time lapse phase contrast cinematography. Exp. Cell. Res. 26:534–540.

Howard, A. and Pelc, S. R., 1953. Synthesis of desoxyribonucleic acid in normal and irradiated cells and its relation to chromosome breakage. Symposium on Chromosome Breakage. Heredity 6 (Suppl.):261–273.

Howard-Flanders, P., 1957. Effect of nitric oxide on the radiosensitivity of bacteria. Nature 180:1191–1192.

Howard-Flanders, P. and Alper, T., 1957. The sensitivity of microorganisms to irradiation under controlled gas conditions. Radiat. Res. 7:518–540.

Hsu, T. C., 1963. Longitudinal differentiation of chromosomes and the possibility of interstitial telomeres. Exp. Cell Res. (Suppl. 9):73–85.

Hsu, T. C., Dewey, W. C., and Humphrey, R. M., 1962. Radiosensitivity of cells of Chinese hamster in vitro in relation to the cell cycle. Exp. Cell Res. 27:441–452.

Hsu, T. C., Humphrey, R. M., and Somers, C. E., 1964. Responses of Chinese hamster and L cells to 2'-deoxy-5-fluoro-uridine and thymidine. J. Nat. Cancer Inst. 32:839–855.

Hsu, T. C. and Somers, C. E., 1961. Effect of 5-bromodeoxyuridine on mammalian chromosomes. Nat. Acad. Sci. (U.S.), Proc., 47:396–403.

Hsu, T. C. and Somers, C. E., 1962. Properties of L cells resistant to 5-bromodeoxyuridine. Exp. Cell Res. 26:404–410.

Huennekens, F. M., Bertino, J. R., Silber, R., and Gabrio, B. W., 1963. Antimetabolites in the chemotherapy of leukemia. Exp. Cell Res. (Suppl. 9):441–461.

Hughes, A., 1952. The Mitotic Cycle. Butterworths, London, 1952. 232 p.

Hughes, C. and Spragg, S. P., 1958. The inhibition of mitosis by the reaction of maleic hydrazide with sulphydryl groups. Biochem. J. **70**:205–212.

Inoué, S., 1952. The effect of colchicine on the microscopic and submicroscopic structure of the mitotic spindle. Exp. Cell Res. (Suppl. **2**):305–314.

Iwamura, T., 1955. Change of nucleic acid content in *Chlorella* cells during the course of their life-cycle. J. Biochem. **42**:575–589.

Iwamura, T., 1960. Distribution of nucleic acids among subcellular fractions of *Chlorella*. Biochim. Biophys. Acta **42**:161–163.

Ives, D. H., Morse, P. A., and Potter, Van R., 1963. Feedback inhibition of thymidine kinase by thymidine triphosphate. J. Biol. Chem. **238**:1467–1474.

Iyer, V. N., and Szybalski, W., 1963. A molecular mechanism of mitomycin action: linking of complementary DNA strands. Nat. Acad. Sci. (U.S.), Proc., **50**:355–362.

Iyer, V. N. and Szybalski, W., 1964. Mitomycins and porfiromycin: chemical mechanisms of activation and cross-linking of DNA. Science **145**:55–58.

Izawa, M., Allfrey, V. G., and Mirsky, A. E., 1963. Composition of the nucleus and the chromosomes in the lampbrush stage of the newt oocyte. Nat. Acad. Sci. (U.S.), Proc., **50**:811–817.

Jacobson, W. and Webb, M., 1952. The two types of nucleoproteins during mitosis. Exp. Cell Res. **3**:163–183.

James, W. O., 1953. Plant Respiration. 282 pp. Clarendon Press, Oxford, 1953.

Kaufmann, B. P. and Das, N. K., 1955. The role of ribonucleoproteins in the production of mitotic abnormalities. Chromosoma **7**:19–38.

Kaufmann, B. P., Gay, H., and McDonald, M., 1960. Organizational patterns within chromosomes. Int. Rev. Cytol. **9**:77–127.

Kaufmann, B. P., McDonald, M., and Gay, H., 1948. Enzymatic degradation of ribonucleoproteins of chromosomes, nucleoli and cytoplasm. Nature **162**:814–815.

Kaufmann, B. P., McDonald, M., and Gay, H., 1951. The distribution and interrelation of nucleic acids in fixed cells as shown by enzymatic hydrolysis. J. Cell Comp. Physiol. **38**(Suppl. 1):71–87.

Kautz, J. K. and De Marsh, Q. B., 1955. Fine structure of the nuclear membrane in cells from the chick embryo: on the nature of the so-called "pores" in the nuclear membrane. Exp. Cell Res. **8**:394–396.

Kay, E. R. M., 1961. Incorporation of deoxyribonucleic acid by mammalian cells *in vitro*. Nature **191**:387–388.

Keir, H. M., Omura, H., and Shepherd, J. B., 1963a. Inhibition of a mammalian deoxyribonucleic acid nucleotidyltransferase by actinomycin D. Biochem. J. **89**:425–430.

Keir, H. M., Shepherd, J. B., and Hay, J., 1963b. Deoxyribonucleic acid nucleotidyltransferase activities from calf-thymus nuclei and cytoplasm. Biochem. J. **89**:9P–10P.

Keir, H. M. and Smith, Sister Marian José, 1963. Characteristics of the DNA nucleotidyl-transferase activity in non-aqueous type calf-thymus nuclei. Biochim. Biophys. Acta **68**:589–598.

Kersten, H., 1962. Action of mitomycin C on nucleic acid metabolism in tumor and bacterial cells. Biochim. Biophys. Acta **55**:558–560.

Kersten, H., Kersten, W., Leopold, G., and Schnieders, B., 1964. Effect of mitomycin C on DNAase and RNA in *Escherichia coli*. Biochim. Biophys. Acta **80**:521–523.

Kessler, B. and Chen, D., 1964. Distribution, properties and specificity of polynucleotide phosphorylase in wheat roots. Biochim. Biophys. Acta 80:533–541.

Kihlman, B. A., 1949. The effect of purine derivatives on chromosomes. Hereditas 35:393–396.

Kihlman, B. A., 1950. Induction of structural chromosome changes with adenine. Hereditas 36:103–105.

Kihlman, B. A., 1951. The permeability of the nuclear envelope and the mode of action of purine derivatives on chromosomes. Symbolae Bot. Upsalienses 11(2): 1–40.

Kihlman, B. A., 1952a. Induction of chromosome changes with purine derivatives. Symbolae Bot. Upsalienses 11(4):1–96.

Kihlman, B. A., 1952b. A survey of purine derivatives as inducers of chromosome changes. Hereditas 38:115–127.

Kihlman, B. A., 1955a. Chromosome breakage in *Allium* by 8-ethoxycaffeine and X-rays. Exp. Cell Res. 8:345–368.

Kihlman, B. A., 1955b. Oxygen and the production of chromosome aberrations by chemicals and X-rays. Hereditas 41:384–404.

Kihlman, B. A., 1956. Factors affecting the production of chromosome aberrations by chemicals. J. Biophys. Biochem. Cytol. 2:543–555.

Kihlman, B. A., 1957. Experimentally induced chromosome aberrations in plants. I. The production of chromosome aberrations by cyanide and other heavy metal complexing agents. J. Biophys. Biochem. Cytol. 3:363–380.

Kihlman, B. A., 1958. The effect of oxygen, nitric oxide, and respiratory inhibitors on the production of chromosome aberrations by X-rays. Exp. Cell Res. 14:639–642.

Kihlman, B. A., 1959a. Induction of structural chromosome changes by visible light. Nature 183:976–978.

Kihlman, B. A., 1959b. On the radiomimetic effects of cupferron and potassium cyanide. J. Biophys. Biochem. Cytol. 5:351–353.

Kihlman, B. A., 1959c. The effect of respiratory inhibitors and chelating agents on the frequencies of chromosomal aberrations produced by X-rays in *Vicia*. J. Biophys. Biochem. Cytol. 5:479–490.

Kihlman, B. A., 1959d. Effect of nitric oxide on the production of chromosomal aberrations by X-rays. Exp. Cell Res. 17:588–590.

Kihlman, B. A., 1959e. Studies on the production of chromosomal aberrations by visible light: the effects of cupferron, nitric oxide, and wavelength. Exp. Cell Res. 17:590–593.

Kihlman, B. A., 1960. The radiomimetic effect of N-nitroso-N-methylurethan in *Vicia faba*. Exp. Cell Res. 20:657–659.

Kihlman, B. A., 1961a. On the radiomimetic effect of adenine in *Vicia faba*. Exp. Cell Res. 25:694–697.

Kihlman, B. A., 1961b. Biochemical aspects of chromosome breakage. Advances Genet. 10:1–59.

Kihlman, B. A., 1961c. Cytological effects of phenylnitrosamines. I. The production of structural chromosome changes in the presence of light and acridine orange. Radiat. Bot. 1:35–42.

Kihlman, B. A., 1961d. Cytological effects of phenylnitrosamines. II. Radiomimetic effects. Radiat. Bot. 1:43–50.

Kihlman, B. A., 1961e. Cytological effects of phenylnitrosamines. III. The effect of X-ray sensitivity at low oxygen tensions. Radiat. Bot. 1:51–60.

Kihlman, B. A., 1962. The production of chromatid aberrations by 5-fluorodeoxyuridine alone and in combination with X-rays and 8-ethoxycaffeine. Caryologia 15:261–277.

Kihlman, B. A., 1963a. The effect of 5-halogenated deoxyuridines on the frequency of X-ray-induced chromosomal aberrations in Vicia faba. Hereditas 49:353–370.

Kihlman, B. A., 1963b. Deoxyadenosine as an inducer of chromosomal aberrations in Vicia faba. J. Cell. Comp. Physiol. 62:267–272.

Kihlman, B. A., 1964. The production of chromosomal aberrations by streptonigrin in Vicia faba. Mutat. Res. 1:54–62.

Kihlman, B. A. and Eriksson, T., 1962. The distribution between cell nuclei of isolocus breaks and chromatid interchanges induced by radiomimetic chemicals in Vicia faba. Hereditas 48:520–529.

Kihlman, B. A. and Levan, A., 1949. The cytological effect of caffeine. Hereditas 35:109–111.

Kihlman, B. A. and Levan, A., 1951. Localized chromosome breakage in Vicia faba. Hereditas 37:382–388.

Kihlman, B. A., Merz, T., and Swanson, C. P., 1957. Experimentally induced chromosome aberrations in plants. II. The effect of cyanide and other heavy metal complexing agents on the production of chromosome aberrations by X-rays. J. Biophys. Biochem. Cytol. 3:381–390.

Kihlman, B. A., Nichols, W. W., and Levan, A., 1963. The effect of deoxyadenosine and cytosine arabinoside on the chromosomes of human leukocytes in vitro. Hereditas 50:139–143.

Kirby, K. S., 1956. Evidence for metallic bonds linking deoxyribonucleic acids to proteins in mammalian tissues. Biochem. J. 62:31P–32P.

Kirk, J. T. O., 1963. The deoxyribonucleic acid of broad bean chloroplasts. Biochim. Biophys. Acta 76:417–424.

Kit, S. and Dubbs, D. R., 1962. Biochemistry of vaccinia-infected mouse (strain L-M). I. Effects of nucleic acid and protein synthesis. Virology 18:274–285.

Kit, S., Dubbs, D. R., Piekarski, L. J., and Hsu, T. S., 1963. Deletion of thymidine kinase activity from L cells resistant to bromodeoxyuridine. Exp. Cell Res. 31:297–312.

Kleinschmidt, A. K., Lang, D., Jacherts, D., and Zahn, R., 1962. Darstellung und Längenmessungen des gesamten Desoxyribonucleinsäure-Inhaltes von T_2-Bakteriophagen. Biochim. Biophys. Acta 61:857–864.

Klenow, H., 1959. On the effect of some adenine derivatives on the incorporation in vitro of isotopically labelled compounds into the nucleic acids of Ehrlich ascites tumor cells. Biochim. Biophys. Acta 35:412–421.

Klenow, H., 1962. Further studies on the effect of deoxyadenosine on the accumulation of deoxyadenosine triphosphate and inhibition of deoxyribonucleic acid synthesis in Ehrlich ascites tumor cells in vitro. Biochim. Biophys. Acta 61:885–896.

Koch, A. L., 1956. The metabolism of methylpurines by Escherichia coli. I. Tracer studies. J. Biol. Chem. 219:181–188.

Koller, P. C., 1953. Dicentric chromosomes in a rat tumor induced by an aromatic nitrogen mustard. Symposium on Chromosome Breakage. Heredity 6 (Suppl.): 181–196.

References

Koller, P. C. and Casarini, A., 1952. Comparison of cytological effects induced by X-rays and nitrogen mustard. Brit. J. Cancer 6:173–185.

Konrad, C. G., 1963. Protein synthesis and RNA synthesis during mitosis in animal cells. J. Cell Biol. 19:267–277.

Kornberg, A., 1957. Pathways of enzymatic synthesis of nucleotides and polynucleotides, p. 579–608. In Symp. on The Chemical Basis of Heredity, W. D. McElroy and B. Glass, eds. The Johns Hopkins Press, Baltimore, 1957.

Kornberg, A., 1960. Biologic synthesis of deoxyribonucleic acid. Science 131:1503–1508.

Krahl, M. E., 1950. Metabolic activities and cleavage of eggs of the sea urchin, *Arbacia punctulata*. A review, 1932–1949. Biol. Bull. 98:175–217.

Krakow, J. S., Coutsogeorgopoulos, C., and Canellakis, E. S., 1962. Studies on the incorporation of deoxyribonucleotides and ribonucleotides into deoxyribonucleic acid. Biochim. Biophys. Acta 55:639–650.

Kramer, P. J., 1956. Permeability in relation to respiration. Handbuch der Pflanzenphysiologie II:358–368. Springer-Verlag, Berlin, 1956.

Kuroda, Y. and Furuyama, J., 1963. Physiological and biochemical studies of effects of mitomycin C on strain HeLa cells in cell culture. Cancer Res. 23:682–687.

LaCour, L. F. and Chayen, J., 1958. A cyclic staining behavior of the chromosomes during mitosis and meiosis. Exp. Cell Res. 14:462–468.

LaCour, L. F., Chayen, J., and Gahan, P. S., 1958. Evidence for lipid material in chromosomes. Exp. Cell Res. 14:469–485.

LaCour, L. F. and Rutishauser, A., 1954. X-ray breakage experiments with endosperm. I. Sub-chromatid breakage. Chromosoma 6:696–709.

Lafontaine, J. G., 1958a. A particulate component found in nucleoli of *Allium cepa* and *Vicia faba*. J. Biophys. Biochem. Cytol. 4:229–230.

Lafontaine, J. G., 1958b. Structure and mode of formation of the nucleolus in meristematic cells of *Vicia faba* and *Allium cepa*. J. Biophys. Biochem. Cytol. 4:777–784.

Lafontaine, J. G. and Chouinard, L. A., 1963. A correlated light and electron microscope study of the nucleolar material during mitosis in *Vicia faba*. J. Cell Biol. 17:167–201.

Lajtha, L. G., 1963. On the concept of the cell cycle. J. Cell. and Comp. Physiol. 62 (Suppl. 1):143–145.

Lan, T. H., 1943. The *d*-amino acid oxidase, uricase, and choline oxidase in normal rat liver and in nuclei of normal rat liver cells. J. Biol. Chem. 151:171–175.

Lark, K. G., 1960. Studies on the mechanism regulating periodic DNA synthesis in synchronized cultures of *Alcaligenes fecalis*. Biochim. Biophys. Acta 45:121–132.

Larsson, A., 1963. Enzymatic synthesis of deoxyribonucleotides. III. Reduction of purine ribonucleotides with an enzyme system from *Escherichia coli* B. J. Biol. Chem. 238:3414–3419.

Laser, H., 1933. Der stoffwechsel von Gewebekulturen und ihr Verhalten in der Anaerobiose. Biochem. Z. 264:72–86.

Laurence, D. J. R., 1963. Chain breakage of deoxyribonucleic acid (DNA) following treatment with low doses of sulfur mustard. Roy. Soc. (London), Proc., A 271:520–530.

Lawley, P. D. and Brookes, P., 1963a. The action of alkylating agents on deoxyribonucleic acid in relation to biological effects of the alkylating agents. Exp. Cell Res. (Suppl. 9):512–520.

Lawley, P. D. and Brookes, P., 1963b. Further studies on the alkylation of nucleic acids and their constituent nucleotides. Biochem. J. 89:127–138.

Lawley, P. D. and Brookes, P., 1965. Molecular mechanism of the cytotoxic action of difunctional alkylating agents and of resistance to this action. Nature 206: 480–483.

Lerman, L. S., 1961. Structural considerations in the interaction of DNA and acridines. J. Mol. Biol. 3:18–30.

Levan, A., 1938. The effect of colchicine on root mitoses in Allium. Hereditas 24:471–486.

Levan, A., 1940. The effect of acenaphthene and colchicine on mitosis of Allium and Colchicum. Hereditas 26:262–276.

Levan, A., 1954. Colchicine-induced C-mitosis in two mouse ascites tumours. Hereditas 40:1–64.

Levan, A. and Steinegger, E., 1947. The resistance of Colchicum and Bulbocodium to the C-mitotic action of colchicine. Hereditas 23:552–566.

Levan, A. and Östergren, G., 1943. The mechanism of C-mitotic action. Observations on the naphthalene series. Hereditas 29:381–443.

Levine, C. and Chargaff, E., 1952. Phosphatide composition in different liver cell fractions. Exp. Cell Res. 3:154–162.

Levine, M. and Borthwick, M., 1963. The action of streptonigrin on bacterial DNA metabolism and on induction of phage production in lysogenic bacteria. Virology 21:568–574.

Lieb, M., 1961. Enhancement of ultraviolet-induced mutation in bacteria by caffeine. Z. Vererbungslehre 92:416–429.

Lieberman, I. and Ove, P., 1960. Enzyme studies with mutant mammalian cells. J. Biol. Chem. 235:1765–1768.

Lilly, L. J. and Thoday, J. M., 1956. Effects of cyanide on the roots of Vicia faba. Nature 177:338–339.

Lima-de-Faria, A., 1953. The regions of special cycle of division of Agapanthus chromosomes. Chromosoma 6:33–44.

Lima-de-Faria, A., 1955. The division cycle of the kinetochore. Hereditas 41:238–240.

Lima-de-Faria, A., 1958. Matrix and kinetochore in living material. Hereditas 45:463–465.

Lima-de-Faria, A., 1959. Differential uptake of tritiated thymidine into hetero- and euchromatin in Melanoplus and Secale. J. Biophys. Biochem. Cytol. 6:457–466.

Lindner, A., 1959. Cytochemical effects of 5-fluorouracil on sensitive and resistant Ehrlich ascites tumor cells. Cancer Res. 19:189–194.

Lipmann, F., 1963. Messenger ribonucleic acid. Prog. in Nucl. Acid Res. 1:135–161.

Loewenstein, W. R. and Kanno, G., 1963. The electrical conductance and potential across the membranes of some cell nuclei. J. Cell Biol. 16:421–425.

Loring, H. S. and Waritz, R. S., 1957. Occurrence of iron, copper, calcium, and magnesium in tobacco mosaic virus. Science 125:646–648.

Lorkiewicz, Z. and Szybalski, W., 1961. Mechanism of chemical mutagenesis. IV. Reaction between triethylene melamine and nucleic acid components. J. Bacteriol. 82:195–201.

Loveless, A., 1951. Qualitative aspects of the chemistry and biology of radiomimetic (mutagenic) substances. Nature 167:338–342.

References

Loveless, A., 1953. Chemical and biochemical problems arising from the study of chromosome breakage by alkylating agents and heterocyclic compounds. Symposium on Chromosome Breakage. Heredity **6** (Suppl.) 293–298.

Loveless, A. and Revell, S., 1949. New evidence on the mode of action of "mitotic poisons." Nature **164**:938–944.

Ludford, R. J., 1936. The action of toxic substances upon the division of normal and malignant cells *in vitro* and *in vivo*. Arch. Exp. Zellforsch. **18**:411–441.

McEwen, B. S., Allfrey, V. G., and Mirsky, A. E., 1963a. Studies on energy-yielding reactions in thymus nuclei. I. Comparison of nuclear and mitochondrial phosphorylation. J. Biol. Chem. **238**:758–766.

McEwen, B. S., Allfrey, V. G., and Mirsky, A. E., 1963b. Studies on energy-yielding reactions in thymus nuclei. II. Pathways of aerobic carbohydrate catabolism. J. Biol. Chem. **238**:2571–2578.

McEwen, B. S., Allfrey, V. G., and Mirsky, A. E., 1963c. Studies on energy-yielding reactions in thymus nuclei. III. Participation of glycolysis and the citric acid cycle in nuclear adenosine triphosphate synthesis. J. Biol. Chem. **238**:2579–2586.

Macgregor, H. C. and Callan, H. G., 1962. The actions of enzymes on lampbrush chromosomes. Quart. J. Microscop. Sci. **103**:173–203.

McLeish, J., 1953. The action of maleic hydrazide in *Vicia*. Symposium on Chromosome Breakage. Heredity **6** (Suppl.) 125–147.

McLeish, J., 1959. Comparative microphotometric studies of DNA and arginine in plant nuclei. Chromosoma **10**:686–710.

McLeish, J., 1964. Deoxyribonucleic acid in plant nucleoli. Nature **204**:36–39.

Magee, P. N. and Vandekar, M., 1958. Toxic liver injury. The metabolism of dimethylnitrosamine *in vitro*. Biochem. J. **70**:600–605.

Maggio, R., Siekevitz, P., and Palade, G. E., 1963a. Studies on isolated nuclei. I. Isolation and chemical characterization of a nuclear fraction from guinea pig liver. J. Cell Biol. **18**:267–291.

Maggio, R., Siekevitz, P., and Palade, G. E., 1963b. Studies on isolated nuclei. II. Isolation and chemical characterization of nucleolar and nucleoplasmic subfractions. J. Cell Biol. **18**:293–312.

Maley, F. and Maley, G. F., 1962. On the nature of a sparing effect by thymidine on the utilization of deoxycytidine. Biochem. **1**:847–851.

Maley, G. F. and Maley, F., 1960. Inhibition of deoxyribonucleic acid synthesis in chick embryos by deoxyadenosine. J. Biol. Chem. **235**:2964–2967.

Maley, G. F. and Maley, F., 1963. Feedback control of purified deoxycytidylate deaminase. Science **141**:1278–1279.

Mangenot, G. and Carpentier, S., 1944. Sur les effets mitoclasiques de la caféine et de la théophylline. Compt. Rend. Soc. Biol. **138**:232–233.

Mantel, N. and Greenblatt, C. L., 1962. Excessive variation in radiation-induced chromosome aberrations. Nature **193**:795–796.

Marquardt, H., 1950. Neuere Auffassungen über einige Probleme aus der Pathologie der Kernteilung. Naturwissenschaften **37**:416–424, 433–438.

Mazia, D., 1941. Enzyme studies on chromosomes. Cold Spring Harbor Symp. Quant. Biol. **9**:40–46.

Mazia, D., 1954. The particulate organization of the chromosome. Nat. Acad. Sci. (U.S.), Proc., **40**:521–527.

Mazia, D., 1955. The organization of the mitotic apparatus. Symp. Soc. Exp. Biol. 9:335–357.

Mazia, D., 1961. Mitosis and the physiology of cell division. *In* The Cell, Brachet J. and Mirsky, A. E., eds., III:77–412. Academic Press, New York, 1961.

Mazia, D., 1963. Synthetic activities leading to mitosis. J. Cell. Comp. Physiol. 62 (Suppl. 1):123–140.

Mazia, D. and Hinegardner, R. T., 1963. Enzymes of deoxyribonucleic acid (DNA) synthesis in nuclei of sea urchin embryos. Nat. Acad. Sci. (U.S.), Proc., 50:148–156.

Mennigmann, H. D. and Szybalski, W., 1962. Molecular mechanism of thymineless death. Biochem. Biophys. Res. Commun. 9:398–404.

Mensinkai, S. W., 1939. The conception of the satellite and the nucleolus, and the behavior of these bodies in cell division. Ann. Bot. 3:763–794.

Merz, T., 1961. Effect of mitomycin C on lateral root-tip chromosomes of *Vicia faba*. Science 133:329–330.

Miescher, F., 1874. Die Spermatozoen einiger Wirbelthiere. Ein Beitrag zur Histochemie. Verhandl. natur. forsch. Ges. Basel VI:138–208.

Miescher, F., 1897. Die histochemischen und physiologischen Arbeiten. Vol. 1. Wissenschaftlicher Briefwechsel, 138 p.

Miller, L. A. and Goldfeder, A., 1961. Adenylate kinase of nuclei and its distribution in several subcellular fractions of neoplastic tissue. Exp. Cell Res. 23:311–317.

Mirsky, A. E. and Pollister, A. W., 1946. Chromosin, a desoxiribose nucleoprotein complex of the cell nucleus. J. Gen. Physiol. 30:117–148.

Mirsky, A. E. and Ris, H., 1947. Chemical composition of isolated chromosomes. J. Gen. Physiol. 31:7–18.

Mirsky, A. E. and Ris, H., 1949. Variable and constant components of chromosomes. Nature 163:666–667.

Mirsky, A. E. and Ris, H., 1951. The composition and structure of isolated chromosomes. J. Gen. Physiol. 34:475–492.

Mizrahi, I. J. and Emmelot, P., 1962. The effect of cystene on the metabolic changes produced by two carcinogenic N-nitrosodialkylamines in rat liver. Cancer Res. 22:339–351.

Molé-Bajer, J., 1958. Cine-micrographic analysis of C-mitosis in endosperm. Chromosoma 9:332–358.

Monné, L., 1942. Über die Doppelbrechung der Kernhüllen. Ark. Zool. 34 B No. 2:1–8.

Moore, E. C. and Reichard, P., 1963. Cofactor requirements of the cytidine diphosphate (CDP) reductase system. J. Biol. Chem. 238: PC 2244–PC 2245.

Morris, N. R. and Fischer, G. A., 1961. Studies on the inhibition by deoxyribonucleosides of the reproduction in culture of neoplastic mammalian cells. Fed. Proc. 20:358.

Moses, M. J., 1963, p. 162. *In* Radiation Induced Chromosome Aberrations, S. Wolff ed. Columbia University Press, New York, 1963.

Moses, M. J. and Taylor, J. H., 1955. Desoxypentose nucleic acid synthesis during microsporogenesis in *Tradescantia*. Exp. Cell Res. 9:474–488.

Muir, R. M. and Hansch, C., 1953. On the mechanism of action of growth regulators. Plant Physiol. 28:218–232.

References

Mukerji, K. B. and Dhar, N. R., 1925. Die Zersetzung der salpetrigen Säure im Lichte und in Gegenwart von Katalysatoren. Z. Elektrochem. **31**:255–259.

Mukherjee, K. L. and Heidelberger, C., 1962. Studies on fluorinated pyrimidines XV. Inhibition of the incorporation of formate-C^{14} into DNA thymine of Ehrlich ascites carcinoma cells by 5-fluoro-2'-deoxyuridine-5'-monophosphate and related compounds. Cancer Res. **22**:815–822.

Munch-Petersen, Agnete, 1960. Formation *in vitro* of deoxyadenosine triphosphate from deoxyadenosine in Ehrlich ascites cells. Biochem. Biophys. Res. Commun. **3**:392–396.

Muramatsu, M., Hodnett, J. L., and Busch, H., 1964. Studies on the "independence" of nucleolar ribonucleic acid synthesis. Biochim. Biophys. Acta **91**:592–597.

Nass, M. M. K. and Nass, S., 1963*a*. Intramitochondrial fibers with DNA (deoxyribonucleic acid) characteristics. I. Fixation and electron staining reactions. J. Cell Biol. **19**:593–611.

Nass, M. M. K. and Nass, S., 1963*b*. Intramitochondrial fibers with DNA (deoxyribonucleic acid) characteristics. II. Enzymic and other hydrolytic treatments. J. Cell Biol. **19**:613–629.

Neary, G. J. and Evans, H. J., 1958. Chromatid breakage by irradiation and the oxygen effect. Nature **182**:890–891.

Nebel, B. R. and Ruttle, M. L., 1938. The cytological and genetical significance of colchicine. J. Hered. **29**:3–9.

Nebel, B. R. and Coulon, E. M., 1962. The fine structure of chromosomes in pigeon spermatocytes. Chromosoma **13**:272–291.

Neish, W. J. P., 1948. On the solubilization of aromatic amines by purines. Rec. trav. Chim. **67**:361–373.

Nierlich, D. P. and McFall, E., 1963. Repression of an enzyme of purine biosynthesis in L cells. Biochim. Biophys. Acta **76**:469–470.

Nowell, P. C., 1964. Mitotic inhibition and chromosome damage by mitomycin in human leukocyte cultures. Exp. Cell Res. **33**:445–449.

Novikoff, A. B., 1961. Lyosomes and related particles. *In* The Cell, J. Brachet and A. E. Mirsky, eds., **II**:423–488. Academic Press, New York, 1961.

Nuti-Ronchi, V. and D'Amato, F., 1961. New data on chromosome breakage by acridine orange in the *Allium* test. Caryologia **14**:163–165.

Odmark, G. and Kihlman, B. A., 1962. Respiration-rates of bacteria, bean roots, and bean root mitochondria as a function of oxygen concentration. Nature **194**:595–596.

Odmark, G. and Kihlman, B. A., 1965. Effects of chromosome-breaking purine derivatives on nucleic acid synthesis and on the levels of adenosine-5'-triphosphate and deoxyadenosine-5'-triphosphate in bean root-tips. Mutation Res. **2**:274–286.

Okazaki, R. and Kornberg, A., 1964. Deoxythymidine kinase of *Escherichia coli*. J. Biol. Chem. **239**:269–274.

Olszewska, M. J., 1960. Recherches sur le caractère chimique de la plaque cellulaire. Acta Soc. Botan. Poloniae **29**:249–261.

Ontko, J. A. and Moorehead, W. R., 1964. Histone synthesis after inhibition of deoxyribonucleic acid replication. Biochim. Biophys. Acta **91**:658–660.

Östergren, G., 1944. Colchicine mitosis, chromosome contraction, narcosis and protein chain folding. Hereditas **30**:429–467.

Östergren, G., 1950. Considerations on some elementary features of mitosis. Hereditas **36**:1–18.

Östergren, G. and Östergren, K., 1966. Mitosis with undivided chromosomes. III. Inhibition of chromosome reproduction in *Tradescantia* by specific mutations. *In* Chromosomes Today, Darlington, C. D. and Lewis, K. R., eds., Vol. 7:128–130. Oliver & Boyd, Edinburgh 1966.

Östergren, G., Koopmans, A., and Reitalu, J., 1953. The occurrence of the amphiastral type of mitosis in higher plants and the influence of aminopyrin on mitosis. Bot. Notiser **1953**:417–419.

Östergren, G., Molé-Bajer, J., and Bajer, A., 1960. An interpretation of transport phenomena at mitosis. Ann. N.Y. Acad. Sci. **90**:381–408.

Östergren, G. and Wakonig, T., 1954. True or apparent sub-chromatid breakage and the induction of labile states in cytological chromosome loci. Bot. Notiser **1954**: 357–375.

Osterhout, W. J. V., 1925. Is living protoplasm permeable to ions. J. Gen. Physiol. **8**:131–146.

Overgaard-Hansen, K., 1964. The inhibition of 5-phosphoribosyl-1-pyrophosphate formation by cordycepin triphosphate in extracts of Ehrlich ascites tumor cells. Biochim. Biophys. Acta **80**:504–507.

Overton, E., 1899. Über die allgemeinen osmotischen Eigenschaften der Zelle, ihre vermutlichen Ursachen und ihre Bedeutung für die Physiologie. Vierteljahrschr. Naturforsch. Ges. Zürich. **44**:88–135.

Overton, E., 1902. Beiträge zur allgemeinen Muskel- und Nervenphysiologie. Pflügers Arch. Ges. Physiol. **92**:115–280.

Painter, T. S., 1964. Fundamental chromosome structure. Science **144**:565.

Paul, J. and Hagiwara, A., 1962. A kinetic study of the action of 5-fluoro-2′-deoxyuridine on synthetic processes in mammalian cells. Biochim. Biophys. Acta **61**: 243–249.

Pechmann, H. von, 1895. Ueber Diazomethan. Ber. d. deutsch. chem. Ges. **28**:855–861.

Pelc, S. R. and Howard, A., 1952. Chromosome metabolism as shown by autoradiographs. Exp. Cell Res. (Suppl. **2**):269–278.

Pelc, S. R. and Howard, A., 1956. Metabolic activity of salivary gland chromosomes in *Diptera*. Exp. Cell Res. **10**:549–552.

Pelling, G., 1959. Chromosomal synthesis of ribonucleic acid as shown by incorporation of uridine labelled with tritium. Nature **184**:655–656.

Perry, R. P., 1962. The cellular sites of synthesis of ribosomal and 4S RNA. Nat. Acad. Sci. (U.S.), Proc., **48**:2179–2186.

Perry, R. P., 1963. Selective effects of actinomycin D on the intracellular distribution of RNA synthesis in tissue culture cells. Exp. Cell Res. **29**:400–406.

Plaut, W., 1963. On the replicative organization of DNA in the polytene chromosome of *Drosophila melanogaster*. J. Mol. Biol. **7**:632–635.

Plaut, W. and Mazia, D., 1956. The distribution of newly synthesized deoxyribonucleic acid in mitotic division. J. Biophys. Biochem. Cytol. **2**:573–588.

Plaut, W. and Nash, D., 1964. Localized DNA synthesis in polytene chromosomes and its implications, p. 113–135. *In* "The Role of Chromosomes in Development." Growth Symposium No. 23, M. Locke, ed. Academic Press, New York.

Pollard, C. J., 1964. The deoxyribonucleic acid content of purified spinach chloroplasts. Arch. Biochem. Biophys. **105**:114–119.

Polli, E. and Ratti, G., 1953. Studien über Leucocyten. I. Die Fettfraktionen in intakten Zellen und in isolierten Zell-Kernen bei normalen und pathologischen Zuständen. Biochem. Zeitschr. **323**:546–554.

Pollister, A. W., 1952. Nucleoproteins of the nucleus. Exp. Cell Res. (Suppl. 2):59–70.

Pomerat, C. M. and Willmer, E. N., 1939. Studies on the growth of tissues *in vitro*. VII. Carbohydrate metabolism and mitosis. J. Exp. Biol. 16:232–249.

Porter, K. R., 1961. The ground substance; observations from electron microscopy. *In* The Cell, J. Brachet and A. E. Mirsky, eds., II:621–675. Academic Press, Inc., New York, 1961.

Porter, K. R. and Kallman, F., 1952. Significance of cell particulates as seen by electron microscopy. Ann. N.Y. Acad. Sci. 54:882–891.

Porter, K. R. and Machado, R. D., 1960. Studies on the endoplasmic reticulum. IV. Its form and distribution during mitosis in cells of onion root-tip. J. Biophys. Biochem. Cytol. 7:167–180.

Possingham, J. V. and Brown, R., 1958. The nuclear incorporation of iron and its significance in growth. J. Exp. Bot. 9:277–284.

Potter, Van R., 1963. Feedback inhibition of thymidine kinase by thymidine triphosphate. Exp. Cell Res. (Suppl. 9):259–261.

Poulson, D. F. and Bowen, W. T., 1952. Organization and function of the inorganic constituents of nuclei. Exp. Cell Res. (Suppl. 2):161–179.

Prescott, D. M. and Bender, M. A., 1962. Synthesis of RNA and protein during mitosis in mammalian tissue culture cells. Exp. Cell Res. 26:260–268.

Prescott, D. M. and Bender, M. A., 1963. Autoradiographic study of chromatid distribution of labeled DNA in two types of mammalian cells *in vitro*. Exp. Cell Res. 29:430–442.

Pricer, W. E. and Weissbach, A., 1963. The effect of lysogenic induction with mitomycin C on the DNA and DNA polymerase of *Escherichia coli* K 12 λ. Biochem. Biophys. Res. Commun. 14:91–95.

Prusoff, W. H., 1959. Further studies on the inhibition of nucleic acid biosynthesis by azathymidine and by deoxyadenosine. Biochem. Pharmacol. 2:221–225.

Puck, T. T., 1964. Phasing, mitotic delay, and chromosomal aberrations in mammalian cells. Science 144:565–566.

Pullman, B. and Pullman, A., 1958. Electron-donor and -acceptor properties of biologically important purines, pyrimidines, pteridines, flavins and aromatic amino acids. Nat. Acad. Sci. (U.S.), Proc., 44:1197–1202.

Quastler, H. and Sherman, F. G., 1959. Cell population kinetics in the intestinal epithelium of the mouse. Exp. Cell Res. 17:420–438.

Rabinovitch, M. and Plaut, W., 1962a. Cytoplasmic DNA synthesis in *Amoeba proteus*. I. On the particulate nature of the DNA-containing elements. J. Cell Biol. 15:525–534.

Rabinovitch, M. and Plaut, W., 1962b. Cytoplasmic DNA synthesis in *Amoeba proteus*. II. On the behavior and possible nature of the DNA-containing elements. J. Cell Biol. 15:535–540.

Radding, C. M., 1963. Incorporation of H³-thymidine by K 12 (λ) induced by streptonigrin, p. 22. *In* "Genetics Today," S. J. Geerts, ed. Pergamon Press, Oxford, 1963.

Rao, K. V., 1959. Streptonigrin. Chem. Eng. News 37:20.

Rao, K. V., Biemann, K., and Woodward, R. B., 1963. The structure of streptonigrin. J. Amer. Chem. Soc. 85:2532–2533.

Rasch, E., Swift, H., and Klein, R. M., 1959. Nucleoprotein changes in plant tumor growth. J. Biophys. Biochem. Cytol. 6:11–34.

Read, J., 1961. Chromosome size, structure and radiation damage, p. 217–226. *In* "Effects of Ionizing Radiations on Seeds." International Atomic Energy Agency, Vienna, 1961.

Rees, K. R., Rowland, G. F., and Varcoe, J. S., 1963. The metabolism of isolated rat-liver nucleoli and other subnuclear fractions. The active site of amino acid incorporation in the nucleus. Biochem. J. **86**:130–136.

Reich, E., 1964. Actinomycin: Correlation of structure and function of its complexes with purines and DNA. Science **143**:684–689.

Reich, E., Shatkin, A. J., and Tatum, E. L., 1961. Bacteriocidal action of mitomycin C. Biochim. Biophys. Acta **53**:132–149.

Reichard, P., Canellakis, Z. N., and Canellakis, E. S., 1961. Studies on a possible regulatory mechanism for the biosynthesis of deoxyribonucleic acid. J. Biol. Chem. **236**:2514–2519.

Reichard, P., Sköld, O., and Klein, G., 1959. Possible enzymic mechanism for the development of resistance against fluorouracil in ascites tumours. Nature **183**: 939–941.

Reichard, P., Sköld, O., Klein, G., Révész, L., and Magnusson, P-H., 1962. Studies on resistance against 5-fluorouracil. I. Enzymes of the uracil pathway during development of resistance. Cancer Res. **22**:235–243.

Reiter, J. M. and Littlefield, J. W., 1964. Nuclear RNA synthesis in partially synchronized mouse fibroblasts. Biochim. Biophys. Acta **80**:562–566.

Revell, S. H., 1953. Chromosome breakage by X-rays and radiomimetic substances in *Vicia*. Symposium on Chromosome Breakage. Hereditas **6** (Suppl.) 107–124.

Revell, S. H., 1955. A new hypothesis for "chromatid" changes, p. 243–253. *In* Proc. Radiol. Symp. Liège, 1954, Bacq, Z. M. and Alexander, P., eds. Butterworths, London, 1955.

Revell, S. H., 1959. The accurate estimation of chromatid breakage, and its relevance to a new interpretation of chromatid aberrations induced by ionizing radiations. Royal Soc. (London), Proc., B. **150**:563–589.

Rickenberg, H. V. and Maio, J. J., 1961. The transport of galactose by mammalian tissue culture cells, p. 409–422. *In* Membrane Transport and Metabolism, Kleinzeller and Kotyk, eds. Academic Press, London and New York, 1961.

Rieger, R. and Michaelis, A., 1962. Die Auslösung von Chromosomen-Aberrationen bei *Vicia faba* durch chemische Agenzien. Die Kulturpflanze **10**:212–292.

Rieger, R. and Michaelis, A., 1964. On the distribution amongst cells of chemically induced chromatid aberrations in *Vicia faba* root tip meristems. Mutation Res. **1**:109–112.

Ris, H., 1957. Chromosome structure, p. 23–62. Symp. on The Chemical Basis of Heredity, W. D. McElroy and B. Glass, eds. The Johns Hopkins Press, Baltimore, 1957.

Ris, H., 1961. Ultrastructure and molecular organization of genetic systems (The annual Invitation Lecture). Can. J. Genet. and Cytol. **3**:95–120.

Ris, H. and Plaut, W., 1962. Ultrastructure of DNA-containing areas in the chloroplasts of *Chlamydomonas*. J. Cell. Biol. **13**:383–391.

Ritossa, F. M. and Spiegelman, S., 1966. Localization of DNA complementary to RNA in the nucleolus organizer region of *Drosophila melanogaster*. Nat. Acad. Sci. (U.S.), Proc., **53**:737–745.

Roberts, J. J. and Warwick, G. P., 1963. The reaction of β-propiolactone with guanosine, deoxyguanylic acid and RNA. Biochem. Pharmacol. **12**:1441–1442.

Robertson, J. D., 1959. The ultrastructure of cell membranes and their derivatives, p. 3–43. *In* The Structure and Function of Subcellular Components, Biochem. Soc. Symp. No. 16, E. M. Crook, ed. University Press, Cambridge.

References

Roth, L. E. and Daniels, E. W., 1961. Infective organisms in the cytoplasm of *Amoeba proteus*. J. Biophys. Biochem. Cytol. 9:317–323.

Rottman, F. and Guarino, A., 1964. The inhibition of purine biosynthesis *de novo* in *Bacillus subtilis* by cordycepin. Biochim. Biophys. Acta 80:640–647.

Salzman, N. P. and Sebring, E. D., 1962. The coupled formation of deoxyribonucleic acid, nuclear ribonucleic acid and protein in animal-cell cultures. Biochim. Biophys. Acta 61:406–413.

Sarkar, N. K., Mukundan, M. A., and Devi, A., 1963. Role of deoxyribonuclease in synthesis of deoxyribonucleic acid. Nature 200:1205–1206.

Sax, K., 1939. The time factor in X-ray production of chromosome aberrations. Nat. Acad. Sci. (U.S.), Proc., 25:225–233.

Sax, K., 1940. An analysis of X-ray induced chromosomal aberrations in *Tradescantia*. Genetics 25:41–68.

Sax, K., 1941. Types and frequencies of chromosomal aberrations induced by X-rays. Cold Spring Harbor Symp. Quant. Biol. 9:93–101.

Sax, K. and Enzmann, E. V., 1939. The effect of temperature on X-ray induced chromosome aberrations. Nat. Acad. Sci. (U.S.), Proc., 25:397–405.

Schneider, W. C., 1946a. Intracellular distribution of enzymes. I. The distribution of succinic dehydrogenase, cytochrome oxidase, adenosine-triphosphatase, and phosphorus compounds in normal rat tissues. J. Biol. Chem. 165:585–593.

Schneider, W. C., 1946b. Intracellular distribution of enzymes. II. The distribution of succinic dehydrogenase, cytochrome oxidase, adenosinetriphosphatase, and phosphorus compounds in normal rat liver and in rat hepatomas. Cancer Res. 6:685–690.

Schneider, W. C. and Hogeboom, G. H., 1951. Cytochemical studies of mammalian tissues: the isolation of cell components by differential centrifugation: *a review*. Cancer Res. 11:1–22.

Schoental, R., 1961. Interaction of the carcinogenic N-methyl-nitrosourethane with sulphydryl groups. Nature 192:670.

Schwartz, H. S., Sodergren, J. E., and Philips, F. S., 1963. Mitomycin C: Chemical and biological studies on alkylation. Science 142:1181–1183.

Scott, D. and Evans, H. J., 1964. On the non-requirement for DNA synthesis in the production of chromosome aberrations by 8-ethoxycaffeine. Mutation Res. 1:146–156.

Scott, G. H., 1940a. Mineral distribution in some nerve cells and fibers. Proc. Soc. Exp. Biol. and Med. 44:397–398.

Scott, G. H., 1940b. An electron microscope study of calcium and magnesium in smooth muscle. Proc. Soc. Exp. Biol. and Med. 45:30–31.

Serra, J. A., 1947. Composition of the chromonemata and matrix and the role of nucleoproteins in mitosis and meiosis. Cold Spring Harbor Symp. Quant. Biol. 12:192–210.

Serra, J. A., 1955. Chemistry of the nucleus. Handbuch der Pflanzenphysiologie 1:413–444. Springer-Verlag, Berlin, 1955.

Setterfield, G. and Duncan, R. E., 1955. Cytological studies on the antimetabolite action of 2.6-diaminopurine in *Vicia faba* roots. J. Biophys. Biochem. Cytol. 1:399–419.

Shatkin, A. J., Reich, E., Franklin, R. M., and Tatum, E. L., 1962. Effect of mitomycin C on mammalian cells in culture. Biochim. Biophys. Acta 55:277–289.

Shiba, S., Terawaki, A., Taguchi, T., and Kawamata, J., 1959. Selective inhibition of formation of deoxyribonucleic acid in *Escherichia coli* by mitomycin C. Nature 183:1056–1057.

Shigenaga, M., 1937. An experimental study of the abnormal nuclear and cell divisions in living cells. Cytologia 1:464–478.

Shigeura, H. T. and Gordon, C. N., 1962a. Hadacidin, a new inhibitor of purine biosynthesis. J. Biol. Chem. 237:1932–1936.

Shigeura, H. T. and Gordon, C. N., 1962b. The mechanism of action of hadacidin. J. Biol. Chem. 237:1937–1940.

Shimamura, T. and Ôta, T., 1956. Cytochemical studies on the mitotic spindle and the phragmoplast of plant cells. Exp. Cell Res. 11:346–361.

Shinke, N. and Shigenaga, M., 1933. A histochemical study of plant nuclei in rest and mitosis. Cytologia 4:189–221.

Sibatani, A., 1963. Ribonucleic acids of cancer cells. Exp. Cell Res. (Suppl. 9): 289–329.

Sibatani, A., de Kloet, S. R., Allfrey, V. G., and Mirsky, A. E., 1962. Isolation of a nuclear RNA fraction resembling DNA in its base composition. Nat. Acad. Sci. (U.S.), Proc., 48:471–477.

Siebert, G., 1963. Enzymes of cancer nuclei. Exp. Cell Res. (Suppl. 9):389–417.

Simonet, M. and Guinochet, M., 1939. Anomalies morphologiques et caryologiques provoquées, sur les jeunes plantules, par les dérivés halogènes des carbures cycliques. Compt. Rend. Soc. Biol. 131:222–224.

Sirlin, J. L. and Jacob, J., 1964. Sequential and reversible inhibition of synthesis of ribonucleic acid in the nucleolus and chromosomes: effect of benzamide and substituted benzimidazoles on Dipteran salivary glands. Nature 204:545–547.

Sirlin, J. L., Jacob, J., and Kato, K.-I., 1962. The relation of messenger to nucleolar RNA. Exp. Cell Res. 27:355–359.

Sirlin, J. L., Kato, K., and Jones, K. W., 1961. Synthesis of ribonucleic acid in the nucleolus. Biochim. Biophys. Acta 48:421–423.

Sirlin, J. L., Tandler, C. J., and Jacob, J., 1963. The relationship between the nucleolus organizer and nucleolar RNA. Exp. Cell Res. 31:611–615.

Sköld, O., 1963. Studies on resistance against 5-fluorouracil. IV. Evidence for an altered uridine kinase in resistant cells. Biochim. Biophys. Acta 76:160–162.

Smellie, R. M. S., 1961. Biosynthesis of deoxyribonucleic acid (DNA). Proc. Ann. Reunion Soc. Chim. Phys. 11:89–95.

Smith, H. H., Kugelman, B. H., Commerford, S. L., and Szybalski, W., 1963. Incorporation of 5-iododeoxyuridine into DNA of plant cells. Nat. Acad. Sci. (U.S.), Proc., 49:451–457.

Smith, H. H. and Lotfy, T. A., 1955. Effects of beta-propiolactone and ceepryn on chromosomes of *Vicia* and *Allium*. Amer. J. Bot. 42:750–758.

Smith, H. H. and Srb, A. M., 1951. Induction of mutations with β-propiolactone Science 114:490–492.

Smith, Sister Marian Jose and Keir, H. M., 1963. Deoxyribonucleic acid (DNA) nucleotidyltransferase in nuclei and cytoplasm prepared from thymus tissue in nonaqueous media. Biochim. Biophys. Acta 68:578–588.

References

Somers, C. E. and Hsu, T. C., 1962. Chromosome damage induced by hydroxylamine in mammalian cells. Nat. Acad. Sci. (U.S.), Proc., 48:937–953.

Somers, C. E., Cole, A., and Hsu, T. C., 1963. Isolation of chromosomes. Exp. Cell Res. (Suppl. 9):220–234.

Stacey, K. A., Cobb, M., Cousens, S. F., and Alexander, P., 1958. The reactions of the "radiomimetic" alkylating agents with macromolecules *in vitro*. Ann. N.Y. Acad. Sci. 68:682–701.

Stadler, L. J., 1932. On the genetic nature of induced mutations in plants. Proc. 6th Int. Cong. Genet. pp. 274–294.

Stedman, E. and Stedman E., 1943. Probable function of histone as regulator of mitosis. Nature 152:556–557.

Stedman, E. and Stedman, E., 1947. The chemical nature and functions of the components of cell nuclei. Cold Spring Harbor Symp. Quant. Biol. 12:224–236.

Steffensen, D., 1953. Induction of chromosome breakage at meiosis by a magnesium deficiency in *Tradescantia*. Nat. Acad. Sci. (U.S.), Proc., 39:613–620.

Steffensen, D., 1955. Breakage of chromosomes in *Tradescantia* with a calcium deficiency. Nat. Acad. Sci. (U.S.), Proc., 41:155–160.

Steffensen, D. and Bergeron, J. A., 1959. Autoradiographs of pollen tube nuclei with calcium-45. J. Biophys. Biochem. Cytol. 6:339–342.

Stein, O. L. and Quastler, H., 1963. The use of tritiated thymidine in the study of tissue activation during germination in *Zea mays*. Amer. J. Bot. 50:1006–1011.

Steinegger, E. and Levan, A., 1947. Constitution and C-mitotic activity of isocolchicine. Hereditas 33:385–396.

Steinegger, E. and Levan, A., 1948. The C-mitotic qualities of colchiceine trimethyl colchicinic acid and two phenanthrene derivatives. Hereditas 34:193–203.

Steinert, G., Firket, H., and Steinert, M., 1958. Synthèse d'acide dèsoxyribonucléique dans le corps parabasal de *Trypanosoma mega*. Exp. Cell Res. 15:632–635.

Stenlid, G., 1949. The effect of 2.4-dinitrophenol upon oxygen consumption and glucose uptake in young wheat roots. Physiol. Plant. 2:350–371.

Stern, H., Allfrey, V., Mirsky, A. E., and Saetren, H., 1952. Some enzymes of isolated nuclei. J. Gen. Physiol. 35:559–578.

Stern, H. and Kirk, P. L., 1948. The oxygen consumption of the microspores of *Trillium* in relation to the mitotic cycle. J. Gen. Physiol. 31:243–248.

Stern, H. and Mirsky, A. E., 1952. The isolation of wheat germ nuclei and some aspects of their glycolytic metabolism. J. Gen. Physiol. 36:181–199.

Stern, H. and Mirsky, A. E., 1953. Soluble enzymes of nuclei isolated in sucrose and non-aqueous media. J. Gen. Physiol. 37:177–187.

Stoneburg, C. A., 1939. Lipids of cell nuclei. J. Biol. Chem. 129:189–196.

Studzinski, G. P. and Love, R., 1963. Accumulation of acid-soluble nucleic acid precursors in HeLa cells inhibited by 5-fluoro-2'-deoxyuridine. Exp. Cell Res. 32:190–192.

Swann, M. M., 1954. The control of cell division, p. 185–196. *In* Recent Developments in Cell Physiology, J. A. Kitching, ed. Butterworths, London, 1954.

Swann, M. M., 1957. The control of cell division: a review. I. General mechanisms. Cancer Res. 17:727–757.

Swanson, C. P., 1961. The Cell. Prentice-Hall, Englewood Cliffs, N. J., 1960. 114 p.

Swanson, C. P. and Merz, T., 1959. Factors influencing the effect of β-propiolactone on chromosomes of *Vicia faba*. Science 129:1364–1365.

Swift, H., 1953. Quantitative aspects of nuclear nucleoproteins. Int. Rev. Cytol. 2:1–76.

Szybalska, E. H. and Szybalski, W., 1962. Genetics of human cell lines, IV. DNA-mediated heritable transformation of a biochemical trait. Nat. Acad. Sci. (U.S.), Proc., 48:2026–2034.

Szybalski, W., 1962. Properties and applications of halogenated deoxyribonucleic acids, p. 147–171. *In* The Molecular Basis of Neoplasma. University of Texas Press, Austin, 1962.

Szybalski, W. and Szybalska, E. H., 1961. A new chemotherapeutic principle for the treatment of drug-resistant neoplasms. Cancer Chemother. Rep. 11:87–89.

Takahashi, T., Swint, R. B., and Hurlbert, R., 1963. Synthesis of RNA in isolated nuclei of the Novikoff ascites tumor, Exp. Cell Res. (Suppl. 9):330–344.

Tanaka, N. and Sugimura, A., 1956. The effect of azaserine on mitotic cells of *Tradescantia paludosa*, with special reference to restoration of and protection against the damage caused by azaserine. Proc. Int. Genet. Symp., 1956:189–195.

Taylor, J. H., 1953a. Autoradiographic detection of incorporation of P^{32} into chromosomes during meiosis and mitosis. Exp. Cell Res. 4:164–173.

Taylor, J. H., 1953b. Intracellular localization of labeled nucleic acid determined with autoradiographs. Science 118:555–557.

Taylor, J. H., 1957. The time and mode of duplication of chromosomes. Amer. Nat. 91:209–221.

Taylor, J. H., 1958a. Incorporation of phosphorus-32 into nucleic acids and proteins during microgametogenesis of *Tulbaghia*. Amer. J. Bot. 45:123–131.

Taylor, J. H., 1958b. The mode of chromosome duplication in *Crepis capillaris*. Exp. Cell Res. 15:350–357.

Taylor, J. H., 1958c. Sister chromatid exchanges in tritium-labeled chromosomes. Genetics 43:515–529.

Taylor, J. H., 1960a. Nucleic acid synthesis in relation to the cell division cycle. Ann. N.Y. Acad. Sci. 90:409–421.

Taylor, J. H., 1960b. Asynchronous duplication of chromosomes in cultured cells of Chinese hamster. J. Biophys. Biochem. Cytol. 7:455–463.

Taylor, J. H., 1962. Chromosome reproduction. Int. Rev. Cytol. 13:39–73.

Taylor, J. H., 1963a. The replication and organization of DNA in chromosomes. *In* Molecular Genetics, J. H. Taylor, ed., Part. 1:65–111.

Taylor, J. H., 1963b. DNA synthesis in relation to chromosome reproduction and the reunion of breaks. J. Cell. Comp. Physiol. 62 (Suppl. 1):73–86.

Taylor, J. H., 1963c. Control mechanisms for chromosome reproduction in the cell cycle. Symp. Int. Soc. Cell Biol. 2:161–177

Taylor, J. H., Haut, W. F., and Tung, J., 1962. Effects of fluorodeoxyuridine on DNA replication, chromosome breakage, and reunion. Nat. Acad. Sci. (U.S.), Proc., 48:190–198.

Taylor, J. H. and Taylor, S. H., 1953. The autoradiograph—a tool for cytogeneticists. J. Hered. 44:129–132.

Taylor, J. H., Wood, P. S., and Hughes, W. L., 1957. The organization and duplication of chromosomes as revealed by autoradiographic studies using tritium-labeled thymidine. Nat. Acad. Sci. (U.S.), Proc., 43:122–128.

References

Terra, N. de and Rustad, R. C., 1959. The dependence of pinocytosis on temperature and aerobic respiration. Exp. Cell Res. 17:191–195.

Thoday, J. M., 1954. Radiation-induced chromosome breakage, desoxyribosenucleic acid synthesis and the mitotic cycle in root-meristem cells of *Vicia faba*. New Phytol. 53:511–516.

Thomas, L. E. and Mayer, D. T., 1949. The proteins of mammalian spermatozoa and cellular nuclei. Science 110:393–394.

Tooze, J. and Davies, H. G., 1963. The occurrence and possible significance of haemoglobin in the chromosomal regions of mature erythrocyte nuclei of the newt *Triturus cristatus cristatus*. J. Cell Biol. 16:501–511.

Ts'o, P. O. P., Helmkamp, G. K., and Sander, C., 1962. Interaction of nucleosides and related compounds with nucleic acids as indicated by the change of helix-coil transition temperature. Nat. Acad. Sci. (U.S.), Proc., 48:686–698.

Ts'o, P. O. P. and Lu, P., 1964. Interaction of nucleic acids. I. Physical binding of thymine, adenine, steroids, and aromatic hydrocarbons to nucleic acids. Nat. Acad. Sci. (U.S.), Proc., 51:17–24.

Van't Hof, J., Wilson, G. B. and Colon, A., 1960. Studies on the control of mitotic activity. The use of colchicine in the tagging of a synchronous population of cells in the meristem of *Pisum sativum*. Chromosoma 11:313–321.

Vendrely, R. and Vendrely, C., 1948. La teneur du noyau cellulaire en acide désoxy-ribonucléique à travers les organes les individus et les espèces animales. Experientia 4:434–436.

Vincent, W. S., 1952. The isolation and chemical properties of the nucleoli of starfish oocytes. Nat. Acad. Sci. (U.S.), Proc., 38:139–145.

Vincent, W. S., 1955. Structure and chemistry of nucleoli. Int. Rev. Cytol. 4:269–298.

Vincent, W. S., 1957. Heterogeneity of nuclear ribonucleic acid. Science 126:306–307.

Vincent, W. S. and Baltus, E., 1960. A function for the nucleolus. Biol. Bull. 119:299–300.

Volkin, E., 1963. Biosynthesis of RNA in relation to genetic coding problems. *In* Molecular Genetics, J. H. Taylor, ed., Part I, pp. 271–289.

Wada, B., 1952. The effect of chemicals on mitosis studied in *Tradescantia* cells *in vivo*. II. Hydrazino-tropone compounds. Cytologia 17:279–286.

Wallace, H. and Birnstiel, M. L., 1966. Ribosomal cistrons and the nucleolar organizer. Biochim. Biophys. Acta 114:296–310.

Wang, T. Y., Kirkham, W. R., Dallam, R. D., Mayer, D. T., and Thomas, L. E., 1950. Acidic proteins of cellular nuclei. Nature 165:974–975.

Wang, T. Y., Carver, M. J., Ramsey, R. H., Funckes, A. J., and Thomas, L. E., 1952. Lipoproteins of cellular nuclei. Fed. Proc. 11:306.

Wang, T. Y., Mayer, D. T., and Thomas, L. E., 1953. A lipoprotein of rat liver nuclei. Exp. Cell Res. 4:102–106

Waring, M. J., 1964. Complex formation with DNA and inhibition of *Escherichia coli* RNA polymerase by ethidium bromide. Biochim. Biophys. Acta 87:358–361.

Warren, L., 1961. Nucleotides and nucleosides. *In* Metabolic Pathways, D. M. Greenberg, ed., II:459–524. Academic Press, New York, 1961.

Watson, J. D. and Crick, F. H. C., 1953. Molecular structure of nucleic acids. Nature 171:737–738.

Watson, M. L., 1955. The nuclear envelope. Its structure and relation to cytoplasmic membranes. J. Biophys. Biochem. Cytol. 1:257–270.

Webb, R. B. and Kubitschek, H. E., 1963. Mutagenic and antimutagenic effects of acridine orange in *Escherichia coli*. Biochem. Biophys. Res. Commun. 13:90–94.

Weil-Malherbe, H., 1946. The solubilization of polycyclic aromatic hydrocarbons by purines. Biochem. J. 40:351–363.

Whaley, W. G., Mollenhauer, H. H., and Leech, J. H., 1960a. The ultrastructure of the meristematic cell. Amer. J. Bot. 47:401–419.

Whaley, W. G., Mollenhauer, H. H., and Leech, J. H., 1960b. Some observations on the nuclear envelope. J. Biophys. Biochem. Cytol. 8:233–244.

Whaley, W. G. and Mollenhauer, H. H., 1963. The Golgi apparatus and cell plate formation. J. Cell Biol. 17:216–221.

Wheeler, G. P., 1962. Studies related to the mechanisms of action of cytotoxic alkylating agents: a review. Cancer Res. 22:651–688.

White, M. J. D., 1947. The Chromosomes, 3rd ed. Methuen & Co., Ltd., London, 1947. 124 p.

Wieland, H., 1911. Tetraphenylhydrazin und Hexaphenyläthan. Liebig's Ann. Chem. 381:200–216.

Williams, H. H., Kaucher, M., Richards, A. J., Moyer, E. Z., and Sharpless, G. R., 1945. The lipid partition of isolated cell nuclei of dog and rat livers. J. Biol. Chem. 160:227–232.

Williamson, M. B. and Gulick, A., 1942. The estimation of alkaline earth minerals in thymus nuclei. J. Cell. Comp. Physiol. 20:116–118.

Wilson, G. B. and Morrison, J. H., 1961. Cytology. Reinhold Publishing Corporation, New York, 1961. 297 p.

Wimber, D. E., 1961. Asynchronous replication of deoxyribonucleic acid in root tip chromosomes of *Tradescantia paludosa*. Exp. Cell Res. 23:402–407.

Wimber, D. E. and Quastler, H., 1963. A thymidine-14C and -3H double-labeling technique in the study of cell proliferation in *Tradescantia* root tips. Exp. Cell Res. 30:8–22.

Wolff, S., 1960. Radiation studies on the nature of chromosome breakage. Amer. Nat. 94:85–93.

Wolff, S., 1961. Radiation genetics. *In* Mechanisms in Radiobiology, M. Errera and A. Forssberg, eds., 1:419–475. Academic Press, New York and London.

Wolff, S., 1963, p. 111–112. *In* Radiation-induced Chromosome Aberrations, S. Wolff, ed.

Wolff, S. and Luippold, H. E., 1955. Metabolism and chromosome-break rejoining. Science 122:231–232.

Wolff, S. and Luippold, H. E., 1964. Chromosome splitting as revealed by combined X-ray and labeling experiments. Exp. Cell Res. 34:548–556.

Woodard, J., Rasch, E., and Swift, H., 1961. Nucleic acid and protein metabolism during the mitotic cycle in *Vicia faba*. J. Biophys. Biochem. Cytol. 9:445–463.

Woods, P. S., 1959. RNA in nuclear-cytoplasmic interaction. Brookhaven Symp. Biol. 12:153–171.

Woods, P. S. and Schairer, M. V., 1959. Distribution of newly synthesized deoxyribonucleic acid in dividing chromosomes. Nature 183:303–305.

References

Wyss, O., Clark, J. B., Haas, F., and Stone, W. S., 1948. The role of peroxide in the biological effects of irradiated broth. J. Bacteriol. **56**:51–57.

Yakusizi, N., 1936*a*. Über die Verteilung von Eisen und Zink in Blutplasma, dem Protoplasma der Blutkörperchen und ihren Kernen bei den verschiedenen Tieren. Keijo J. Med. **7**:276–288.

Yakusizi, N., 1936*b*. Über die Verteilung von Eisen und Zink im Plasma, Protoplasma und Kern verschiedener Eiterarten und die biologische Bedeutung dieser Metalle. Keijo J. Med. **7**:289–300.

Yost, H. T., 1951. The frequency of X-ray induced chromosome aberrations in *Tradescantia* as modified by near infrared radiation. Genetics **36**:176–184.

Zagury, D., 1957. A liporibonucleoprotein complex with sulfhydryl groups inside the nucleolus. Compt. Rend. Acad. Sci. **244**:1825–1827.

Zeuthen, E., 1958. Artificial and induced periodicity in living cells. Advances Biol. Med. Phys. **6**:37–73.

Zeuthen, E., 1963. Independent cycles of cell division and of DNA synthesis in *Tetrahymena*, p. 1–7. *In* Cell Growth and Cell Division, R. J. C. Harris, ed. Academic Press, New York, 1963.

LATE ADDITION:

Eigsti, O. J. and Dustin, P., Jr., 1955. Colchicine—in agriculture, medicine, biology, and chemistry. Iowa State College Press, Ames. 470 p.

236

List of Abbreviations

A = adenine
G = guanine
H = hypoxanthine
C = cytosine
T = thymine
U = uracil
AR, GR, IR, CR, UR = the ribosides of adenine, guanine, hypoxanthine,
        cytosine, uracil
AMP, GMP, IMP, XMP, CMP, UMP = the riboside-5′-monophosphates
        of adenine, guanine, hypoxan-
        thine, xanthine, cytosine,
        uracil
ADP, etc. = the riboside-5′-diphosphates of adenine, etc.
ATP, etc. = the riboside-5′-triphosphates of adenine, etc.
AdR, GdR, CdR, TdR, UdR = the 2′-deoxyribosides of adenine, guanine,
        cytosine, thymine, uracil
dAMP, dGMP, dCMP, dTMP, dUMP = the 2′-deoxyriboside-5′-mono-
        phosphates of adenine, gua-
        nine, cytosine, thymine, uracil
dADP, etc. = the 2′-deoxyriboside-5′-diphosphates of adenine, etc.
dATP, etc. = the 2′-deoxyriboside-5′-triphosphates of adenine, etc.
H^3-TdR = tritium-labeled thymidine
SAMP = adenylosuccinic acid
R-1-P = ribose-1-phosphate
dR-1-P = deoxyribose-1-phosphate
PRPP = 5-phosphoribosyl-1-pyrophosphate
DNA = deoxyribonucleic acid
RNA = ribonucleic acid
mRNA = messenger RNA
rRNA = ribosomal RNA
sRNA = soluble or transfer RNA
DNase = deoxyribonuclease
RNase = ribonuclease

NAD = nicotinamide-adenine dinucleotide
NADP = nicotinamide-adenine dinucleotide phosphate
FA = folic acid

DHFA = dihydrofolic acid
THFA = tetrahydrofolic acid
TCA cycle = tricarboxylic acid cycle

AO = acridine orange
AO-VL = acridine orange-visible light
Apt. = aminopterin
AP = 2-aminopurine
AS = azaserine
BPL = β-propiolactone
BU = 5-bromouracil
BUdR = 5-bromodeoxyuridine
CA = cytosine arabinoside
CF = cupferron
CUdR = 5-chlorodeoxyuridine
DEPE = di(2.3-epoxypropyl)ether
DIECA = diethyldithiocarbamate
DMNA = dimethylnitrosamine
DNP = 2.4-dinitrophenol
DPNA = diphenylnitrosamine
DRB = 5.6-dichloro-1-(β-D-ribofuranosyl)benzimidazole
EOC = 8-ethoxycaffeine
FU = 5-fluorouracil
FUdR = 5-fluorodeoxyuridine
HA = hydroxylamine
HC = hadacidin
HN2 = di(2-chloroethyl)methylamine or nitrogen mustard
IUdR = 5-iododeoxyuridine
MC = mitomycin C
MH = maleic hydrazide
MNNG = 1-methyl-3-nitro-1-nitrosoguanidine
MPNA = N-methylphenylnitrosamine
SN = streptonigrin
TEM = triethylenemelamine
TMU = 1.3.7.9-tetramethyluric acid
ER = endoplasmic reticulum
SU = sister (chromatid) union
NU = nonunion (of sister chromatids)
NUd = NU distal
NUp = NU proximal

S = the period of DNA synthesis during interphase
G_1 = interphase period between telophase and S
G_2 = interphase period between S and prophase

Author Index

Wyss, O., 139, *236*

Y

Yakusizi, N., 29, *236*
Yost, H. T., 70, *236*

Z

Zagury, D., 27, 40, 150, *236*
Zahn, R., *221*
Zeuthen, E., 22, 23, 88, 101, *218*, *236*
Zimmerman, S. B., *210*

Subject Index